THE **ROZZERS** COLLECTION

FIVE TRUE STORIES by
D I E M   B U R D E N

SHRIVEN
B O O K S

A catalogue record for this book is available from The British Library.

THE ROZZERS COLLECTION

END OF THE ROAD
Soldier image © Vladimir Ivanov | Dreamstime.com
Police Officer image © Editorial | Dreamstime.com
Police Car image © Alan Mathews
Landscape image © Yorkman | Yaymicro.com
Sky image © Mykola Mazuryk | Dreamstime.com

COPS DON'T RUN
Police Officers image © iStockPhoto.com
Cambridge scene image © Rainprel | Dreamstime.com

ONE FOR THE ROAD
Background image © Peter Clark | Dreamstime.com
Police Officer/uniform part 1 image © Viorel Sima | Dreamstime.com
Police Officer/uniform part 2 image © Camrocker | Dreamstime.com

THIEF TAKER
Scrote image © Ammentorp | Dreamstime.com
Cop image © Richard Thomas | Dreamstime.com
Cop's face image © Ammentorp | Dreamstime.com
Victor Bravo Four Alpha image © Keith Curtis

COP OUT
Cop's face image © Smikey26 | iStockPhoto
Cop's eye image © Diem Burden | Shriven Books

Logo feather © Ruslan Tsyganov | Dreamstime.com

ISBN-13: 978-1-5272-6230-0

DISCLAIMER

These short stories are based, in part, upon actual events and persons.
I have tried to recreate events, locales and conversations from
my memories of them. In order to maintain their anonymity in all
instances, I have changed the names of individuals and places. I may
have changed some identifying characteristics and details such as
physical properties, occupations, and places of residence,
as well as other descriptive details. Some of the events and characters
are also composites of several individual events or persons.

Throughout this book I generally refer to police officers in the male
form. This is not intended as disrespectful to the many female officers
doing the same job: it is purely for ease of writing and protection of
some individuals' privacy in the absence of permissions.
I have nothing but admiration for all police officers,
male and female, who do an amazing job fighting not only the criminal
but also the bureaucracy that's dumped on them from above.

For mum and dad

"The police are the public and the public are the police;
the police being only members of the public who are paid to give
full time attention to duties which are incumbent on
every citizen in the interests of community welfare and existence."

SIR ROBERT PEEL, 2nd Baronet, FRS

CONTENTS

END OF THE ROAD   1

COPS DON'T RUN   35

ONE FOR THE ROAD   91

THIEF TAKER   153

COP OUT   259

BOOKS IN THIS SERIES   351

COMING SOON   352

CONTACT THE AUTHOR   353

ACKNOWLEDGEMENTS   354

Book One in THE ROZZERS Series

END
of the
ROAD

A TRUE STORY by
DIEM BURDEN

END OF THE ROAD *is dedicated to the memory of Mr RV Mellor (1937–2006): a true teacher and a genuine English eccentric. Many years ago, he saw something in me that I couldn't see for myself. If it hadn't been for his selfless intervention, this book – along with all those to come – would never have been written. Thank you, Bob, for making a difference.*

END of the ROAD Chapter One

Salisbury Plain, 1998

THE SUN HAD DIPPED BELOW THE HORIZON. The sky turned a sharp orange as darkness spread out across the desolate plain. Overtaking us in the distance was the black outline of a familiar Gazelle helicopter as it flew back to the nearby Army Air Corps base.

I glimpsed a sign for Stonehenge, which marked the halfway point. We'd soon be back in camp, showered and dressed, and out in Andover town centre with its limited pubs, yet numerous girls.

As the alcohol took hold of hungry men drinking too quickly, the debate between Pizza and Donk over the advantages of computers versus plant equipment became more and more animated.

Pizza was the baby of the group – a young, funny lad of about eighteen years of age who had earned his nickname on account of his poor complexion, and had never once challenged it. That was the kind of guy he was.

"Nah," said Donk. "You dunna want none of that bollocks. Waste of bloody time, computers."

Hilariously, Donk was proud of being called Donk, which we all knew was short for *donkey*. Built like a horse, he naively believed he'd earned the moniker on account of the size of his penis. He hadn't – it was because he had a very long face that vaguely resembled that of a donkey. We never had the heart to correct him.

"Construction's where the money's at," Donk continued. "With the qualifications you've got, just top 'em up with a trucker's licence on your pre-release course. Get a top job anywhere in the world with those quals, mate."

What Donk was saying made perfect sense, and the free, month-long course given to all army leavers meant I could gain a qualification in almost anything I wanted. I had just twelve months to decide, and having to put my name down for a course was another reason I needed to make some decisions about my future, and soon.

"A mate of mine took a course in London with computers," said Pizza, undaunted. "Did the lot, he did, and got loads of certificates at the end."

"And became what? *A bleedin' secretary?*" scoffed Donk.

"He's right though, Dave," said Cat. "Like it or not, computers will be everywhere in the next few years. Could be useful to have computer skills – never know where it might lead."

Corporal 'Cat' Stevens was a newly qualified truck driver who had enthusiastically jumped at driving that day, although the unexpected beers (which I'll come to shortly) had made him wish otherwise. Cat was my top drinking partner. Everybody liked Cat, and boy could he drink.

I sighed. "You're probably right, Cat, but *computers?* I mean, what am I gonna do with a shit-load of computer certificates?" In comparison, a trucker's licence had merit – it was a *real* qualification.

"How about the *Old Bill?*" asked Cat. "My mate's in his first year with the Manchester lot – loving every minute of it, apparently."

I stared at Cat, speechless. *The police? Me?*

"Dave a *Rozzer?*" Donk said, laughing. "Could you seriously see *him* as a *cop?*" He had a point – I had broken a fair few laws in my time, *and* I hated the sight of blood.

"Get stuffed, you ginger prick," I said, good-naturedly, as I turned and stared out of the window at the emptiness of Salisbury Plain. I listened absent-mindedly as the argument continued, and felt the warmth of something that had been missing from my life for several years creeping over me – real job satisfaction.

It was early September 1988, shortly after my twenty-third birthday. I remember it well because, on that day, a seed was planted – a seed that should never have seen the light of day. That seed only needed a small amount of nurturing to begin its life, and that nurturing came from the most unexpected of places, as indeed did the damned seed.

Apart from the sergeant, all the guys in the cab were my regular drinking buddies. We lived together, worked together, fought together, and socialised together. We knew each other inside out, and probably would have died for each other if war had come our way. Thankfully, it never did, and, like all good military relationships (pre-computers), I was to lose contact with each and every one of them as soon as I left the army behind.

We were bantering about women, life, and sex, easy and relaxed in each other's company. The man in charge was Sergeant 'Smudge' Smith, a diminutive career man who had been with us for so long that he was like part of the furniture. For a sergeant, he wasn't all that bad, despite his size. He was the man handing out the cans of beer we'd been given earlier, blatantly ignoring army regulations, which forbade drinking in military vehicles.

"But, Dave, seriously," said Smudge. "You've got your pre-release interview with *The Old Man* next week, for Christ's sake! You *need* to decide something!"

He was right, of course. I had to have something to say to the boss. In twelve months time, I'd be out of the army and on *Civvy Street*, and the Major expected to hear of my plans for the future.

But, *what,* exactly?

As much as the dull routine of army life had bored me for the previous five years, I couldn't help but feel satisfied at that day's work. We'd been assigned to 'civil aid', which roughly means the army helping the civilian population in some way. We'd arrived in a tiny village in the middle of Salisbury Plain, in a huge tipper-truck, towing an enormous tilting-trailer with one of our camouflage-green earth-moving machines on the back.

The twelve-ton digger had spent the day knocking out the crumbling wall of the local churchyard and digging the earth out, as we prepared the foundations for the vicar to have a new wall built. We also carted off all of the leftover rubble. Cat won the kitty for guessing the exact quantity of skeletons we'd pull out of the ground – zero, if you didn't count the small finger bone. I tapped my pocket. *A keepsake.*

"It'll come back to haunt you," Smudge had said, laughing.

As we were sweeping the soil off the road, the vicar came out and thanked us all individually, and presented Smudge with a case of bargain beer for our efforts. We were thrilled – British squaddies will drink absolutely anything.

The vicar watched as we routinely and expertly loaded the digger onto the trailer, tethered it down, and jumped up into the spacious cab. After some careful shunting back and forth by Cat, we ended up facing in the right direction and headed off out of the village and up onto the desolate, darkening roads of the plain – back to the dull routine of camp life.

It felt good, and I wanted this feeling to be a regular part of my new life. So what *could* I do? In my panic to escape my previous life at eighteen, I'd ended up here – a squaddy in the British Army, overjoyed at being let out to do a bit of useful work for the day. Joining up was a mistake I was only too aware of.

How I'd turned out to be a combat engineer is down to similar well-thought-out planning. At the army recruiting office I had commented that I liked the look of the Royal Engineer cap in the poster. I was told that I could learn any trade I wanted to in the Engineers. *Nice cap, good trade.* So, into the Engineer Corps I went. As for the trade, I had no idea. Other recruits had said that being a *POM* was the easiest job available. I had no idea what a *POM* was, and I certainly wasn't one to take the easy option, but it seemed like the job everybody in the know was taking.

"You'll have to sign up for six years for those qualifications, son. Army's gotta get its money's worth from its investment, you know." When you are eighteen years of age, six years doesn't seem like a very long time at all, so I took the job of *POM* – which I later learnt stood for *Plant Operator Mechanic*. For the previous five years, I'd been learning how to operate and maintain dozens of huge earth-moving equipment, along with all the other jobs we sappers did.

I briefly thought of going back to college, but soon laughed at the thought. Being a squaddy changes you in subtle ways. I would never be able to fit in with a bunch of immature, adolescent college kids again.

My rambling thoughts were silenced as efficiently as Donk and Pizza's argument – by the huge metallic crash from somewhere just behind us, as something slammed through the whole truck. It smashed all thoughts from my wandering mind.

We froze, brows furrowed, trying to identify the origin of the sound. Cat was startled enough to ease off the throttle.

"What the fuck was *that*?" I asked, quietly, looking at Cat. He was checking his mirrors as he double-declutched his way down the gearbox, carefully bringing the vehicle to a stop. There was apprehension on his face.

"Did any cars pass us, Cat?" I asked, suddenly fearful. Despite the very thorough first aid training we did every year, I dreaded having to deal with injured people. I always panicked when confronted with a realistically made-up battlefield casualty, guts spilling out through his hands.

"Dunno," replied Cat. "I didn't notice any."

I turned and, standing up, looked through the rear window of the cab, across the back of the cargo area to where the digger's cab should have been visible. It took a moment for me to comprehend.

"It's gone! The digger! It's fucking gone!"

The colour drained from Cat's face. We all knew what this meant – we were in deep, military-coloured crap. We'd lost the digger due to loose chains, and we'd have to take full responsibility, especially the driver and the sergeant in charge.

"Fuck, fuck, fuck, *fuck*!" screamed Cat, as he activated the truck's hazard lights. On the empty, darkening road, in the middle of nowhere. He punched the dashboard as we jumped down from the cab into the silence of the plain, throwing beer cans into the darkness in panic. When a squaddy throws his beer away, you know it's deadly serious.

"Pizza! Run on ahead, and wave down any approaching traffic!" I shouted. "We don't want anyone piling into the digger." I watched him disappear, swiftly, into the darkness.

I turned to the next man. "Donk, you do the same – behind us – until we know what we've got." He quickly ran off in the direction we had come from.

I left Smudge inside the truck, flapping over the beers, and anxiously throwing cans out of the window.

Cat and I legged it to the rear of the truck, where we stopped and stared at the empty space behind it. The digger hadn't just *fallen* off the trailer as we had feared, it had completely vanished, along with the trailer it was sitting on!

Cat and I looked into each other's eyes without saying a word – we both knew that this meant even bigger trouble than we'd initially thought. We'd lost the *complete* trailer! The whole damned thing had come uncoupled. Cat bent down to check the truck's towing eye. He had to know – had he failed to lock it shut with the securing pin?

As he did so, the scream came out of nowhere, and stopped him dead. Its volume was amplified in the absolute silence and darkness of the plain. It was right on cue, and it scared the hell out of the pair of us. It was the most dreadful, painful, drawn-out male scream I had ever heard, and it came from the darkness, just fifty yards behind us.

We stared into that void, acutely aware of just how isolated we were out there on the plain, as the nightmare was unfolding around us.

END of the ROAD Chapter Two

THE TRAILER AND DIGGER combination – about twenty tons in all – had obviously flown off the side of the empty road, landing harmlessly on the grasses of the huge, empty plain. There was nothing but rabbits for miles around here, so who the hell was screaming, and why?

"OK, so nobody passed us, but was there anybody behind us, Cat?" I asked.

"No, definitely not," said Cat. "I'm sure I would have noticed."

I believed him – Cat was a conscientious enough driver to be aware of what was behind him at all times.

The sergeant reappeared, his nervousness clear. "What the hell is that?" he whispered.

Six eyes searched the darkness along the road. We were all wishing we were still at the church.

"Anyone got a torch?" asked Cat.

We both shook our heads.

"Shit," he said. He took a deep breath. "Well, there's only one way we're gonna find out who that is and why the hell they're screaming like that."

I swallowed and looked at the other two. We nodded in unison, each drawing strength from the others. This is how I imagined war would be, as we set off at a you-go-first pace into the darkness, none wanting to be the first to find the screamer, and all completely terrified of what we'd discover.

I jumped – we all did – when, after about twenty yards, a large shape loomed out of the darkness, at rest in the middle of the road. It was black and mangled, about as big as an old TV set. Before any of us could guess what it was, the scream came again, further along the road, closer now. We ignored the lump of metal and walked on – *it* wasn't screaming, whatever it was.

About thirty yards further on, a larger black shape began to appear before us. The thing seemed to grow in size as we approached it, rising to about four yards in height and wide enough to completely block the road before us. It was digger- and trailer-sized.

"I think we've found it," whispered Smudge, hardly breathing.

Another scream made us all jump again – the sound was coming out of the black shape just in front of us. This time, it didn't stop – the casualty must have heard or sensed our presence. He wasn't shouting for help, as you might expect from someone in trouble. He just screamed, and screamed, and screamed.

We stepped closer and, slowly, the image of a car's rear end formed, protruding from the black mass before us. So, a car *had* passed us. Unfortunately, it was now wedge-shaped, its front reduced to a squashed point by the twenty tons of heavy metal lying across the top of it.

The front end of the car was buried somewhere under our digger, and the trailer – still attached to the bottom of the digger – was now lying across the road, on its side. I felt oddly relieved that the securing chains hadn't, as we'd initially feared, actually come undone. In fact, they had done an amazing job of remaining intact throughout this enormous crash.

Finally, we acted – as men do when there is no other way to delay the inevitable. We ran to the car, but found we couldn't open what was left of the doors. The screaming continued as we frantically searched for a way in. It was far more intense now. Or just closer. Damned close.

The backhoe – excavator arm – was squashing the roof down at the exact spot where any front seat passenger would have been. There was only one scream coming from the car – there couldn't have been two. The only way in was through the smashed rear window. Cat took the initiative and clambered into the back seat. I squeezed through after him.

We were two burly squaddies squashed onto a tiny back seat, and one that had been much reduced in size due to the impact. We could hardly move, and had to bend down so as not to hit our heads on the crumpled roof. The feeling of weight bearing down on us was very real. Once inside, we felt around the dark interior.

My hands touched something warm and soft – the driver. The darkness in the car was more intense than outside, so we could feel him but not see him. He was pressed so close to the lowered roof of the car that, if it hadn't been for the noise coming from him, I'd have guessed he was dead. Fortunately, he proved to be very much alive.

"We need a light," said Cat.

I searched the rear of the roof and found an interior light. I clicked the switch and, amazingly, it still worked.

Only now could we see what was causing the man to make so much noise. He was pinned into his seat, and the squashed-down roof of the car was less than two inches from his face and the whole of his torso. We couldn't see his lower legs though – they vanished under the weight of the digger.

"Help me, please, help me!" he cried, trying to turn his head towards Cat.

"It's OK. It's OK! Try not to move – you might make matters worse. We'll get you out of here. Just try to stay calm, OK?" said Cat.

The man was terrified and confused. "Where am I? Where am I?"

"There's been an accident," said Cat. "Help is on its way."

I had five years of highly realistic first aid training to draw on, so I should have been prepared for this, but those dolls and actors never screamed like this, and their legs were always reachable. Also, they were never in danger of dying in my hands like this man was. And that just scared the crap out of me. OK, OK, so what do we do? He's going to die unless we help him. We're totally alone, and it's up to us now. Come on! Think, man, think! Whether this man lives or dies depends on what *we* do next.

Breathing, bleeding, breaks, and burns! That's it – the mantra that had been rammed down our throats, year after year, so that we wouldn't forget what to check first. It worked. I hadn't forgotten it.

Take it one step at a time – *Breathing* first. Check. Yes, he was definitely breathing.

Bleeding. Check. He was certainly bleeding, from his face, his arms, and his hands – from everywhere! OK, keep calm – it's blood, but it's not pouring out, just seeping. Not enough leakage to kill him, from what I could see. I glanced further down his body, to where his legs vanished under that huge machine, lying on the flimsy roof. There was no way of knowing if his legs were still actually attached to him. For all we knew, he didn't have any legs left, and he'd be dead in no time, no matter what we did.

"Try the seat, Cat," I said. "See if you can release it somehow. Slide it back." It was an automatic reaction, a desperate attempt to get a dying man out of a crumpled car.

Cat blindly groped around the base of the deformed seat for the release handle, but found it to be jammed. As we worked together, pulling on the seat, he eventually managed to force the lever open. It was difficult to find a position to apply leverage – a bit like trying to push a small refrigerator door open with your feet, from the inside. I pleaded for the seat to come back, away from the oppressive weight of that digger.

The seat jolted backwards a few inches, causing the man to yell out in abject pain, tearing something awful inside of me. I fought the urge not to try again – we had no choice. Fortunately for him, it wouldn't budge but, *un*fortunately, we still couldn't see his legs.

I was pleased that we'd managed to release some pressure from his legs, if only slightly. Then I realised that perhaps we shouldn't have done that. He might well bleed to death down there now, and there would be nothing we could do about it. I didn't want the driver to know this, but I did want Cat to realise it.

"Check for any bleeding around his legs, Cat," I said. "See if you can get your hand through, and have a feel around." Cat didn't need telling twice – he tentatively checked around, squeezing his fingers into the gap between the man's legs and the roof. The driver yelled at his touch.

"Sorry, just checking for damage," Cat told him. He pulled his hand out and held it up to the light.

I dreaded seeing blood dripping from his fingers. They *were* red, but it was just smeared blood. I breathed out – we hadn't killed him.

OK, breathing and bleeding sorted. Now for the breaks and burns.

Breaks. Under the present circumstances, I didn't think it mattered too much if the guy had any broken bones. He wasn't going to be moved any time soon, and I was sure he wasn't going to die from any broken bones, even if his legs were all smashed to pieces.

Finally – *Burns.* He had no burns to worry about because there was no fire. Fire? I could smell the fuel. It was actually quite overpowering, but I hadn't been aware of it until that point. The whole car was sitting on a lake of fuel – gallons of the stuff – that had leaked from the two impacted vehicles. If this thing did catch fire, the poor bastard would burn to death, and there'd be nothing we could do to help him. If we didn't get caught up in the inferno and perish with him, we'd have to sit on the side of the road and listen to him die.

I wanted to panic – it was the easiest option – but I forced myself to focus. I knew the digger was full of diesel, and there was no way diesel would ignite. I knew this for a fact. However, the car was full of petrol, as most cars were back then, and petrol *does* catch fire. *Easily.* As a POM, I was able to tell the difference between diesel and petrol just from the smell, but that basic skill failed me when I needed it most.

I silently and pointedly sniffed the air at Cat's face. He sniffed back and frowned at me. I shrugged. *Which is it?* He shook his head. *No idea.* We both understood that we were completely powerless at that point, and that we needed professional help, and fast. I remembered we were not alone.

"Sarge!" I yelled out of the back window.

It took a while for him to reappear. He'd been with Donk, asking motorists to turn around, find a phone box in the nearby village, and call for an ambulance.

"Sarge, we need serious help here! Driver's well trapped and badly injured. We need Fire and Rescue, and quick!" I considered telling him about the fuel too, but I didn't want to add to the driver's worries. Nothing could be done about that until Fire and Rescue arrived anyway.

"Need the first aid kit from the truck?" he shouted back, helpfully.

I knew the box of plasters he was on about. "No, a waste of time. We need a medic, and we need one now!"

"Hang in there – the ambulance should be well on its way. I'll chase up the fire brigade!" He ran off back to Donk at the head of the line of traffic, briefed him, and then ran to the other end of the road to Pizza, and did the same.

We didn't know exactly where we were or which village was closest. We just needed somebody to get to a phone and make the call. We didn't know if any of the drivers were making the calls. None came back to tell us they had, but of course they weren't able to, not with the huge traffic queues that had built up. We just hoped they had.

Smudge briefly reappeared and asked if we were all right. We weren't. We were very worried. It'd be at least thirty minutes before the first emergency services arrived at our isolated accident site. We honestly believed that this man would die before any help got remotely near us.

There was little we could do except talk to him, keep him calm, and offer some kind of reassurance. It was quite a task, trying to take his mind off the twenty tons of machinery lying two inches from his face as fuel dripped onto the tarmac beneath us, mixing with his blood.

"Is there anybody we can contact for you?" asked Cat. "A wife, or someone we can call, to come here?"

That was good thinking – if the guy was to die, he might want to do it holding hands with the one he loved, and not a couple of terrified, sweating squaddies. I looked at the squashed passenger seat next to him, and hoped she was at home.

He battled with his thoughts for a few moments, then spoke. "Robin. The name's Robin."

"You want us to call Robin?" I asked.

"No," he said, fighting back the pain of talking. "It's my name. I'm Robin."

In all the panic and fear, we hadn't even asked the guy his name.

"I'm Dave, and this is Cat. OK, Robin – who can we call for you?"

I fished out the small notebook and pencil I always carried with me when working. With great effort, he gave me a name, address, and telephone number, which he said was his wife's. As I finished jotting it down, a loud female voice made me jump.

"Hey, hey, *hey*!" she cried out. "Calm down, will you? I'm just trying to help you."

I looked out of the shattered rear window and saw a man and woman in the moonlight. The woman was trying to shine a torch into the face of a tall soldier I didn't recognise. A bit of a scuffle ensued, and the soldier cursed the civilian woman, swinging his arms violently, knocking her away. I stared at them, speechless.

"Who the hell are *they*?" I whispered.

"Buggered if I know," said Cat. "Go and check it out. We'll be all right in here."

I hesitated, but Cat was insistent, so I scrambled out of the back window and stood on the road, breathing in the fresh air. Smudge reappeared and joined me and, together, we approached the strangers on the road.

The smartly dressed civilian woman proudly stated that she was a first aider and had stopped to help. She said that the man with her was seriously hurt. The agitated soldier was walking off along the road, talking to himself and waving his arms about. I stepped in front of him and saw that he was obviously in need of help. Blood was running down the side of his face from a head injury, and he was mumbling incoherently to himself, his left hand cupping his left eye.

"Let me see. Let me see," I pleaded, calmly and firmly, knowing that soldiers responded to that kind of tone. I gently removed his hand from his face to see where all the blood was coming from, but he quickly pulled it back.

The woman, who was carrying a torch, rejoined us, causing the man to pull away from me slightly.

"It's OK, I'm just gonna take a look," I said, trying to sound calm. "But I need the torch, OK?"

He accepted my help, but still glared at the woman as she shone the torch on his face.

I removed his hand again, but something momentarily stuck to it, then swung free and hung down his left cheek. It took me a few seconds to recognise what I was looking at – it was his left eye, hanging out of the socket and dangling on a bit of bloody thread. I swallowed deeply and turned away to compose myself before turning back.

"OK, we need to take a look at that," I said, surprising myself. "This lady's a medic – she's gonna help you." I was only too glad to hand him over to somebody better qualified than me.

I encouraged him to sit down on the side of the road, speaking constantly, the training finally kicking in. He was clearly in shock. Talking to people I could do, but a dangling eye was something else.

I think he understood that I was another soldier, and that he needed help. I managed to get through to him, calm him down, and hand him over to the first aider. She pushed me aside, but I let it go – I was glad to leave him in the hands of someone who claimed to know what she was doing. She seemed able to attend to such injuries, whereas I had no idea what you do with an eye that's hanging out. I don't think I wanted to know.

She set about him with authority – she clearly knew what she was doing, and the casualty was now accepting of her.

I stood up to speak to Smudge. "Where the bugger did *he* come from?" I asked.

I looked around and saw nothing but the black mass of the squashed civilian car with our digger resting on top of it. There were no other vehicles to be seen.

"Could he have been in the car?" asked Smudge, indicating the squashed vehicle beneath our digger.

"No, not possible." I knew he couldn't have been in the front seat: he couldn't have survived. But neither could he have been in the back seat: there wasn't a drop of blood on it – I would have noticed. "You haven't seen any other smashed-up vehicles on your travels, have you?" I asked.

Smudge shook his head.

I bent down to the casualty and spoke gently, noting the three stripes on his epaulet. "Listen, Sergeant. Where exactly did you come from?"

The woman attending to him looked at me. She appeared irritated.

"What?" he replied, confused.

"You're not with us. You're not from that," I said, indicating the pile-up behind me. "So where, exactly, did you come from?"

"The bloody army Land Rover, obviously," he snapped.

I stood up and looked around. "*What* bloody Land Rover?"

"Tommo. Where's Tommo?" the man suddenly called out, looking around and trying to get to his feet, causing the first aider to let go of a bandage she had been fastening around his head.

She stared at me, angrily. I put my hands on his shoulders to prevent him from standing. He sat back down.

"Tommo?" he whispered, looking up at me, questioningly, clearly worried, and not making much sense. He then began sobbing uncontrollably.

I ignored the woman's protests and looked at Smudge. 'Tommo' was the standard nickname for anybody in the army whose surname was Thomas or Thompson, and we both knew that a Land Rover was the standard mode of transport for the military, but *who* was Tommo, and *what* Land Rover was he talking about? Then I remembered.

"Oh shit, of course." I turned to Smudge. "That lump of metal that we passed earlier, back there in the road? The TV thing?"

Smudge nodded.

"I think I know what it is! It's the engine block of a Land Rover – *his* Land Rover."

"So, where the hell is the rest of it, then?" asked Smudge.

We instinctively looked around. Our truck was parked further up the road, its hazard lights still flashing. The outline of the engine block could just be seen in its amber lights, between the truck and us. Beyond that, on the brow of a hill, we could see car headlights as Pizza stopped the traffic, spoke to the drivers and turned them around. Behind us was the main accident site, with Cat still inside the car, illuminated by the interior light. Beyond that, more cars were being stopped and turned around by Donk. Out to the sides, we saw nothing but the darkness of the plain.

"Where did he come from?" I asked the first aider.

She dismissively pointed over the squaddy's shoulder into the darkness, loath to speak to me. I wanted to slap her. I stared at her, my eyes demanding a better answer.

"He just appeared from out of the darkness, over there," she said, primly, pointing. "He scared the *poo* out of me," she said, trying to swear. As she spoke, a huge figure ran from around the back of the digger and trailer, startling all three of us.

"Fucking hell, Donk – you scared the shit out of us!" snapped Smudge.

"Sorry, Sarge. Don't wanna miss all the action, do I?" he said, excited and eager to get involved.

A few minutes earlier, a helpful civilian had stopped his car and volunteered his services to Donk, at which point Donk had legged it down the road into the darkness, leaving the poor Good Samaritan standing alone on the road, turning traffic around. Donk wanted to be involved more, and resented being stuck on traffic control well away from the accident. He couldn't take his eyes off the guy's blood-soaked, bandaged head.

"Who's he?" he asked, too loudly.

I looked at the injured soldier and recalled his earlier aggression. An excitable Donk was the last thing we needed right now. *Damn that helpful civilian for releasing Donk.*

"Sarge, if it's all right with you, I'll take Donk and go look for the other guy – this *Tommo*? Could you stay here with the lady?" I asked, tactfully, nodding at the soldier's back. Smudge understood my meaning, and

15

accepted. He seemed relieved at my suggestion.

"Donk, you're with me. We need to find a Land Rover with a guy called Tommo in it, check out if he's OK."

Donk smiled and nodded enthusiastically.

"Any chance of lending us your torch?" I asked the first aider.

"No chance, sorry. I can't do my work in darkness," she said, leaving no room for argument.

"You got a torch, Bruce?" I asked, using Donk's correct name, although I always thought that Donk sounded far nicer than Bruce. He hadn't. I looked up. We could have done with the moonlight, but clouds obscured it again.

"OK, mate, let's spread out a bit. There must be an engineless Land Rover out there somewhere. If we find that, we'll likely find Tommo."

We walked off into the darkness, eyes straining to see something, anything, minds hoping not to. What I'd seen so far was more than enough horror for one lifetime, but was there more to come? I had to brace myself for what we might see, for what we might have to deal with out there on that big, empty plain. I regretted not paying more attention in our first aid classes now, and cursed the police for not being there yet. The crash seemed to have happened so long ago, but, in truth, only about thirty minutes had passed since that first impact.

Come on, Tommo, where the hell are you? I called out his name, thinking that if he was lying on the grass injured somewhere, he might hear me and respond. Instead it was Donk who answered.

"Dave! Dave! Over here!"

END of the ROAD Chapter Three

AS I HURRIED TOWARDS DONK'S VOICE, the moon reappeared, thankfully casting some light on the grasses of the plain. Just ahead of me, another large, dark shape loomed. I ran closer, and a Land Rover appeared, in a very sorry state. It looked like it had been bombed out, but had defied the explosion and remained upright, its doors hanging open.

"Donk?" I shouted.

His voice came back from the other side of the vehicle. I quickly joined him and found him kneeling on the grass, leaning over a dark shape, giving mouth-to-mouth resuscitation to the lifeless figure.

Tommo.

I kneeled next to them, my heart beating madly. I watched Donk as he blew air into the man. My mind was in a whirl – I was about to apply CPR for real, for the first time in my life. I desperately looked up and down the road for any sign of blue lights. Nothing. I tried to recall which of the ever-changing rates of heart compressions I should use, as my fingers felt tentatively along his chest for the right place to compress.

"Too hard, Donk, you're blowing too hard!"

He was – you didn't need to be a medic to know this, but he didn't hear me. I took the guy's wrist to feel for a pulse. It was stone cold. I frowned and leaned over Tommo to check his injuries, having to forcibly push Donk off. Donk angrily pushed me back – he was determined to bring this guy back.

"Donk, wait! Just a second, will you?"

The man's head flopped unnaturally to one side. Even in the darkness I could see how young he was and how freely his head moved. He had dark, matted hair – blood-soaked I assumed. I probed around his head with my fingers, ignoring the blood. I then discovered a huge hole in the back of his head.

"Come on! I gotta breathe for him!" shouted Donk.

The man's injury was clearly fatal. There was no way he could have survived that, and there was obviously nothing we could do to bring him back.

"He's dead," I said, defeated, staring at the young man's peaceful face.

"He can't be – not till a doctor says!" Donk pushed me aside and restarted his over-ambitious mouth-to-mouth. He was determined to bring him back to life, and repeatedly blew air into the guy in ever more desperate breaths.

I watched his futile efforts as I questioned my judgement. Donk was right, of course – we were always told to carry on mouth-to-mouth until a doctor said stop – *we* couldn't say he's dead, but everything about him told me he was beyond help. Should we continue?

I looked across at the battered Land Rover. There could be others inside that vehicle – guys who *did* have a chance. Maybe this wasn't even Tommo?

"Donk, leave it. He's gone, mate. He's gone."

Donk blew again. He wasn't going to give up that easily. Donk was a big guy, strong as an ox, and, in desperation, he blew harder and harder. He was blowing so hard into the corpse that the man's eyes began to come out of their sockets. I wanted to vomit again. That would have been far too many eyes hanging out on one night. I put my hand on Donk's shoulder and shook him, looking into his eyes.

"Bruce," I practically growled. "Leave it, mate. There's nothing we can do for him. He's gone. He's fucking brown bread." I stared into Donk's eyes as he slowly realised the truth of what I was saying. I nodded towards the Land Rover. "There might be others who need our help in that thing. Come on, mate, give us a hand. I don't wanna do this alone."

His shoulders slumped as he stared down at the body lying before him. We stood up together, and I became aware of a bloody handprint on Donk's shoulder where I'd shaken him. I bent down and wiped my hand clean on the grass.

18

I took a deep breath and looked at the wreck of the vehicle. I didn't want to go in there and see more horrors. I prayed that there weren't any more people involved. Donk was subdued and obviously in shock, so I spoke to him gently.

"Now, help me search this *Landy* for any more people – OK, mate?"

Donk nodded, and I grasped his clean shoulder as we moved towards the Land Rover.

"Where are the fucking cops?" I asked, staring off at the long line of car headlights stretching into the distance, just visible beyond the hill. It seemed like everybody had come to this remote spot tonight – everybody except for the Goddamned emergency services.

Donk went to the rear of the vehicle whilst I climbed in through the open driver's door. I kneeled on the seat and looked around. It was full of chaotic darkness, shapes, and shadows. I fumbled for the light, found it, and flicked it on, as Donk lifted the rear canvas flap, which was hanging down over the open tailgate. We knew that soldiers routinely travelled in the back of these vehicles, and this vehicle contained a lot of military webbing – belts and equipment, stuff that was darkly camouflaged, making a search of the vehicle quite difficult, even with the cab light on.

There were large, dark stains on the far doorframe and dashboard, where the passenger – presumably the guy with the eye injury – must have smacked his head open. I decided to stay away from that side of the seating.

The front was clearly empty, both occupants now accounted for. Separating me from Donk was a heavy-duty metal panel, used to fix huge military radios on. I leaned over to look in the back and help Donk, accidentally casting a dark shadow over the rear.

"Fucking 'ell, Dave!" hissed Donk, annoyed at losing the light.

I twisted in the seat with the intention of getting out and joining him at the rear. As I did so, I put my hand on the grey-coloured metal frame, and jumped back as if electrocuted.

"What's up?" asked Donk, concerned.

I didn't reply. I raised my hand up to the cab light, and my stomach heaved. I fell out of the Land Rover and threw up in the grass. Donk ran to me.

"Dave?" He was full of concern. "What's up? What is it?"

The palm of my hand was covered in cold, sticky, light-coloured goo.

I frantically tried to wipe it off onto the grass, but it resisted.

I looked from my hand to the nearby body. I remembered the hole in the back of his head. His proximity to the driver's door meant he had obviously been the driver. This sticky matter had been on the metal frame just behind the driver's head. I vomited again, desperately wiping every last trace of the poor man's brains from my hand.

"I'll be fine in a sec," I said to a worried Donk, between breaths. "Is the back clear?"

"Yeah, there's no one in there – just him, I guess."

"Thank God for that." I slowly got to my feet and looked at Tommo, lying like a discarded animal in the middle of Salisbury Plain, his skull smashed in. As I wiped my hand on my trousers one last time, I felt such sorrow at the loss of this guy. He was younger than me, just a lad, and his family didn't even know of his death yet. I thought of the poor sod that would have to tell his mother, and of the family's anguish.

We stood staring at him. A ridiculous urge to say something over his broken body was interrupted by the sound of a distant siren.

"About bloody time. Come on, Donk. We need to tell them about him." I then remembered the guy trapped in the car and Cat sitting in there on top of all that fuel. It seemed like so long ago. Surely they must be out of the vehicle by now? No, this was the first siren I'd heard – no other emergency crews had arrived, and that guy was still trapped in there. With Cat.

I ran like hell.

END of the **ROAD** Chapter Four

IT WAS A COP CAR, A TRAFFIC PATROL CAR NO LESS. The blue strobe lights were visible for miles, and I stood, impatiently, as it crawled past the stationary queue of traffic. Its progress was occasionally hampered by more than one frustrated driver deciding to do a U-turn, often right in front of the approaching cop car, despite its blaring siren.

I ran past the fuel-soaked car, towards the start of the line of traffic. As I did so, I sent a silent thought of encouragement to Robin, still trapped inside, hoping he was still alive. If he were, he'd have heard the emergency siren approaching too. If *I* felt relieved that they were finally here, how the hell did *he* feel? I also sent Donk back to be with Smudge, as they were both looking more and more stressed.

The cop car came to a casual stop, angled across the road, its headlights illuminating the cause of the tailback. *Come on, guys, this is frigging serious.* I ran forwards as two male cops, both wearing fluorescent yellow jackets, ambled out of the patrol car. They looked up and down the road at the mess in front of them, and, finally, as I approached them, at me.

It was probably the after-effects of the adrenalin, but I was very angry that a young soldier was lying dead out there, all alone in the darkness. I was angry that we had been so helpless and isolated, abandoned to deal with this hell alone. I was angry because they hadn't been here, doing what they were paid to do. And their seemingly casual attitude was the final straw.

"What the hell took you so long?" I shouted. "This bloody thing …" I indicated the carnage a few yards behind me, "… happened about forty fucking minutes ago!" I wasn't really angry with them, but, like most members of the public unexpectedly dropped into a surreal, tragic situation, I hit out at the cops – those who had arrived first to help us. It was all I could do.

"All right, all right, son, calm down. We're here now," said the passenger. He was mid-thirties, calm, smart, and friendly. "We came as soon as we got the call – all the way from the other side of Salisbury. We were the nearest traffic unit. Update me, please. What we got?"

I looked from him to the driver, who turned away and spoke into his pocket radio as he went to the rear of the cop car and opened the boot. I looked back at the passenger cop. *Salisbury*? I knew how far away Salisbury was. *Seriously*? You've come *that* far? I felt bad – they had actually got here very quickly indeed, considering that distance. I regretted my outburst.

Update? Military speak. The training kicked in again.

"One dead – a squaddy, out there in the darkness. Nothing to be done for him."

The cop looked like he was about to ask me a question, and I guessed what it was. *How do you know he's dead?* Somehow, he knew I knew – I saw it in his eyes.

"More importantly," I continued, "we've got one man trapped beneath *that* lot, and I mean seriously trapped. We don't know the extent of his leg injuries for sure, but they're probably life-threatening, although he's conscious and talking – or he was when I last spoke to him." I looked back. Poor sod. "It doesn't look good. My mate's in there with him, and the place reeks of fuel – not sure if it's petrol or diesel, or a mixture of both, but it's all over the road."

As I spoke, the cop scanned the wreckage in front of him, his mind clearly working quickly. I anticipated his next question. "The digger's diesel, but I think the car is petrol. We can't get him out of there. We've tried. We need heavy lifting gear to get that thing off him." I glanced back at the mess and lowered my voice. "Or you'll have to cut his legs off, if they're still attached to him." I paused for breath and listened as the cop spoke rapidly into his radio.

"Believed one fatality at this location. Further casualty trapped with fuel leak. Request Fire and Rescue and heavy lifting gear." He turned to me. "How heavy's that thing?"

"Twelve-ton digger. Maybe fifteen max, with trailer."

"Sufficient for eighteen tons, plus ambulance, and a supervisor, please."

He was passing on my update to his control room. He spoke in a language I recognised and appreciated – a concise, accurate, and efficient language that military personnel use on radios. I realised that what I was saying to this officer was important enough to cause a man to die if I got it wrong. I seriously concentrated as the driver returned with heavy-duty torches, and a decent-looking first aid kit.

"There's another guy with a serious head-cum-eye injury over there. There's an arsy civilian first aider with him, although she seems to know what she's doing. He's another squaddy, and his eye's hanging out." I forced the image from my mind. The driver made to go until I said, "He's OK, though. He's in good hands. Nothing more to be done for him now until he gets to hospital."

"Whiskey Tango one-nine further," said the passenger.

"Go ahead," came back the female voice.

"Will need two ambulances at this location. Repeat: two. We have one further casualty with a serious head and/or eye injury. The road is completely blocked. Will need to close it both ends at ..."

As he continued updating his control room, the driver asked me to show him what was what. He switched his radio off so as not to ignite the fuel vapours as we walked around the fuel-soaked pile-up. He leaned in through the rear window and spoke, introducing himself, reassuring Robin that help was on its way and that he'd be out of there soon. I was so relieved to hear Robin's voice respond.

"Is there anyone we can contact to meet you at the hospital?" asked the cop.

"Oh yeah," I said. "I've got that here." I ripped out the page from my notebook and held it out to the cop. "It's Robin's wife's details." My hand trembled. The cop looked from my hand to my face before taking the paper. He shone a pocket torch on it, checking its legibility.

"Nice one – thanks." He put his head back inside the car. "We'll get a car around there straight away. OK, Robin?"

I heard a muffled reply.

The officer turned to me and squeezed my shoulder as we walked towards the small group huddled around the injured sergeant.

"Nearly done, soldier, nearly done." He looked me in my eyes, and I felt his strength and understanding. "Now, just go with my colleague and show him where the fatality is, will you? I'll get this sorted out." He waved the paper at me and smiled. I felt another hand on my shoulder, and turned to see the other cop again.

"Come on, son – show me where he is. Did you know him?"

"No, he's not one of ours," I replied, privately relieved. I led him off the side of the road as he illuminated the plain with his monster torch. We spotted the Land Rover straight away – it was about twenty yards from the road. We made directly for it and found Tommo where we'd left him. The cop kneeled and examined him.

"Poor sod. At least he didn't suffer."

I wondered how often he'd had to do this sort of thing, and how he managed to deal with it. Traffic cops – must be a way of life for them.

"No doubt here, soldier. He's definitely deceased." He looked up at me. "What's your name, son?"

"Sapper Burden, Officer."

"Well, Sapper Burden, I was hoping you had a *name*."

I smiled. "Sorry, it's Dave." For a moment, I forgot that we were chatting to each other over a dead body. Such was the need for intimacy.

"Well, Dave, my friends call me Jonesy. I often get called other things, but Jonesy suits me just fine." He smiled at me as we stood up. I took comfort in his presence. "Did you pull him out of the Land Rover?"

"No, I didn't. Donk – that's the guy who found him – might have. He was with him when I arrived. Or the driver might have done – that's the guy with the eye injury – he appeared out of the darkness some time after the accident."

"Has anybody searched the Land Rover and the surrounding area for any more casualties?"

"Yeah, we have. We've searched everywhere, but without torches."

"OK, better make sure you didn't miss anything." He stood up and flashed his torch around the smashed-up vehicle, the beam illuminating the area clearly as he spoke into his radio.

"Whiskey Tango one-nine. Confirmed – one fatality at this location. Military personnel."

"Roger, one-nine. Confirmed – one fatality. Will notify RMP."

The Royal Military Police were now on their way. Like most soldiers, I had an irrational fear of the RMP. I thought of the interrogation Cat would have to go through. Presumed guilty before they even got here.

"Good, there are no others," said Jonesy.

We both looked up at the sound of a siren. More blue lights could be seen approaching in the distance.

"Ambulance. Thank God." I couldn't see the vehicle, just its blue lights. I looked at the cop, quizzically.

"It's the sound, Dave. When you've been doing this job for as long as I have, you get to recognise the sound of an ambulance approaching. Sometimes, you pray for that sound." He stared into the distance as the ambulance duly appeared over the rise.

"You see." He smiled. "Come on, there's nothing we can do for him now. It's the living who need our help." We headed back to the main crash site.

On arrival, I was surprised to find so many people there. We had been isolated for so long that the small group of people standing on the road seemed like a crowd. The other cop was taking details from the injured sergeant. He was much calmer, and had been bandaged up quite neatly. Where his dangling eye was, I had no idea.

Donk and Smudge were standing with several civilians I hadn't seen before. Passers-by I guessed. I went up to Smudge and introduced him to the cop.

"Jonesy, this is the man in charge of us: Sergeant Smith." They shook hands.

"You and your men have handled this very well, Sergeant Smith. Well done."

I looked into Smudge's eyes and realised he wasn't looking too good. He was in shock – real shock, not the simulated shock I was used to. He too was a victim, yet he had had to keep playing his part, playing the sergeant. He might have been a military man, but he was just a career construction man – never seen action in his life – and he was really suffering that night. He'd been through what I'd been through, but he also carried the burden of responsibility for all of us, and his job was on the line too.

Was *I* in shock? Were we *all* suffering? I looked at the civilian first aider. *Yes*. I looked at Donk and Pizza who were milling around. *Yes*. I glanced back at Cat, still inside the squashed car. *Yes, of course.* Everybody caught up in this tragedy was suffering from shock – everybody, it seemed, except for these two cops, these two men, who seemed to be in complete control.

I glanced after the other cop, who was now directing the reversing ambulance up to the back of the toppled digger. So in control, directing and organising. *Me?* I just wanted to sit down at the side of the road and have a good cry. Is that how we all felt? When did the cops cry? *Do cops cry?*

The paramedics removed Cat from the back of the car before climbing in themselves. If anybody should be crying, it should be Cat. He walked towards me, and I hugged him. A great big, man hug.

We all turned and looked up at more approaching sirens. So many blue lights flashing through the darkness almost made me dizzy.

"Here come the cavalry," said Jonesy. "Sergeant, keep all your men together. Your work's done for now, but we'll need to speak to you all before we're finished up here, and this might take some time. I presume that's your truck?" He nodded up the road at our semi-illuminated lorry. "Get everybody in there and wait around, would you? Take a breather, but, whatever you do, do not move that truck from where it is."

"Understood," replied Smudge.

We walked along the road in total silence, heads down. Back to our truck, a place of warmth and comfort, a place that had been full of jovial, meaningless conversation less than an hour ago. Several tears were shed by those big, strong soldiers on that short walk back to normality. Nobody said a word until we reached the truck.

Cat went to the rear to examine the towing eye again. I joined him there. I frowned as I bent down to see what he was looking at. I couldn't initially understand what he was holding in his hand.

"Cat! Can you believe it?" I shouted, relieved. He just smiled back at me, his relief clear even in the darkness.

I reached into my pocket and took out the souvenir I'd taken from the churchyard earlier. I briefly looked at it before chucking it into the ditch at the side of the road.

"Now, where the hell did you throw all of that beer, Sarge?" I asked, and the sergeant forgave me my cheek, and laughed heartily.

We all did.

END of the ROAD Chapter Five

I SWALLOWED DEEPLY, AS I ALWAYS DID before entering any office of authority, and this man was *the* authority – *The Old Man*, the boss, the officer in command of my squadron: Major 'Arty' Cummins.

"Come in!" came the reply to my respectful tap.

I entered and saluted smartly. "Lance Corporal Burden, reporting for pre-release interview, Sir."

"Ah, yes, good man. Come in, Corporal Burden, and close the door behind you, would you? There's a good chap. Oh, and pull up a pew."

I did as I was ordered, as the major turned to the new computer at his side. I watched as he scowled at it, before hitting the keyboard hard, several times.

"Useless ruddy thing." He smacked the keyboard one last time, much harder. "Waste of space, if you ask me. More trouble than they're ruddy worth."

He turned towards me, smiling mechanically, as he opened a file on his desk. He briefly scanned the contents in silence before looking over his half-rimmed glasses, directly at me.

"So, you're leaving us, are you? Don't suppose there's any chance I can convince you to stay on, is there?"

"No, Sir – absolutely none."

"I see." He looked down again, disappointed with my firm stance against his beloved army. "Married now, aren't you?"

I nodded. You should know. I had to get *your* permission, in writing.

"Good, good. So, what are you planning to do with yourself on the other side, then? Huh?"

I knew this question was coming, and I had prepared for it. "The Prison Service, Sir."

"The ruddy *Prison Service*? Whatever for?" He removed his glasses and stared at me. He looked as if I had just told him I was going to join the Argentinean Navy. I hadn't been expecting this response.

"Well, er … a secure job, Sir? Good pension?"

He smiled a tolerant smile at me. "Yes, I suppose security is important, what with a young family to support, and so on." He put his glasses back. "But, the *Prison* Service?" He shook his head in disbelief.

I had never really cared much for what he thought, but the fact that he was so shocked and disappointed at my choice concerned me. I didn't know what more to say, so I just shrugged. I felt like a child in the headmaster's office.

"Look, Corporal Burden, let me be frank with you." He removed his glasses once again, and stared at me for a few seconds. "I don't think for a minute that you will be happy to go to work every morning for the rest of your working days knowing that you are going to spend ten hours locked up in an overcrowded Victorian building, full of the scum of society, who all hate your guts, and who would think nothing of sticking a knife in your back the minute your head is turned. And all for a ruddy pension." As he spoke, his voice rose in pitch.

I winced. I hadn't been committed to it – it was just a thought, something to tell him. However, Major Cummins had just established that I would never be joining the Prison Service, because what he had just said to me was absolutely the bloody truth. It just wasn't for me. My new career would have lasted less time than my sixth form studies had. I looked at my boss with grudging respect.

"Put like that, Sir, maybe I'll think of something else."

He stared at me. "Listen, I'll let you into a secret." He glanced at the closed door behind me, for effect. "The squadron is going back out to Belize for six months next year, just about the time you are due to leave us. You were there the last time, weren't you, back in '85?"

I nodded. At the tender age of nineteen, it had been my first taste of 'abroad', and it was an amazing experience. The thought of going back out there again for six months, seeing the old places and exploring the country anew was very tempting, not to mention that Mexico would be just across the border.

However, I wasn't married back then, and I'd seen what the six-month separation had done to some marriages the last time round. *The Old Man* saw the flicker of interest spark in my eyes before being extinguished under the heavy weight of responsibility. He upped the ante.

"Maybe – and no promises here – but, *maybe,* you could go on tour with a *second* stripe on your arm?" He glanced down at my single stripe and raised his eyebrows.

I stared at him. Was he serious? I'd been a lance corporal for over eighteen months now and had never believed I'd ever see another promotion. I was too non-conformist. However, the money was good, it was one step before sergeant, and it was a respected rank. It was very tempting: Belize *and* promotion. It was also a good way of putting off this impossible choice I had to make.

Major Cummins had been my boss for about nine months at that point, and I'd never spoken to him, and I doubt he even knew I existed before that day. As one of his two hundred or so men, I was a nobody, yet here he was offering me a promotion to encourage me to stay in the army! I pushed my luck.

"Only a *maybe*, Sir?"

"I say *maybe* because I'd need to see a serious change in you, Corporal Burden. I'd be taking a chance as it is. Look, I know you are against most of what the army stands for. You can't deal with the boredom of a peacetime army, yet none of us hopes for war. But, whilst we are waiting for another Argentinean-type event to prove ourselves, we need to keep the men entertained. Stop them from getting bored and so on."

It was then that I understood what was on offer. With the new stripe, I'd be expected to give up who I was. I'd have to become one of the army-barmy fools I so despised, just to keep the men from getting bored. Get them to polish the vehicles down with diesel – there's a good chap. A yes-man. A so-not-me man.

"Thank you, Sir, but no thank you. I can't leave my wife behind, not with a baby on the way and all."

"Ah, yes, if I recall, you turned down the Kenya tour for the same reason?"

I hadn't. I'd seriously wanted to spend three months in Kenya, but I couldn't go. I'd had to turn it down for an important course – more qualifications I might have needed. But he was doing all right, the major. The fact that he knew I hadn't gone on the tour impressed me considerably.

"That's right, Sir," I lied.

He stared at me for several seconds, and I saw resignation on his face. "So, you're one hundred percent committed to getting out then." It was a statement, not a question, but I nodded all the same. "Construction work doesn't interest you?"

I shook my head.

"No, I didn't think so. Look, Burden, there's a place in the world for everybody. Mine happens to be in the army for now, and yours isn't. Whatever you do next, don't make the same fucked-up decision you made to get here." He had my full attention and admiration at that point. "You have responsibilities now, and from what you've said so far, I can see that you are taking them seriously."

I nodded in agreement. His astuteness just kept on impressing me. "So, what about your pre-release course – what are your thoughts on that? As you know, there are thousands to choose from, and you might actually find something to qualify in that might not only prove *useful* to you, but be something you might actually *fit* into."

"I thought maybe I'd do a computer course, Sir." I was serious. A month living in London and studying at an official institute, gaining certificates in all aspects of computing not only sounded like a great month out, but it would also give me the chance to get my hands on one of those damned things at last. Pizza had won.

He glanced at the Amstrad and scowled. "Good choice. Those things are the future, although they don't seem to be much use at the moment." He looked at me. "I guess they'll improve though, and, if you learn how to use one, you could always pop back and show me what I'm doing wrong."

We both smiled and sat in silence for a few seconds.

"Awful business, that accident," he said. It had been several weeks since the soldier had died and I'd wiped his brains off my hand.

"Yes, Sir, it was. Very sad. Great that Corporal Stevens didn't face any charges, though."

"Yes, good news indeed. Conducted yourself rather well, I understand?"

I was surprised. Of course he was aware of the accident – his men had spent the whole of the next day writing out statements for the Military Police – but how much did he know of what actually happened?

"Yes, according to Sergeant Smith, you did very well. You kept calm, provided help, put yourself at risk in that car, supported your colleagues throughout, and even bollocked the cops for being late!" He smiled. "You did the regiment proud, David."

I blushed, unaccustomed to an officer using my first name, not to mention praising me.

He sat back. "Yes, if you ask me, you have all the makings of a cop …"

"A *cop*?" The smile fell from my face. I was so shocked that I forgot to add the 'Sir' bit.

"Yes, why not? Security, great pay, good pension. Plus, no two days are the same." He leaned forward. "Think about it – you are out and about, making your own decisions, living off your wits, helping people out. You'll be away from the upper ranks, and you'll be your own boss for most of the day. I think it's right up your street, Corporal Burden. Seriously."

All I could see was another uniform. More men at the top without principles, and pointless bullshit below, not to mention the fact that I'd have to give first aid now and again. I really didn't want to be able to recognise the sound of an ambulance approaching.

I shook my head and smiled at him. "Thanks, but there's absolutely no chance of that happening, Sir."

END of the ROAD Epilogue

THE CAUSE OF THE ACCIDENT WAS ATTRIBUTED to metal fatigue in the neck of the trailer's towing eye, which caused it to shear in two. Once the trailer had separated from the towing vehicle, gravity forced the towing arm to drop down onto its single wheel, causing the front of the trailer to veer out to the right, as if overtaking our truck, and directly into the path of the oncoming traffic. The heavy-duty towing arm that swung out was fashioned into a point, like an arrowhead, but made of steel girders.

This deadly point met the oncoming Land Rover head on, slamming into the front of the flimsy vehicle as it was passing our truck, effectively slicing it in two. The engine section went in one direction, and the rest of the vehicle was thrown across the plain.

The driver was killed instantly, whilst the passenger remained strapped into his seat as the vehicle rolled over and over, coming to a stop off the road. He was lucky to get away with 'just' a serious head injury. Had their vehicle been a second faster or slower, the trailer would have missed them altogether. I never found out if the casualty's eyesight was saved.

The impact of the Land Rover spun the trailer further to its right through 45 degrees, leaving it travelling along and across the road at 90 degrees. Robin had been following the Land Rover. As the Land Rover was knocked off the road in front of him, he slammed into the side of the trailer at about 60 mph. This low-point impact stopped the trailer dead, causing the whole combination to tip over onto his car, squashing it to less than half of its original height. Another few inches and he'd have been killed instantly.

Cat's career didn't suffer as a result of the accident. It wasn't the first time metal fatigue had caused the towing eye to break off that type of military trailer. He later applied to become a pilot at the Army Air Corps, but failed the course for being 'too mechanical'. Shortly afterwards, he left the army and joined the police service.

Donk rose rapidly through the ranks and remained a committed career man.

Sergeant Smudge Smith eventually achieved the rank of Warrant Officer and retired to a well-paid civilian construction job.

Pizza's story is unknown.

I have no idea why the first aider was so unpleasant towards us. She was, however, the first to park her car up and come down and help. She also helped the injured soldier greatly, and, for these reasons, I will always be grateful to her. I never heard anything more of the casualties in this story – it's not something the Royal Military Police excel at: updating the common soldier. Sadly, I don't even know if Robin survived.

I will be eternally grateful to Major Cummins for talking me out of joining the Prison Service. How I even considered it reminds me of just how lost I was back then.

First aid, however, still scares the hell out of me.

L/Cpl Burden in 1988

Book Two in THE ROZZERS Series

COPS DON'T RUN

A TRUE STORY by
DIEM BURDEN

This book is dedicated to each and every man and woman who took the brave decision to become a police officer, even if ultimately you didn't make it through basic training. You wanted to make a difference, and, for that, I applaud you.

COPS DON'T RUN Prologue

I LEFT THE GARRISON TOWN OF TIDWORTH for the last time, and headed off over to Cambridge to start a new life. I'd applied to join the police shortly after my army boss had told me it was the right job for me. That had been a year earlier. The selection process had been long and rigorous, and I hadn't expected to get through it: competition was fierce. When the letter arrived offering me a position with the Cambridgeshire Constabulary, I was stunned. As my time in the army was over, and with nothing else available, I decided to take them up on their offer and become a cop.

On arrival in Cambridge, I was allocated a police house in a marvellous rural setting, in a very upmarket village just outside of the city. In comparison to my army house it was enormous. I was given a week to settle in before reporting for duty at Cambridge Police Station as probationary Police Constable 424 Burden.

My training was based on the new modular system. The induction module, conveniently labelled module one, lasted for four weeks, and took place at my intended police station. The first week of this module dealt with admin matters: allocation of uniform and equipment, getting sworn in, allocation of police warrant card, and touring the station to meet the relevant heads of department. The second week was spent away from the police station, in civilian attire, attached to outside agencies. I spent a fun day in a fire engine, another with a reporter from the local newspaper, and one more with a mental health charity.

Although dressing up as a fireman for a day was fun, it was the third week that proved the most memorable for me. I was put into my new uniform and sent out on patrol with my future colleagues, as a cop. That first week out on the streets both excited and terrified me. I was introduced to my new shift at briefing, and spent the rest of the week out and about with them, observing the day-to-day routine of a patrol officer. With no training whatsoever, the idea was to give me a taste of patrol work, in order to get a feel of what lay ahead for me as a police officer.

Allocated to a tutor-constable to look after me, my brief was to quietly observe, to stay out of trouble, not to get involved in anything, and, above all, to enjoy the experience. That was easier said than done.

COPS DON'T RUN Chapter One
Cambridge, September 1989

"JEREMY'S A LOSER, A COMPLETE WASTER," said Danny as we responded to a lunchtime call of a street disturbance. "A washed-up druggy who usually only comes to our attention nowadays for petty domestic stuff – along with his fat, ugly missus. Used to be a handful in his time did our Jeremy," he added, almost in admiration. "But this'll be a load of crap, a waste of our time. Just you see."

I'd known PC Danny Green for exactly two days at this point. I knew he had nothing against Jeremy; it was people in general he disliked. Danny was my tutor – a world-weary cop who was, on account of his length of service, 'qualified' to take new recruits out on patrol. As the new boy, I was – naturally – in total awe of him. With an expanding waistline, he was dry, apparently humourless, completely unexcitable, and hated everything and everybody, including – it seemed – being burdened with excitable, incompetent new recruits.

For the last two mornings, we'd been patrolling the northern half of the city – the rough council estates – in our little Ford Escort panda car. Yesterday, my first day out on patrol with Cambridgeshire Police, had been dull and routine: tons of paperwork that Danny had to complete whilst I sat and watched, trying to look interested, interspersed with false intruder alarms activated by cleaning staff. This call was different though. This sounded like real police work.

As Danny cut through the chaotic streets of the council estate like a racing pro, I kept glancing at a little switch on the dashboard. This was no ordinary switch; this was the switch that activated our blue light. It had remained permanently off since day one and I was bitterly disappointed that we hadn't used it yet. Surely this was such an occasion? No matter how much I willed it, our solitary blue light remained switched off, much to my dismay. I think Danny knew what I was thinking and detested me even more for it. I later discovered Danny's aversion to any form of excitement, and activating a blue light would just draw unnecessary attention down on us. So it stayed off.

Before long, we turned into a small cul-de-sac packed with too many houses. It looked like the constructor had thrown all the houses up into the air, and built them where they'd landed.

"That looks like the scrote there," Danny said, indicating a man on the pavement fifty yards ahead of us who was attempting to open a tall, wooden, garden gate. I had no idea what a *scrote* was, and I had no time to ask as Danny continued his brief. "Yeah, Jeremy's the tall guy standing by the gate – his gate – and that looks like his stupid wife on the other side of it, if I'm not mistaken."

I was sitting in the passenger seat with the window down, which also happened to be the closest window to where Jeremy was standing, as we approached at an unimpressive pace.

"You mean him?" I asked, pointing. "The one with the *axe*?"

"An axe? He *hasn't* … Oh, God, he *has*, hasn't he? OK, don't get out." Danny said all this in exactly the same tone and volume as before, and I never did understand why he thought that I might have actually got out of the car at that precise moment.

Jeremy was now fully aware of the cop car slowly crawling towards him along the quiet street. As if to prove it, he looked menacingly at the axe in his hand, before raising it high above his head and slamming it into the top of the wooden gate several times, splintering the wood. He turned his head and stared directly at me, the nearest 'cop'. I did what any person would have done in my situation; I crouched down in my seat and acted invisible. I was just about to close the window and lock the door when Danny leaned across me and called out of the window.

"Come on now, Jeremy. Put the axe down. Don't be stupid," he said, sounding inconvenienced. I wondered at his choice of words – surely calling an axe-wielding scrote 'stupid' wasn't something we'd be taught at police college?

Confirming my assessment, Jeremy yanked the axe out of the gate, turned, and marched directly towards us – towards *me*. Danny must have anticipated this response because he calmly put the panda into reverse, and backed out of the cul-de-sac just fast enough to keep ahead of Jeremy, but not too fast to get noticed. After a short distance, Jeremy gave up and returned to his gate. I breathed out again.

I was armed with nothing more than a small, wooden truncheon hanging from my belt – a police weapon invented one hundred and fifty years earlier. Nobody had taught me how to use it, just how to loop it around your belt so that it didn't fall down the inside of your leg and trip you up when running. I hoped we wouldn't be expected to take on this six-foot tall, axe-wielding, ex-druggie scrote with only our pathetic pieces of wood for defence.

That's it, then. Time to call in the specialists, take this loony out.

Then Danny did something unexpected. He drove back towards Jeremy the Axe. My eyes were white. What the hell was he thinking? He hadn't even called for back-up, *and* the blue light was still off. He stopped the car in exactly the same place, leaving Jeremy the Axe just a few yards from my half-open window.

"Jeremy, don't be bloody stupid. Put the axe down, will you?" There was *that word* again. Danny's voice went up a tad in volume, but still showed no sign of fear or excitement – or even interest, come to think of it.

As I stared at the axe splitting the gate, I began to have serious concerns about having chosen the wrong police force. I'd assumed that Cambridge would be full of students, and old ladies drinking tea, and that absolutely nothing ever happened there. The fact that Jeremy the Axe was happening to me on my second day out on patrol, and the calm, matter-of-fact way Danny was dealing with it, made me really worried – was it *always* like this?

We reversed a bit further this time, on account of Jeremy chasing us a bit further, before he gave up again and returned to his rapidly deteriorating gate. This time, Danny did get on the radio, but asking for assistance came hard to him.

"Yeah, control, Jeremy has an axe and won't put it down. I think we're gonna need a bit of help here." (I soon learnt that police radio messages, especially urgent calls, *always* began with the word *Yeah*. I have no idea why.)

I smiled. I pictured dogs, helicopters, and dozens of beefy cops equipped in full riot gear. I anticipated seeing Jeremy, the axe-wielding scrote, being unceremoniously de-axed and dragged away screaming, bundled into a waiting police van, and carted off to prison, sobbing. Pats-on-the-back all round. That always happened on the TV series *The Bill*, and now I had a front row seat as a real-life police drama unfolded before me, a real blue-light job! I looked at that switch and smiled. I was rather looking forward to this next bit.

COPS DON'T RUN Chapter Two

I WAS SMIRKING AT JEREMY from the relative safety of the police car, parked just out of his reach. If only he'd known what was about to happen.

"Zulu 147 on scene," boomed the voice over the radio, startling me – much to Danny's amusement.

"Ah, just the man," said Danny, turning in his seat to look at his requested 'someone else', as a vehicle pulled up behind us. I looked back and saw a solitary white Escort van. It could have been the local baker on his rounds. Its blue light was also off.

A single gangly officer stepped out of the van. I followed Danny's lead as he got out of the car, trying to look as confident as he did. In reality, I was relieved to be out of the confines of the car and able to run away if Jeremy came at us again.

"Hello, John. Long time, no see," said Danny to the new arrival. I stared at the cop. He was tall and thin, with no special equipment, and *alone*? I looked up and down the road for his colleagues, but there were none – no distant sirens, no deep thuds of helicopter rotors. *Nothing*.

"Where is he?" asked the new arrival, without once glancing at me.

"That's the prick – over there, by the gate," said Danny. We were about fifty yards away now, and Jeremy was still chopping up his gate, but with less enthusiasm. He was warily watching us out of the corner of his eye. The skinny cop went to the back of his van and vanished from sight. Danny turned and watched Jeremy watching us.

"This'll be good," said Danny, dryly. "Just stay out of the way, don't say nothing, and you might even learn something." His tone told me he didn't think that last part was possible.

I had no idea what was about to happen, and I couldn't imagine that the two veterans were about to take on Jeremy the Axe alone. It all seemed too risky.

"Watch your back," said Danny. It wasn't a warning, a command, or a request – just a statement, calmly spoken. I casually turned to see what it was I should be careful about, and jumped aside – too quickly for Danny's liking.

The waist-high wolf was dragging the skinny cop down the side of the Escort van, salivating as it came towards me. I felt foolish – it was just a police dog after all, and it was on *our* side. As I tried to recover my composure, Danny pushed me aside quite forcefully. I didn't understand – the creature was a cop dog and I was a cop! I was in uniform, after all – we were on the same team.

"You've obviously never been bitten by an eight-stone German Shepherd, have you?" sneered the tall cop, as he was dragged past me towards Jeremy who had now completely forgotten about the gate. I wasn't aware that I was making the same foolish assumption made by all new cops.

Now that I had been removed from the dog's line of sight, the beast instinctively headed directly for Jeremy. Jeremy was no fool – he'd obviously been there before. As soon as the beast's radar was fixed on him, he turned and legged it into the confusing alleyways of the council estate. Foolishly, he took the axe with him.

"Stay behind me," ordered Danny. "Keep quiet and, whatever you do, stay well out of the way of *The Exocet*." I did as I was told. It was on that little walk around the rambling council estate that I learnt a valuable lesson: that contrary to popular belief, police dogs don't love cops and bite crooks – they bite *anybody* who gets in their way. Months later, The Exocet not only took a chunk out of about twelve people at an illegal rave gathering, but munched on three cops in the crowd as well.

With a dog trained to bite leading the way, and a mad axe-man hiding from us somewhere nearby, my senses were on a high state of alert. Behind the dog was the dog-handler, with Danny close behind him. I walked at the back of the line, constantly checking behind me to see if Jeremy had looped around us and felt like attacking the little guy at the back.

After several disorientating circuits of the estate, we arrived back at the two police cars. The nutter had vanished, and there was nothing to be done until he turned up again. The damaged gate was his own gate, so we couldn't even get a complaint of damage. I watched as The Exocet was being put safely back into the cage in the back of the van, whilst trying to calm my beating heart down.

Then the radio room called us up. They were speaking to Jeremy on the phone. He wanted to say he was sorry and to give himself up, but not to the dog. The operator was able to tell us precisely which public call box he was calling from, so, while they kept him talking, we took a direct route to him. The dog seemed to understand the operator because, as soon as we got the update, it began salivating again.

Before we reached the phone box, we bumped into Jeremy walking across the green towards us, hands up in surrender. The dog somehow knew this was Jeremy the Axe, despite the axe not being visible, and went crazy. The handler had to hold onto the dog with all of his strength, as we edged closer to an increasingly worried Jeremy.

"Where's the axe? Where's the fucking axe?" shouted the dog-handler.

Jeremy put his two hands out in front of him in a defensive gesture, and they were both clearly empty. None of us could tell if he had the axe or not, but the dog didn't care – he wanted this guy so badly. I stood back and watched, as a passing spectator might, my eyes wide open.

"Show us the axe, Jeremy! Show us the fucking axe!"

Even with my limited experience, I could see how this was going to end. The more Jeremy wasn't showing us the axe, the more the dog-handler screamed at him to show it. The more the dog-handler shouted, the more excited and aggressive the dog became. The more frightening the dog became, the more terrified Jeremy became. He'd scream back that he didn't have the axe, which in turn really upset the dog. Danny, amazingly, remained calm throughout the whole drama.

The gap between us was now down to about ten yards, and Jeremy was beginning to panic, as the salivating beast got closer to him. And then he did something stupid. He started to back away. Even *I* knew this was the wrong thing to do. *Just show us you don't have the damned axe – lift up your shirt, and turn around!* But no, Jeremy decided to back off, away from the cops and the terrifying demon. *Fight or flight.* He had chosen, and he had to be apprehended.

I anticipated that moment, as did the other three. They ran at him and, in that moment, I realised that Jeremy wasn't so stupid after all, because just before the dog reached him, I saw him stand dead still and cup his balls in both hands. For an instant I admired his bravery and forward thinking. I didn't know at that time, but what Jeremy had just done was very advisable, because if the dog bites you there – and they often do, it's just at the right height for them – then it hurts, seriously hurts, and can prove problematic later on. Jeremy knew what he was doing – he was an old pro at this, and he liked his balls just the way they were.

Fortunately for him, the dog didn't bite him there, but it did bite his thigh muscle. I saw the fang go all the way in, then back out again, leaving a deep muscular hole which immediately filled with scarlet blood. *Oh great, blood.* Jeremy screamed and stared at his leg in horror, as the dog-handler manhandled the wolf off him. It had tasted blood and had become a demented demon. I believe that, had it broken free, it would have eaten Jeremy, on that grass, just next to the local infants' school.

I didn't know who to watch – the dog-handler dragging the raving mad dog across the green, or the prisoner now sitting on the grass, openly bleeding, with his hands cuffed behind his back. Danny finished searching him. He didn't have the axe with him.

"You silly little sod – you only had to show us you didn't have the axe with you. It didn't have to come to this, Jeremy," Danny said, in his usual low monotone.

"How could I fucking show you I *didn't* have the fucking axe with me if I didn't *have* the fucking axe with me to fucking show you?!" yelled Jeremy. He had a point. He was clearly annoyed, as he stared at the blood spreading out across the front of his jeans. I wasn't sure if he was pissed off at the dog bite, or the seeming unfairness of the cops asking him to show them something he didn't have.

"You dickhead. All you had to do was turn around and lift up your T-shirt. Come on, on your feet."

And that was it – the first arrest I witnessed whilst in uniform. It all seemed so dangerous, so violent, so exciting, and all over too quickly. My eyes were like saucers and I was speechless, but Danny, he was as cool as a cucumber. In all the time I was with him, I never once saw him get ruffled.

Many weeks after this baptism, as we ambled through the beautiful city centre thronging with shoppers and tourists, a member of the public excitedly told us 'One of your guys is getting a right pasting' just around the corner from us. We had been heading towards a report of a shoplifter being detained, and the update of possible trouble made our arrival even more urgent. Danny was obviously anticipating my next movement. I wanted to run to help, but my body language gave me away.

"Don't you dare," hissed Danny, out of the corner of his mouth. Like a scolded puppy, I stayed where I was.

"But?" I asked, confused. There were hundreds of shoppers milling around us, all aware of our presence as we marched through the crowds towards a potentially violent incident just around the corner from us.

"Cops don't run," Danny said, leaving no room for argument. It was true, some cops never ran, and I didn't whilst with him. Once free of him, however, I never stopped running.

COPS DON'T RUN Chapter Three

MOST PEOPLE ARE UNCOMFORTABLE WITH CHANGE but will eventually come to accept it. Cops, on the other hand, seem completely averse to change, which is understandable if you take into account two things: First, they are – naturally – a suspicious lot, so when they learn that change is coming they think the worst. Second, British policing had hardly changed since the world's first professional police force was established, way back in 1798, in London. Trying to convince such cops that change is actually good for them can prove difficult.

When I joined the police back in 1989 nobody had cared to force real change on the police. Most officers could serve out their whole career without as much as a whiff of any outside interference. Nothing changed, ever. It was quite simple: you had a uniform which hadn't changed since forever; a wooden truncheon to bash people over the head with; and the legal right to go out and make people do what you required them to do. You were part of a Police *Force,* and force was always available if folk failed to co-operate with you.

But, the end of the 1980s brought a new awakening in UK society. It heralded the beginning of political correctness, open government, and the right to ask questions. The British public was being bombarded with bad news almost daily, and the time had come to start asking difficult questions. The year I joined the police was certainly a good year to begin asking.

It began dreadfully. In January 1989, an airliner was blown apart over

Lockerbie, in Scotland, killing 270 innocent people. This was followed four days later by another airline disaster, as a Boeing 737 crashed onto the motorway on approach to East Midlands Airport, killing another 44 people. It was the year that author Salman Rushdie received his *fatwa* for writing a book. And the IRA blew up a military barracks, injuring 50 soldiers. Another 6 people died as trains collided at Purley. Then, a month later, 96 football fans died and 766 were injured at a football match in Sheffield, whilst Wolverhampton and Dewsbury suffered rioting. Fifty CID officers were suspended or transferred, as the West Midlands Serious Crime Squad was disbanded, following repeated allegations of fabrication of evidence. Then, in August, a pleasure boat sank on the river Thames, resulting in the deaths of 51 people. Yet another IRA bomb killed 11 soldiers in Deal, Kent, just a month before the 'Guildford Four' were released from prison due to unsafe convictions.

It was also a monumental time for me as I quietly left the army and moved to Cambridge, but obviously nobody noticed amongst all that strife. Even the country's ambulances were staffed by military personnel, because every crewmember had gone on strike. Margaret Thatcher's ten-year term in office was increasingly under threat. And then, to cap the year off, the Berlin Wall fell, heralding a declaration that the Cold War was over. All of this happened in the year that I joined the police.

With so many questions being asked, and the inevitable mud being slung at the police, the government decided to do something about it. The first thing they came up with was to change the name. It was the word 'force' that was too strong, too *police*. Maybe it had been the long, drawn-out fight with the striking miners that had caused the rethink – the image of the *Dixon of Dock Green* bobby had been dented forever in that dreadful, long-running dispute that left ten people dead. Along with other questionable incidents that year, police actions were constantly being challenged, not least by the gutter press. Maybe the police were relying on the use of *force* too much when, instead, they should be delivering a *service*? It was in this growing climate of mistrust of the police that change was instigated, causing much disquiet amongst the established ranks.

Policing by consent is the cornerstone of British policing, and that stone was being constantly eroded, so naturally *something* had to be done. If we lost that unique policing aspect – an unarmed police service as can only be found in Great Britain and three other countries in the world – then we'd all have to carry a gun, and nobody wanted that, not least the officers walking the streets.

The answer was amazingly simple: from 1989 the police could no longer *force* people to do things, but would *ask* them politely to do it, only resorting to force as a very last resort. And afterwards, we were required to sit around and talk about what had happened, so that we could learn from our mistakes. So, the centuries-old terminology was discarded: we were no longer to refer to ourselves as a police *force*. Instead, we were to be known as a police *service*, and then the general public would revert to respecting us once more.

Next in line was the mindset of the people providing this new service: *incoming* police officers. As the government bods were well aware, any attempt at changing the working practices of an old, cynical cop would have been a waste of time, so a gradual transition from *force* to *service* was called for. Bring in better-educated, open-minded new blood, mould them to the required way of thinking, and sit back and watch everybody love the police once more. Just let the old guard slowly fade away on their way to retirement. So, with the change of name came the change in training. The old military system of training was abolished, and in came the modern, touchy-feely style, as the old cops distastefully referred to it. Even saluting senior officers was quietly dropped, as it was deemed far too martial.

It was on this new modular system that I found myself, only the second batch in our force – sorry, *service* – to have started it. We were the guinea pigs, and we were constantly being monitored by everybody who had come before us for signs of being too soft. One officer even suggested we were 'more like social workers than cops', a phrase that was said with utter contempt. I began to have an idea as to why Danny disliked me – he, like everybody else, had gone straight to police college to study law, then returned to division and found his place out on patrol. Nearly two years later, they had all attended another course, then returned to the force where they were confirmed by the Chief Constable. That was it: they were then fully fledged cops. It was a tried and tested method, and it had produced real men (and later, women) since time immemorial.

I had no idea what awaited me that Monday morning, when I was driven to the station to report for duty for the first time. My pregnant wife had driven me there.

"But why do *I* have to drive you there?" she whined, on the way into the city.

"Because, my dear, I don't actually know *where* the police station *is*." It was true. I'd only ever been into the city twice before, and both times were for the cinema.

"Not very good, is it?" she laughed. "You being a cop and all, and not even knowing where the cop shop *is*." She had a point, but even so, I didn't actually feel like a cop yet. I was just looking forward to exploring the police station, meeting my new colleagues, and getting out and about in this idyllic, quiet town known all over the world for its architectural beauty and famous university.

There were a few of us starting that day. Our first week had been a leisurely, albeit exciting, one. We got to know one another over numerous mugs of coffee, as we met key personnel and senior officers, and signed for our new uniforms. I remember trying mine on in the Quartermaster's store, and standing in front of a full-length mirror. Standing before me was a fully uniformed, stern-looking officer of the law, his gaze fixed directly on me. My natural impulse was to flee. Most of my life had been spent avoiding cops. The only times I had actually spoken to any had been when I was doing something I shouldn't have been doing – which was quite often. I usually ran or cycled or drove away quickly. Had I been caught, I wouldn't have been able to choose that particular career, but I never had been. I'd always managed to get away, but not this time. This time, the cop had truly got me.

We took great delight in wearing our crisp new uniforms around the station, feeling the suspicious eyes of the old guard following us around everywhere. We stood out so much, and not just because of our starched uniforms. We were young, eager, and full of something that you lose a little of each year in the job: positivity. You could usually tell the length of service of a British bobby, just by gauging the amount of positivity he had left in him. If he had none, then it was safe to assume that he had been a cop for at least four years.

Towards the end of the first week, I was instructed to prepare for a familiarisation visit to the local Magistrates' Court. I was to meet the court's officer downstairs, who would take me there. I did as I was told and met a WPC (even the 'W's were in the process of being dropped, out of political correctness) who was wearing a civilian jacket over her uniform, and pushing a bicycle.

"Oh," she exclaimed, you're coming like *that*?" I looked down to see what I'd done wrong, confused. "We're *walking* over?" she explained. I still didn't understand. She relaxed. "I suppose it'll be OK, it's only a short distance."

Nobody had warned me that we would be walking there. I was in full uniform, complete with the famous and extremely uncomfortable large 'tit' helmet. It was no more than a five-minute walk through the city centre, but it was a momentous walk for me – and terrifying. It was the first time I'd been outside of the police station in my uniform, and there I was, walking down the street with another officer who was, for all intents and purposes, completely hidden from the public's view. How many times I got stopped by members of the public to ask me directions I can't recall, but each enquiry left me bumbling like a buffoon.

"Excuse me, officer, could you tell me where the bus station is?"

"Er, sorry … I, er …" I stammered to a halt.

"Yes," interjected my disguised colleague. "It's just there, right behind you." The man looked at her, then back at the bus station just across the road. It was indeed right behind him. He looked back at me, smiling.

"Thanks," he said directly to me, even though the lady had answered him.

"Could you point me in the right direction for the police station, please? I've got to pay this parking ticket," asked another man, waving his ticket at me, quite cheerfully. I smiled: it was just along the road behind us, still in sight. Now, *that* I could do. I stood tall.

"Yes, sir, just follow this road along here, and you'll find it on the left, just before the fire station. Big, ugly, grey building. Can't miss it." I smiled at the man. I was really proud. I actually felt like a cop, and I had just carried out my first public service!

"Er, actually …" chimed in the real cop. "If it's a parking ticket you have, you can't pay it at the station. You'll have to pay it at the Magistrates' Court." She gave him directions to the court, leaving me feeling like a complete novice. I didn't know the city, I didn't know the law, and I certainly didn't know anything of police procedures. How on earth would I learn all of that?

My colleague quickly ushered me through the throng of shoppers and, within a few minutes, we arrived at what I thought would be the sanctuary of the court. It wasn't. It was packed with angry people who had been put there by us – the police. Their hatred of *us* was all too clear. It was the first time I'd felt such contempt directed at me from complete strangers (if you discount the instructors in basic military training). I remembered the words of my old army Major, when I'd told him I was thinking of joining the prison service. Thankfully, I'd taken his advice, as I couldn't wait to get out of that courthouse with its bubbling, concentrated anger. Imagine a whole prison wing full of such people?

My guide gave me the quickest of tours before arranging for me to be transported back to the police station in the relative safety of the back of a police van. I rested my head back and closed my eyes – I was hidden from view and safely locked inside the cargo area. The opening of a small hatch made me jump. It was the front seat passenger who smiled back at me.

"Hopefully, we'll get you back to the nick before any urgent calls come in, but we're the only unit free at the moment. If we get a call, just hang on tight back there; you'll have to come with us." As the hatch closed, I crossed my fingers. *Please, no …* Fortunately, the ride was only five minutes long, and no calls did come in.

As soon as I arrived back behind the thick walls of the station, I went straight to the canteen for a strong coffee. I spoke to my fellow recruits about what I'd been doing, trying to put into words how it feels to have every pair of eyes on you as you walk out of the police station in full uniform, and the uncomfortable feeling inside the court house. None of them could understand *why* I had walked out in full uniform, and all thought it hilarious.

The following week, we were sent out to work with different outside agencies. This had such a great impact on me that I can only remember three of them. One day was spent with a weird reporter from the local newspaper, whizzing all over town in a tiny Rover Mini. The second day was spent at a mental health workshop, where I helped ill people make things to sell at a local shop. Another day was spent dressed as a fireman, either being thrown around in the back of a fire engine racing to various incidents, or sitting around the station, bored. I only recall two of the incidents: one was to a child whose finger was stuck in a classroom door. As I walked in dressed as a fireman, all the concerned teachers turned to me for help and advice. I was quickly discovering that, if you wear a uniform, even for a day, the public will automatically assume that you are the real deal. The other was to a sixth-form college for a fire alarm test. We parked up in the playground and got swamped by curious, flirty, female sixth-formers. It took us ages to complete the test.

The third week was when I got to meet Jeremy the Axe, and the final week was a debriefing of our experiences. Naturally, I got to do most of the talking on account of Jeremy. We all agreed that the month had been an eye-opener for everybody. We couldn't wait to go to police college, get trained up, and come back and get stuck in for real.

The end of the module had arrived too quickly. It was time to say goodbye to our families and new colleagues, and head south for ten weeks. It was time to learn how to be a cop. It was time for police college. Little did I know that I was about to make police college history – for all the wrong reasons.

COPS DON'T RUN Chapter Four

Ashford Police Training Centre, Kent

ASHFORD POLICE TRAINING CENTRE IN KENT is now closed down. Built around an 1875 mansion, the site had been used in various roles before being acquired by the Home Office in 1973, to be used as the regional training centre for the police forces of South East England. Its function was to give new recruits a thorough grounding in various police skills, including law, physical fitness, self-defence, life-saving, and first aid.

In 1989, the training changed. I was on the second course of the new system, which was done through classroom-based discussions, self-study, or practical simulations. I was looking forward to a relaxing ten weeks sitting around discussing points of law and procedure, and repeating the story of Jeremy over many coffee breaks. Much to my surprise, we also had to learn to march. Drill, as it was known, was second nature to an ex-soldier such as myself, but for others it was a painful thing to be put through, and even more painful for ex-soldiers to have to witness.

I couldn't understand it; marching went against everything that the Home Office was trying to achieve with the new *service*. Surely it should have been phased out, too? But, to my horror, I soon found myself standing to rigid attention in front of an ex-military Drill Sergeant, resplendent with vertical peaked cap and pace-stick, screaming at us in a booming voice. What's more, we were to waste numerous hours each day on the parade square, learning how to march! I'd just spent six years of my life marching, and I wasn't overly impressed with this pointless charade.

Our intake was huge, and we were divided into several classes of fifteen probationers, each class formed up in three ranks on the parade square. The classes were made up of a mix of officers from various forces. I was the only one in my class from the Cambridgeshire force, so everybody was new to me. We hit it off straight away, despite the varying standards and requirements of each individual force's recruiting process. We were very much alike, each full of enthusiasm, and all wanting to make a difference.

As I shivered on that chilly parade square whilst waiting to be inspected, the first doubts began to surface. This was not what I had joined for, and I was beginning to have serious regrets about having joined *another* army.

I watched the Drill Sergeant out of the corner of my eye as he walked along the front rank, making small adjustments here and there, and criticising the turnout of some officers – most deservedly so. I noticed that the sergeant generally left us ex-army folk alone – there were three in our class, and we did stand out from the other students. By that, I mean we knew how to *wear* a uniform, stood to attention properly, and at least knew the difference between 'left turn' and 'right turn', something that one WPC never managed to get right until the very last day of the course.

The sergeant stopped at the student standing directly in front of me – he was wearing his tunic like a black bin liner and, quite rightly, needed to be told so. He looked the bloke up and down, the disgust on his face clear for all to see. I did actually feel sorry for the recruit – he was about to get the bollocking of his life.

"Did you brush your tunic this morning?" asked the sergeant, quietly, as he moved to within inches of the poor boy's face, whilst picking a hair off his lapel.

"Yes, Staff!" squealed the victim, almost trembling. The sergeant stared into the man's face. The tension was electric. He looked up and down the ranks before looking back at the recruit.

"What with? A Jack-fucking-Russell?!"

The tension broke in an instant, as fourteen officers wet themselves laughing, all at the expense of the poor chap in front of me. From that moment on, I liked the sergeant because when he told the joke, I could see the smile in his eyes. He was enjoying the moment – it wasn't an offence worthy of getting locked up for. This wasn't the army, after all.

After parade, we were shown to our classrooms. The first thing I noticed was our seating arrangements: in the army we sat in rows facing the sergeant, but in the police we sat in one great circle, which *included* the sergeant. We still had to address him as 'Staff', and he still wore three stripes on each arm, but it was meant to make us feel less military-like, despite the early morning parade square shenanigans.

Our ten weeks there were supposed to prepare us for our next five weeks out on patrol, where we'd be doing hands-on police work under close supervision. We were to be instructed on the various aspects of being a police officer, with the practical aspects being recorded on video. This meant that the whole class could sit around and giggle over your dreadful performance immediately afterwards.

Our biggest concern wasn't whether we'd cope or not out on the mean streets, it was the old guard. It varied from force to force, but the general feeling was that our allocated tutor-constables for those first five weeks back on division hadn't in fact been fully trained to deal with the new system we were being subjected to.

'They should be' we were repeatedly reassured, without anyone really knowing how prepared the various forces were.

The end of the ten weeks came quickly, and we couldn't wait to get back to our forces, away from the parade square and false practicals, and back to reality, to the job we'd joined to do. We were to spend five weeks on our respective streets before returning to Ashford for a final five-week stint, which, from what we'd heard, was nothing more than a five-week debrief of what we'd all been up to out on division.

It meant we had to say our goodbyes for a while, and as we'd bonded so well, it was difficult. We knew we were all heading out to dangerous streets, and that anything could happen to any of us. If the Jeremy the Axe incident had happened in my quiet city, what sort of craziness happened in places like London or Luton? Being human, our final night together had to be a memorable one. Being British, it involved copious amounts of liquid refreshment, and it all began in the extremely cheap campus police bar.

Now, strictly speaking, female officers were not allowed into the men's dormitory, but after quaffing so much alcohol, we felt justified in what we did next. We knew it was against the rules, we knew we'd be in trouble if we got caught, but there was no way we could consider leaving the three female officers from our class out of our little farewell event. We'd survived ten weeks of police college together, and we were off to do dangerous work in dangerous places. We'd seen the 'for-police-eyes-only' videos of numerous British disasters, uncensored recordings hiding nothing from the curious recruits, all in the name of education. We knew how dangerous our jobs were, and we silently feared the awful prospect that maybe one of our classmates might not actually make it back there again. So the *whole* class, including recruits from other classes on our course, ended up back in the corridor of our (male only) dormitory for a corridor party – naturally.

It was going really well, if a little loudly, when the door at the end of the corridor burst open. We all turned to face the intruder, cans of beers swiftly hidden behind backs. We might have got away with it if it hadn't been for Dave. He was standing on a chair in the middle of the corridor, wearing a pair of men's underpants on his head. He'd hidden his beer, but forgotten about the boxers. I have no idea why he was wearing the Y-fronts or indeed whose they were, but he had just been leading us all in a rather enjoyable rendition of some rude rugby song.

The man marched into the corridor, a look of smug satisfaction on his face. It was Staff Red-face, the duty sergeant, and he'd caught us in the act. Staff Red-face was a man who walked around campus with a very angry face. About what, we knew not, but he was a man some said they didn't really want out on the streets. So he had been sent there, out of harm's way. They'd stuck three temporary stripes on his arm, and left him there to his own devices.

"What the hell is going on here?!" he demanded. I thought it was rather obvious.

"Well?" he squealed, looking up at Dave who was still wearing the underpants. Dave suddenly remembered, and sheepishly slid them off his head with an embarrassed smile, hiding them behind his back. Somebody behind Red-face snickered, and others giggled too. It was an extremely funny situation to everybody present, except for Mr Angry. He was out of his depth, but he was the authority that night.

"Sorry, Staff, it's just a bit of fun, that's all …" began Dave.

"Fun? *Fun!*" He was really red now, almost purple. "You'll be arresting people for doing this, next bloody week!"

Evidently he was wrong on that point – this party was a private event on private property, and therefore it would be out of the jurisdiction of the police. We'd just spent the last ten weeks preparing for such scenarios. The recruits all knew this point of law, but obviously law wasn't his strong point.

"You're supposed to be police officers now, setting an example to others, so start acting like officers!" He stared at us all, sensing that nobody really took him seriously or respected him. None of us had signed away our personalities, our culture, our way of life. Yes, we knew that we'd have to set an example to the public, but the public were not at our party. He did the only thing he could do – he put us all in front of an authority we did respect.

The following morning we were all marched into the Commandant's office by Staff Red-face. After learning of our heinous crime, the boss threatened us all with expulsion from the course. None of us wanted that – for each of our positions there had been thousands of applications. We knew we were lucky to be there, but none of us actually believed his threat.

He advised us to show greater self-control back on division, where we'd be in the public eye, and to return for the final module at police college as better probationers than we were showing ourselves to be.

We did as we were advised, and we all went away to fight the bad guys, before returning to college as 'better' people. What happened on my eventual return was the fault of Staff Red-face too, who caused my name to go down in the centre's history.

COPS DON'T RUN Chapter Five

Cambridge

DESPITE THE FACT THAT I NEVER functioned very well in the mornings, by 6.00am I had tied and retied my shoelaces countless times, drunk umpteen cups of coffee, and visited the toilet twice. I was loitering alone amongst the regimented rows of grey metal lockers in the basement, and fidgeting: with my stiff uniform, my noisy equipment, my clip-on tie, and just about everything else that was new and uncomfortable to me.

I'd jump as the echo of silence was occasionally interrupted by blue-section officers crashing through the basement door in a zombie-like trance. They'd been on duty throughout the night, and were rapidly approaching sleep-hour. They had no idea who the stranger was, lurking uncomfortably amongst the lockers, but a nod of the head was offered along with the ubiquitous 'All right, mate?' They didn't care who I was – they were already asleep.

Each section was headed by an inspector and three sergeants, supervising – on paper – a team of about fourteen patrol officers. My section – red section – were congregating around several large wooden tables in the next room, the briefing room. I'd been there on my taster week and had met most of them, yet the prospect of bumbling into that room full of experienced, busy professionals, terrified me. I didn't want to walk into that room alone, unannounced and completely out of my depth.

"Hello, you the new guy?" asked a calm voice. I turned and saw a very tall officer with a warm, friendly face. He was wide-awake; therefore he was red section.

"Yes, yes, I am. I'm Dave," I replied. He took my hand and shook it warmly, a genuine smile lighting up his face. The stress evaporated from me.

"Brian, Brian Buncombe. Come on, we're gonna be late." I scurried after him as he deftly wove his way through the numerous fire doors, before entering the large, busy briefing room.

"Morning, chaps," he beamed, as he plonked his equipment on the table at a gap, and motioned for me to sit on the wooden bench. "This is Dave. Some of you might remember him? Friend of Jeremy's?" he said, as he turned and went to his 'pigeon-hole' (which was basically a place where officers kept their on-going paperwork, and where new papers were put for their attention). Several officers welcomed me back or just smiled before putting their heads back into their respective paperwork. I looked around the table. I recognised a few faces from my earlier attachment, yet others were completely new to me. Danny, the officer who had taken me to meet Jeremy the Axe, wasn't present, so I had no idea who would be tutoring me. I relaxed as Brian re-joined the table, squeezing himself into the space next to me. He had that kind of effect on people.

At exactly 6.45am, I belatedly followed suit as everybody suddenly stood up: the section inspector had just entered the room with the three sergeants in tow. They looked so serious and business-like. We sat back down as the boss stood at the lectern. The first thing he told us was who was allocated to what part of the city. This was done with the issuing of call signs for the day. The officers knew what he was talking about despite its sounding Chinese to me. Then he looked at Brian and me.

"Oh yes, I almost forgot. Dave, isn't it? Welcome back." He looked directly at me, and I nodded, my face burning red. "Well, Brian's gonna be looking after you this week, and hopefully we'll be able to leave you alone a bit to get settled in." I nodded, genuinely pleased. "Brian, you're on C515."

"Marvellous." He smiled, scribbling the details in his pocket notebook.

For the next ten minutes, we were briefed on the night's events: who was locked up, intelligence memos for the day, and the details of stolen cars to look out for. Then came the jobs: crime reports and missing person files were handed out to the officers whose cars covered the geographical area of the relevant enquiry. Our car was a 'spare car', which meant we weren't confined to any one part of the city and could pick up jobs for anywhere.

By 6.55am, the briefing came to a close and officers stood up and went to a small room just off the briefing room. On the door, a plaque proudly boasted it was the 'Radio Room'. One of the sergeants was squeezed into the tiny cupboard, handing out our only means of communication – a decrepit pocket radio. A more useless piece of equipment I couldn't have imagined, unless you count the battery as a separate entity. The small grey box of electronics was handed to me along with a detached cord containing a small microphone and antennae at the end. The sergeant was rapidly removing batteries from a large charging device, testing them to see how full they were, and chucking eighty percent of them into a basket labelled 'For Charging'. Once one produced a green light, it was handed to me. I left the room fumbling with the three pieces of alien equipment.

Brian followed me out shortly afterwards and demonstrated what to do. The battery was clipped onto the base of the radio, the handset attached to its side. The whole thing was then clipped onto a belt clip on my trousers and the handset attached to my epaulet. It felt unnaturally heavy on my belt. I was advised that the batteries were ancient, and even a 'fully charged' battery was unlikely to last a full shift, so it was wise to come back and look for another battery halfway through the day. I was to learn later that this was indeed true. Once the battery reached a certain level of discharge, it cut out to protect itself. As a transmission used far more battery power than merely monitoring the radio, the thing had a disturbing habit of cutting out mid-shift, whenever you needed to tell the control room something, and this something was usually an urgent matter, like 'Hel– '

The small speaker and microphone attached to the epaulet on my shoulder were supposed to allow me to hear the radio and to speak into it with just a slight turn of my head. Fine in theory, but, again, about eighty percent of these had suffered years of damage to the cable, and most refused to work. Many were simply discarded, leaving just the radio dangling from the clip on your belt. To make a transmission, the officer had to unclip the damned thing first, and raise it to his mouth before speaking. I soon learnt that removing the extension left the contacts exposed, just at the place where you put your fingers around the radio. It was great fun if you happened to be touching these when you transmitted, as it would burn your fingers, causing you to almost drop your radio. There had been small covers available to prevent such pain, but they'd been long lost, and, as the whole equipment was obsolete, new parts couldn't be ordered.

I wasn't exactly filled with confidence at that point. Then I was told by Brian to do a radio test, to ensure it was all working. I could hear everybody else doing it over the radio; a call sign followed by 'radio-check', at which point the radio operator would tell them how well they were transmitting. Naturally, I was terrified. Speaking over a professional radio network for the first time has this effect on you. It was the first transmission I did on the police network – another milestone – but not one to be done in front of these wizened cops. However, I had no choice. I was forced to make several transmissions before I too dumped the mic extension and risked burning my fingers.

Located adjacent to the briefing room was the radio room, the home of the people I had just spoken to on the radio. Small, rectangular, and without windows, the place felt more like a dingy cellar than an operations room. It was staffed by one of the sergeants who was now sitting in the throne at the centre of two banks of workstations, which fanned out, forming a flattened 'V' shape. One bank contained two computer screens staffed by a civilian and a police officer who were running the city radio. On the other side of the throne were two officers covering the radio for the southern half of the county. The five people in this isolated room were responsible for the allocation of all jobs to the officers in the city and surrounding area. After being introduced and given a quick rundown of how calls came in and got allocated, Brian read my mind.

"Come on, let's get a coffee," he said. I was relieved. I hated mornings and rarely functioned before several shots of caffeine.

"Brian!" called one of the city operators. "Can you turn out to an intruder alarm in Green Street, please?"

"OK, will do!" said Brian. He turned to me, patting me on the back. "Let's go, young man. Your first job! The coffee will have to wait."

He was just like Danny in that he didn't run, but he did have a sense of urgency about him. I followed him out of the station and jumped into the panda car alongside him. All of the kit he had been carrying was thrown onto the back seat as he fired up the engine. He looked at me with his forever-smile.

"Ready?"

I buckled up, fighting with the seat belt to get it over the strange radio attached to my waistband. "Ready," I replied.

"Marvellous. Hit the blue light, would you? There's a good chap."

I looked at him in surprise. "Really?"

"Really really."

I smacked that button and smiled as we raced out of the station car park to my first priority call.

COPS DON'T RUN Chapter Six

THERE IS ONE CALL THAT ALL POLICE OFFICERS get excited about, no matter how cynical they are. It is guaranteed to get the most agoraphobic of officers out of the station and onto the streets. It is the only call known to empty the police station car park, and it is the call all cops hope to never have to use themselves. Urgent Assistance, or 10/16 in Cambridge code, meant that an officer was in serious danger and needed help immediately. It was one of the first codes Brian drummed into me, with the caveat that I shouldn't use it lightly, if at all. I hoped not to be in a situation where I might need to use it during my five weeks on the streets, but I secretly wanted to experience one.

As I returned for briefings the following days, a pattern for each morning was beginning to reveal itself to me. After briefing, we were usually turned out to an A-grade call – typically an intruder alarm activated by sleepy cleaning staff. Once those had been dealt with, we were required to attend to a constant stream of victims who had suffered overnight crimes, ranging from slight damage to burglaries, all the time being ready to respond to any additional emergencies that came in. Occasionally, we grabbed a quick coffee and, if we were lucky, managed to get back to the staff canteen for a short lunch. My well-planned training schedule took a back seat if the work came in, and boy did it come.

Towards the end of the seven long days of 6.00am starts, I began to suffer. I don't function in the mornings, and once we arrived at work that week it was non-stop action right the way through until 3.00pm. We were run ragged by the control room who only had five cars and a van to deal with all the incoming workload for the city, which was relentless. I was so busy and absurdly enthusiastic that I didn't even notice a wall had just fallen in Berlin.

Brian was a chilled and patient tutor, and, several times, he calmly reminded the dispatcher that he was supposed to have time available to tutor me, but a priority call was a priority call. We had very little time to debrief anything we did, and little choice of what we attended, having to deal with whatever the control room deemed a priority.

Towards the end of this week my wish came true. A 10/16 shout. It is one of the biggest and most exhilarating incidents an officer is likely to attend. They were so rare that in my twelve years of service I only had to call it about three or four times myself.

During a 10/16, everything else stopped – all focus was on the officer in need, and getting to him or her as quickly as possible. Due to the military, I nearly missed my first one.

It was lunchtime, and I was in the staff canteen making a call regarding a trivial administrative matter to a clerk back in the army. Suddenly, all of the patrol officers in the canteen jumped up and fled, abandoning their food and drinks. I really didn't want to have to speak to the army again about this matter, so I kept the conversation going whilst curiously looking at the empty places around the dining room. *Where had they all gone?* As I spoke, I became aware of the amount of radio traffic in my ear. The sense of urgency was noticeable, even to my untrained ear. Then the tannoy burst into life announcing '10/16, Park Street car park. Any officer to assist, please – 10/16'. The remaining officers in the canteen belatedly jumped up and ran after the others – traffic, CID, and so on, obviously not in the habit of listening to radios over a slow lunch.

As I stared after them it suddenly clicked. *Shit!* I importantly told the clerk that an emergency had come up and that I had to go. I hung up and ran after everybody else, hoping not to have missed my first 10/16. I ran down the three flights of stairs and into the station car park, praying that somebody with a vehicle might still be about to leave. I looked around to see if Brian was there, perhaps waiting for me. I wasn't surprised to see he wasn't – you didn't wait for anything or anybody on a 10/16 – you acted the way that you hoped others would react to your own cry for help.

"Dave!" shouted a female voice I recognised. It came from the back of the transit van, its rear doors wide open, as several officers dived into the rear cargo area. As soon as the last one was in, the van began moving forward urgently, doors still wide open, across my path. Several officers were being thrown around in the back, hands waving frantically at me, urging me to get in. As I ran after them the van was forced to stop at the car park exit. I didn't hesitate. I just had to be on this 10/16 call. I sprinted towards it and launched myself at the open doors. It was at this precise moment that the driver decided to leave the car park, accelerating full throttle. As I flew through the air towards the now-moving van, it became apparent that whilst my feet might actually make contact with the rear cargo bay, the rest of me wouldn't.

I was right. My feet entered the vehicle whilst my hands flailed helplessly at the moving doors, just inches out of my reach. I began falling backwards as the vehicle sped away from me. I was about to land in an embarrassing heap in the entrance to the car park, as everybody else raced off to the 10/16.

Two of the officers inside, who themselves were hanging on for dear life, managed to reach back and grab my arms. They yanked me inside the vehicle, where I landed in an undignified heap on the floor. I expected to be ridiculed, but they burst out laughing and applauded me for my gymnastics. Adrenalin was high but, in retrospect, I think I earned some kudos that day, not only for turning out on my own to the 10/16, but also for the effort I put into getting on board that departing van.

The van was the only vehicle in our fleet fitted with an audible warning device, or siren. Incredibly, city patrol cars had none. We were slung around in the back of the van with the siren blaring, unable to hear any updates from the scene, arriving at the specified multi-storey car park shortly after everybody else had, whilst clearly overdosing on adrenalin.

I'd never seen so many cops in that car park. Where had they all been hiding? It transpired that one of the 'shoplifting squad' had been attacked in the car park by a suspect, and had called the 10/16. By the time we arrived, all the suspects had been detained, with one of the cops bleeding from a nose injury. My first urgent assistance call was over and I'd survived it, but only just.

I looked around and found Brian. We debriefed the incident on the return journey to the station, and I made him laugh with the retelling of the van entrance. We discussed the morning – it had been a relatively quiet affair up until that shout, and we'd managed to get a few of the forty-nine tasks on my probationer's list ticked off – boring and minor tasks, yet necessary ones. We were just arriving back at the station when Steve called us up on the dodgy radios.

"Brian, you still got that new lad with you?"

"Dave? Yeah, we're just reorganising. Why? Got something *interesting* for us?" He had, although neither of us could have known just *how* interesting it was going to be. Brian knew that Steve was at a possible sudden death, as he had been monitoring the radio at the same time as listening to my excited debrief of the 10/16. Steve hadn't attended the shout – death is the only thing that takes priority over a 10/16.

"Yeah, I think this'll be good for *him*," said Steve, smiling. I couldn't see him, of course, but I felt his smile, along with its sinister undertone.

"Marvellous. On our way," said Brian. He looked at me. "This'll be interesting," he said, smiling at me as we set off across town. "Ever met a dead person?"

"Well, yeah, quite a few, actually."

"Really?" he asked, surprised.

"Yeah, I saw my first when I was about ten years old. I found a man dead at the wheel of his car as I walked to school. Then, when I was in the army, I was involved in a fatal accident. Awful day."

"Oh, marvellous," he said, almost in admiration. I felt like I had just passed some kind of test. "Well, you're about to see one more."

I did see another corpse, and nothing that I had seen or done up until that point in my life could have prepared me for what I was about to experience.

COPS DON'T RUN Chapter Seven

WE PULLED UP IN THE MIDDLE of another council estate on the other side of the city. Steve was awaiting our arrival in front of a house. I exited the car apprehensively, and watched as Steve spoke quietly to Brian, indicating the open door behind him. I couldn't hear what he was saying so I looked at the door. Inside was a wooden stairway leading up to a first-floor flat.

"The occupant's a bit of a hermit, apparently. Hasn't been seen for a week or two," said Brian, as I approached. "The downstairs neighbour reported a bad smell coming from upstairs." I looked up at the first-floor windows.

"What's all that black stuff on the windows?" I asked.

"Oh that? That's flies," said Steve, calmly.

Flies? Why on earth would there be so many flies on the insides of the windows? I had to ask.

"Flies?"

"Yep, flies, and lots of them," said Steve. "You'll like this." I was soon to learn that whenever anybody said that to me, the opposite would be true.

As soon as I stepped through the downstairs door the smell hit me. I had never experienced anything like it before, but would experience it many times more during the rest of my police career. It's the kind of smell that creeps into your clothes, clogs your pores, and refuses to budge no matter how much you shower afterwards. In fact, I learnt that day that you could put in for a new clothing issue after such an incident, allowing you to throw your old uniform away, or just burn it.

We gingerly ascended the wooden stairs to the upper floor, the stench getting stronger with each step. Brian paused halfway up.

"Why didn't you open the windows?" he called down to Steve, his hand over his nose.

"I did," replied Steve. "You should have smelled it before."

We reached the top and entered another universe. It's how I imagined soldiers lived during The Great War: row upon row of newspapers stretched along the walls in every direction, leaving a narrow, chest-high trench to get around the cluttered flat. There must have been decades of the *Cambridge Evening News* in those walls.

We walked along the gap into what was once a lounge. The large room was packed chest high with compacted papers, with just a small passage threading from the door to the fireplace, where a small clearing contained a single armchair in front of an open fireplace. A strange green shape was just visible in the chair. The room was extremely warm and buzzing with flies, and the smell almost prevented me from breathing.

As we slowly walked along the trench to the clearing, I realised that the shape in the chair was in fact a corpse. We both covered our noses as we got closer. It was the clothes that helped me identify the shape as a man. The corpse was wearing jeans, which were pulled down to its ankles. Its upper body, neck, and face were severely bloated, and its tongue and eyes were being forced out of the body. It looked like it might burst at any moment. The skin was a mottled green marble colour, and the face was forced skywards and was so distorted it looked like it was wearing some kind of giant frog party mask. It was difficult to recognise as human. I'd never seen anything like it before, and wondered how a man could be left undiscovered for so long in modern Britain.

"Why's it so hot?" asked Brian.

"That was on," replied Steve from the relative comfort of the doorway, indicating a small two-bar electrical heater at the foot of the body.

Something moved in the corner of my eye. I turned and looked closer at the body. Was it moving, or *speaking*? Brian spotted it too and we both stared. Bubbles were slowly emerging from the man's open mouth and silently popping, releasing the decomposing gases from deep inside the body. I clasped my hand to my mouth, turned, and hurried out of the room, followed closely by Brian. We fled down the stairs after Steve and out into the fresh air, flapping our arms like demented chickens. It was the smell – it stuck to our clothes and skin like glue.

"When was he last seen?" asked Brian, his face showing genuine discomfort.

"About two weeks ago," said Steve, seeming to smile at our distress, "although it's not uncommon for him not to be seen for days, according to the neighbour. My guess is he's been dead in front of that heater for several days, if not a week." That heater had been continuously heating the corpse, providing the perfect conditions for rapid decomposition.

"The meat wagon's been requested," said Steve. "He's all yours, if you want him?" He seemed to be enjoying this game. The meat wagon was the local police slang for the Coroner's van, which brought mortuary technicians out to collect the bodies that a doctor would not issue death certificates for. Without the certificate, it became a 'sudden death', and only the Coroner could decide on the cause of death in such cases. The attending police officer acts on behalf of the Coroner, and I needed to do this to be able to tick it off on my list.

Brian looked at me, shrugged, and said, "Yeah, OK. Thanks for this, Steve." With these words, I formally took over the role of Coroner's Officer from Steve, accepting full responsibility for the bubbling corpse in the house. We stared after Steve as he got into his police car and drove away, his relief obvious.

"Right, then," Brian said to me. "To work, my man – your first sudden death. Get yourself a sudden death form from the car to fill out, there's a good chap."

I did as I was told, and leaned against the car as Brian helped me to fill in the few details we knew. Once that was done, we knocked on the door of the downstairs neighbour and obtained more details from her, as she was the one who had called the police. After that, we needed to go back inside to search for more details, such as the full name and date of birth of the deceased, and any possible next-of-kin details. They must have been hidden somewhere in that place. We also had to check for any death-related items, or suspicious activity. Any sudden death could be a murder scene, no matter how routine it might seem at first.

We headed back upstairs and into the flat. We spent about twenty minutes searching the kitchen, bathroom, and bedroom. It didn't take long – there was very little there except for walls of old newspapers. Finally, we had to enter the lounge once more, not just for any details we might find, but also for the details we had to write about the body, and the circumstances under which it was found. That meant we had to have a closer look.

The guy had died sitting in his favourite seat – the only place to sit in the whole lounge. It was a black faux-leather armchair, and his trousers were around his ankles. Why I do not know, and some things are better off left alone, out of respect for the dead, whoever they might be. We checked around him, around the floor and the small space containing his chair and the heater. We could find nothing of note and nothing out of the ordinary in this extraordinary house. As police officers, we always had to keep an eye out for the possibility that foul play might have been responsible. If that had been the case, we might have been trampling all over a murder scene.

"Hello!" came a cheerful male voice from the bottom of the stairs, making Brian and I jump. We used the voice as an excuse to go down and get some fresh air again.

The meat wagon had arrived. Two cheery young men in protective clothing greeted us at the bottom of the stairs.

"Smells like a messy one!" said the guy, sniffing the air gratuitously. I stared at him in amazement. How could he be so blasé about it? The two men trotted upstairs, carrying a neoprene-type black body bag between them. We had to follow them up to officially hand the body over to them. Everything had to be done by the book. I watched as the two young men unravelled the body bag onto the part of the floor not covered in newspapers. I was transfixed as they calmly stepped around the body, looking for the best way to lift him off the chair. Were they really going to touch the body in that state? Although I considered myself to be fairly experienced in death, actually touching and moving *any* dead body was still an uncomfortable experience. But one so badly decomposing? I hoped they wouldn't ask for an extra pair of hands. If they had, I knew which of the two officers present would be doing it.

Luckily, I didn't have to worry. These two young men lived and worked amongst the dead. Death was their business, and they knew exactly what they were doing. Once they'd decided on a plan, they set to work, and Brian and I watched as they hefted the body up off the chair. The lack of space was clearly a hindrance, as was the fact that the body refused to change shape or position: it remained stubbornly seated. It was obvious to me that his sitting posture wasn't going to change, even when lifted up and laid out on the bag, and that his rigidity might cause some problems when moving him. But nobody was prepared for what happened next.

As they attempted to lift the body, it resisted them. The weight of the body, combined with the rigor mortis and small space, caused the two slight men great difficulty. They readjusted, took as deep a breath as they could, nodded to each other and gave one large, coordinated lift.

The body came up out of the chair with an almighty rip, followed by a large splash onto the bare floorboards and armchair. We all froze, totally surprised by what had just happened.

What *had* happened?

The corpse's naked thighs had stuck to the plastic-leather of the chair beneath it, the skin detaching itself from the body as it was lifted up. I didn't know at that time, but fluids in a corpse drain to the lowest level and stay there. That's how detectives know when a body has been moved after death – the body will be in a different position but the discolouration remains unchanged.

The splash was the accumulated bodily fluids escaping from the body, like a bucket of foul-smelling water being launched across the floor.

"Oh, officer!" called out one of the technicians, as they struggled with the balance of the rigid corpse whilst standing on a now slippery floor. "That's odd."

It may have been strange, the body may have had a wound in its back that only revealed itself as they lifted him up, but Brian and I were running out of that place as if we'd just discovered a bomb detonator counting down its last five seconds. I felt guilty for leaving them like that, but, amazingly, those guys didn't mind – it was all in a day's work for them.

As Brian and I flapped around the green area of the council flats, the black body bag eventually appeared at the bottom of the stairs. The two men had done a job few would want to do, yet had done it so calmly and professionally. How they managed to get the corpse down the stairs I'll never know – moving a body is really difficult.

I felt awful for the old lady downstairs who had initially complained about the smell. The smell was now in liquid form, seeping through the floorboards towards her ceiling. I couldn't tell her, but we did inform the council so they could come out and clean the place up. I was advised that they would send in a specialist cleaning squad, not only to clean and empty the place, but also to replace those floorboards. I sorely hoped they would. They would also take on the responsibility of tracking down any family members of the poor soul.

Our final action at the scene was to secure the flat. We then followed the wagon down to the local mortuary, which was situated underneath the city hospital. The mortuary was a new experience: death clung to every surface, the air thick with super-strength disinfectant, which was clearly losing its battle with the scent of the dead. The walls contained row after row of metallic, body-sized drawers, each labelled with a number. I stared at them. Was that how it all ended? In that place?

In the next room was our corpse, on its back, its legs still in the sitting position. I watched from a distance as the technicians methodically cut the clothes from the body, and sealed them up in bags. As the green, marble-patterned body was slowly revealed, Brian explained that the coroner would have to perform a post-mortem examination on it, to try and discover the cause of death. He instructed me on the obvious signs of fluid accumulation, the tell-tale signs of discolouration showing that the man was now clearly in a different position to how he had been when he had died. I found it interesting, but considered it irrelevant in this case. The guy was still in the sitting position whilst positioned flat on his back. It didn't take a genius to see he had been seated when he died. We also examined the corpse's back for any signs of suspicious injury, but found none.

Brian gleefully explained that new recruits were taken down there to watch a post-mortem examination. He couldn't explain why, they just were. He slapped me on the back, smiling.

"We might even come back to see *his* PM if we have the chance." I hoped he was joking. I couldn't imagine a worse thing to see. The outside of the corpse was horrific enough; the inside was totally unimaginable. Yet somebody had to do that job. I just didn't think it necessary for me to be there too.

Brian was watching my face out of the corner of his eye for any reaction. I didn't hide it – I didn't need to. Any person who wasn't repulsed by the smell and sight in that room wasn't human. I just kept it measured, professional. I considered the two technicians working methodically around the body. Were they just being professional or had they really become immune to the horrors?

Once the relevant procedures and documentation had been carried out, we returned to the police station for a debrief. Even at the station I could smell death on my clothes and skin, despite the fact that we had not had any physical contact. Brian advised me to burn my clothes, and said we would request a fresh issue of uniform the following day. It was standard procedure under such circumstances.

Brian was impressed at my stoic and mature attitude. Despite the badly decomposing state of the man, I never had problems dealing with that awful experience. Dealing with dead bodies was easy – it was the living that proved more difficult for me. One of the worst aspects of police work was visiting the *living* to tell them about the *dead*. There is no worse experience than telling somebody that a loved one has suddenly and unexpectedly died. But there it was on the list of tasks to complete, and as soon as one came up we would be volunteering to deal with it.

It wasn't something I was looking forward to, and unbeknown to me, the worst incident of its kind was about to come our way.

COPS DON'T RUN Chapter Eight

THE LATE SHIFT WAS INFINITELY MORE EXCITING than working earlies. Working from 3.00pm until 11.00pm meant that, as the evening wore on, more interesting incidents came our way, often exacerbated by alcohol abuse. The only downside was that we were seldom left alone long enough to work through my list of jobs to do. A lot of the work we could instigate ourselves, such as giving a ticket to a motorist, arresting a drink driver and so on, provided we had the time to find them; other jobs, such as road traffic accidents, were usually allocated by the control room to the local car. As I was halfway through my five-week attachment and less than halfway through my list of tasks, Brian had done the right thing: he'd left a list of jobs with the radio dispatcher that he wanted us to be allocated to.

It was about 6.30pm, and I was beginning to get hungry. Brian was using his fine-tuned detective skills to hunt down drivers not wearing seat belts for me to deal with: he could spot one before I'd even spotted the car. I'd seen him issue a Fixed Penalty several times, and now I needed to do one for myself. The only worry for me was that each of the stops proved to be totally different from the other; no two police jobs are ever the same. I only had to deal with one – issue a single ticket. I'd tried twice but, on both occasions, the drivers were just too nice to give a ticket to, the result being that both drivers had been let off with a warning. Brian had just smiled each time. He totally supported my decision, but I had to issue a ticket to be able to tick it off the list.

We were also monitoring the radio about a serious road traffic accident that had occurred on the motorway to the north of the city. It soon became apparent that it had been a fatal accident. I think Brian was considering taking me out there for the experience, but our car wasn't suitably equipped for motorway work.

As we sat in the car, watching a major junction for a suitable, possibly confrontational driver not wearing a seat belt, the control room called us up. They asked Brian to find a phone box and to pass the number to them so that they could call us. This was usual practice for confidential messages, as we had a constant problem with people listening into our insecure police radio network. With a cheap scanner, anybody and everybody could tune into our police radio transmissions, and hear everything that was being said. Brian soon located a box and passed them the phone number. He took the call, jotting down some details, and frowning.

He sat back in the car with me, his usual jovial face now grim.

"Oh, marvellous."

"What is it?" I asked, concerned.

"Agony message," he said, using police jargon for telling the next-of-kin of a death. "I thought it might be, and this is not gonna be fun."

I was worried. He must have passed hundreds of these messages in his career; why should *he* be concerned?

As expected, it was connected with the fatal accident we'd been monitoring. A sixteen-year-old boy had been crossing the motorway when a car struck him, killing him instantly. What was worse was that it had happened beneath a raised roundabout. He could easily have walked over the motorway quite safely but had chosen to cross the actual carriageway on foot instead. Nobody would ever know why.

"We have to go and break the news to his parents," said Brian. I looked at him. How do you *do* something like that? Nothing at college prepared you for that. It wasn't something I wanted to be involved in, yet there I was, a twenty-four-year-old rookie cop about to go and tear the hearts out of some boy's unsuspecting mum and dad.

Brian briefed me on the importance of doing it right, of ensuring that the message of his death sunk in, and advising and supporting them as much as possible. "Procedures – focus them on the procedures. It gives them something to latch onto. And don't use vague language."

I knew very little about procedures for such an incident, but what he said made total sense.

"Wanna do it?" He looked at me, his face serious. It was my job, my duty, to do this. I'd have to learn one day, and I wanted to impress him, not let him down.

"No, if you don't mind, I don't." He didn't, he was good like that.

Five minutes later we parked the panda car in a quiet street of semi-detached council houses. Young children were playing in the street, some cycling around our car, curious. I didn't want to talk to them, and I hoped that they'd stay out of the way until we knocked on the door. We needed to focus. We needed to build up the strength to do this.

As we walked up the front garden towards the door of the house, I thought about the impending and dreaded police-knock at the door. For the last couple of weeks we had had to knock on the doors of many such houses, often to ask the occupants some routine questions, such as whether they'd seen anything the night before when a car was stolen or a burglary had occurred nearby. I never forgot the shadow of fear in the eyes of those occupants as they opened the door and saw the police uniform on their step, the colour draining out of their faces, hands jumping up to their hearts. Some even blurted out, "Oh, God, no. Please, no ..."

I imagined how my mum would react under such circumstances, with four of her five sons living far from home. I soon learned how to instantly reassure them that nothing was wrong, and became, like most officers, a bit of an expert at it.

"Nothing to worry about, sir. Just a routine enquiry about your neighbour's car," he'd say, even before the door was fully open, and with that disarming Buncombe smile.

PC Buncombe and I stood silently at the door to the house, staring at each other. He nodded at me and I took a deep breath before knocking at the door. I prepared myself as best I could, but I was unsure what to say once that familiar fear appeared in their eyes. This *was* bad news, of the worst kind, and we wouldn't be able to dismiss it with a disarming smile.

After a minute's wait, a middle-aged man opened the door, and I braced myself for his fear. After all, his kid hadn't come home for dinner, and our faces would surely confirm his worries.

He beamed at us. "Good afternoon officers. Do come in." He stood aside and joyfully waved us in. We were caught out by his reaction, and passed through into his kitchen. The room smelt homely, comforting, and of freshly cooked food. A few slices of pizza sat unattended on a plate nearby.

"My wife's having dinner." He indicated through the door into the lounge. Our heads mechanically followed his hand. "You don't mind speaking to her whilst she eats, do you?" She was sitting on the sofa, tray on her lap, eating pizza whilst watching the news. I have no idea what his wife was expecting of the police that day but it wasn't what we had come to tell her. The cheerful husband ushered us into the lounge and my heart sank even further.

My mind instantly went back to my own upbringing. I'd lived in just such a house with four brothers, born into a working class family. Two little boys, about seven and eight years of age, were seated at a table near to the kitchen door, arguing over their meal in that way children of that age do. *His younger brothers.* A young girl of about fourteen years sat on the sofa next to her mum, eating dinner. *His sister.* So, they had four siblings, now reduced to three. I couldn't begin to imagine how my own parents would have coped with such awful news.

"Look who's here!" said dad, as two towering police officers, caps respectfully held under arms, intruded on the routine family gathering. Mum greeted us cheerfully as dad sat back down next to his daughter, picking up his food tray as he did so. It was a perfect family setting, warm and friendly, and totally at ease. I was completely lost as to what we should do next, as – it seemed – was Brian.

"So?" asked the father, still smiling, "Are you going to tell us?" He wanted us to tell them something else, not what we had come to say. Whatever he had been expecting would be better news than this. Brian had to take the lead here, and I could sense his unease.

"Well, er, can I speak to you in private, please?" said Brian, hoping to break the news to the father first, away from the rest of the family. We couldn't do it there, not in front of all of them.

It was at that moment that I saw the fleeting glimpse of a shadow, the sudden doubt in his eyes. He quickly and silently counted the heads of his children before looking back at me. I could sense the sudden realisation that he had got it wrong, followed by barely checked fear. No, we weren't there about his neighbour's car or whatever else he was expecting. What we had to tell him was seriously awful, something that was going to tear him in two.

"What's wrong?" asked mum, picking up the tension in an instant. Her hands gripped the sides of her tray, unsure of what was to come.

"Can I speak to you in private?" insisted Brian once more, whilst looking around at the young family surrounding us, the two boys still bickering over their pizza, blissfully unaware of how their world was about to change forever. Even the sister had taken her eyes off the TV long enough to sense the change in atmosphere.

"What is it?" asked the father, fear feeding fear. "Is it … Tommy?" It was Tommy – he was the only one missing. Tommy, their sixteen-year-old son, their eldest, was on his way to the mortuary in the back of the wagon. He won't be returning home again, he'll never walk through that door again. He won't be needing the pizza you've left out for him in the kitchen back there.

"Yes," replied Brian, defeated. "I'm sorry, it is."

"What … what's happened?" whispered the father.

"There's been an accident," said Brian, unable to say anything else.

"Oh my God!" gasped the wife. "Is he, is he …?" She was unable to finish the sentence. I looked from her to their daughter, sitting between them. She was old enough to know what was going on, and she looked terrified.

"Is he OK?" asked the father, quietly.

"No, I'm afraid not," said Brian.

"Oh, God, no." He looked at his wife and back at Brian. "How bad … is it?" he whispered, not wanting to hear the answer.

"The worst it can be," replied Brian, gently.

Mum screamed as she jumped to her feet, her pizza crashing over the floor. She fled from the lounge into the kitchen still screaming, followed by her daughter – the eldest child now.

"Is she …?" asked Brian, nodding towards the kitchen, concerned.

"No, she's … she's OK. She's going to her sister's," he replied, looking through the front window. His wife was running up the middle of the road, still screaming, her daughter close behind her. The local kids were staring after them. They turned and looked back at the house with the cop car parked outside. They were excited now – something interesting was happening on their street.

"Oh, God, no," whispered dad, putting his head in his hands. He was unable to move, not sure of what to do: go after his wife and daughter or stay with his two young sons? Nobody spoke. Nobody knew what to do. The two boys had stopped bickering and were staring at dad, upset by mum's screaming, and suddenly very aware of the two cops standing in their midst.

"How?" dad asked, not sure if he wanted to know.

"It was a traffic accident on the A14. He was crossing the carriageway. It was instant," said Brian, trying to help somehow.

Dad stared at his dinner, before putting it to one side. "He's deaf, you know," he said in the present tense. "He wouldn't have heard the car."

Tears welled in my eyes. Tommy's father, the man who had always looked out for his disabled son in life, now looking out for him in death. I looked away to hide my tears, and saw a small gathering of local kids on the pavement outside, staring into the heart of this devastated family when they needed total privacy. I stepped forward and drew the curtains.

"What's wrong with mummy?" said a tiny voice behind me. I looked back and saw one of the little boys standing in the middle of the room, his brother just behind him. My heart wrenched. I looked at Brian. It was clear that he too was out of his ability-zone.

Dad kneeled on the floor and held his son to him. Tears ran from his eyes as he called his other son over to him. He hugged them tightly to him, before turning his head and looking directly at me.

"What should I *tell* them?" he asked me. *Me*. I was just a boy myself, barely older than his deceased son. All he saw was the uniform – a British cop, a man with all the answers. I had no idea. I was just a kid, completely out of my depth. I just wanted to turn and run away from the situation, from the discomfort I was in, but I remembered Brian's words.

I fought back the tears and looked into the man's eyes. "They'll need to know the truth," I said, quietly, instinctively. "They'll have to know at some point." I hoped it was the right thing to say. I had no idea. Training could never prepare anybody for that.

Dad took my unrehearsed, untested advice without hesitation. He hugged his sons tightly once more and spoke quietly.

"Listen to your daddy, carefully, my little soldiers. It's Tommy," he sobbed. "He won't be coming home again …"

COPS DON'T RUN Chapter Nine

Ashford Police Training Centre, Kent

THE END CAME TOO SOON. The five-week roller-coaster of emotions had been unlike anything I had experienced in my life up to that point, and, by then, I was certain that my life in the police would never be boring. From the heartache of the agony message, to the violence of Jeremy the Axe, I just had no idea of what was to come when I attended briefing each day: dealing with road traffic accidents; giving first aid; arresting drunkards, beggars, and shoplifters; and so on – the list seemed endless.

Going back to college seemed like a cop out, an easy option away from the action. Real policing happened out there on the streets, not back at the sanitised training school with its fake, red-faced sergeants. Surely learning how to be a cop could only happen out there, on the streets? I'd learned so much in such a short time, and yet I knew just how much more I still had to learn.

Despite my desire to stay right where I was, I was looking forward to hooking up with my mates again and sharing our various experiences. If that craziness had happened to me in Cambridge, imagine what might have happened to others in the big inner-city beats many of my friends had gone back to. So, with deep regret, I said my goodbyes to my new colleagues, told my heavily pregnant wife to 'hang on' for five more weeks, and headed south once more for more classroom-based training and lots of talking.

In truth it was a bore, a 'waste of police time'. For five weeks we sat around in a circle trying to outdo one another on incidents. I won, amazingly. Sure, such things happened in the big cities, but the response in such places was enormous when compared to our minimalist approach; the big cities had big resources. We debriefed each incident a thousand times, swaggered through the centre bar every night – as the senior course – and continued to march around and around the parade square in preparation for our final day at college: the all-important passing out parade, or graduation day.

It was mid-module when the Duty Sergeant tracked me down to my room. I had to go home, straight away. My wife had gone into labour.

Within fifteen minutes I was in the car and heading north through thick fog. It was the longest drive of my life. There was minimal visibility all the way to the hospital, where I then spent the night holding my wife's hand, while she spent twenty-four hours in labour. The following day I was a father, but had to return directly to the course.

On arrival back at the centre, I was taken straight to the bar, and made to drink far too much beer to wet the baby's head. The following morning, I sat in class nursing a huge hangover, and with a strong desire to leave the place as soon as possible. If I hadn't felt like being at the centre before the birth, I absolutely hated every minute of it afterwards. It all seemed so utterly pointless, as so much real life was going on back in my new home city. The only highlight was the fact that I came second in the self-defence competition, winning a medal for fighting, followed by and another free night in the bar.

Before I knew it, we were preparing for our graduation day. Friends and family had been invited, hotels were booked, and measurements taken for the obligatory tuxedos. And drill. How much drill did we have to do in that second module in preparation for the military-style passing out parade? And *she* still didn't know her left from her right. I was dreading the parade, surely she'd mess it up in front of everybody and make us all look ridiculous.

The night before the parade was our formal farewell meal, and, the day after, we'd be going our separate ways. We were dressed in tuxedos, drinking heavily, and having a great time. Even the total power cut failed to dampen our spirits. Candles were brought out, and we sat around without any music, and got drunk together. We would probably never see one another again, so it seemed the obvious thing to do. As I carefully staggered out of the hall, still in complete darkness at the end of the night, the red-faced sergeant appeared out of the gloom, staring at me as if he were going to burst.

"What is *that* in your hand?!" he demanded of me, in front of all the other officers and my wife. I nearly told him it was my wife, but bit my tongue. I looked down and realised that I was still carrying a brandy glass, half full.

"Er, brandy?" I replied, not sure if this was the right answer.

"Exactly! On the streets you'll be arresting people for doing precisely this!" The redness of his cheeks was evident even in the moonlight, but I still didn't have a clue what he was talking about.

"Sorry?" I looked at my wife, apologetically.

"You're *stealing* that glass! You can't leave the bar with a glass that doesn't belong to you!" I had to hold myself back from stating – exactly – the legal definition of theft, something that we had been learning verbatim. I had *no intention* of keeping the glass, it was just an *obvious* oversight, and there was certainly *no dishonesty* on my part. Unfortunately, he was too excited that he'd finally caught an 'offender' to see reason. I wasn't surprised that he'd been sent to this college, away from the streets and the public. I had been warmly drunk up until Staff Red-face ruined the night, but I still managed to think carefully about my response, fully aware that this was our last night at training college.

"Yeah, if you say so." I turned to go. He turned deep purple.

"You! You will take that glass back to the bar and–"

"As I'd intended to do." He didn't like the interruption, or the fact that I wasn't addressing him as 'Staff'.

"And! And report to the Commandant first thing in the morning!" Now, that really annoyed me, as I was staying off campus in a hotel, with my wife who had travelled all the way down to see me, leaving the baby with her mother.

"Will there be anything else?" I asked, unperturbed, knowing that he had reached his limit. He nearly exploded in frustration, but slunk off into the shadows after several audible giggles and comments came his way from watching colleagues.

"Prick," I said, as I left the glass on the wall in protest. What more could he do to me?

Had I realised it at the time, I might have thanked the fool. What he had done had just caused me to make college history by being the first, and possibly only, officer ever to appear in front of the Commandant on the final day of each module of the course, and threatened with being kicked off the course on each occasion.

I never believed the Commandant on either occasion, and I returned to division with a feeling of invincibility, and a hatred of injustice, along with a strong desire to make my mark.

COPS DON'T RUN Chapter Ten
Cambridge

IT WAS ALL BEHIND ME. There was no going back to police college anymore. After enjoying a week of leave with my family, I returned to red section at Cambridge. I was back on the streets with the sole objective of becoming a *real* cop. And, to call myself that, I'd have to have the umbilical cord between my tutor and me cut. To be authorised to go out on solo patrol meant revisiting all of the forty-nine tasks and activities, and getting a tick put in level two (competent) or level one (highly competent). Without a minimum level two, my tutorship would be extended beyond the next ten weeks until such time as I did. The countdown was on.

Unfortunately, we wasted an afternoon in the mortuary observing a post-mortem. Brian had taken me along with June, a female probationer from the course just ahead of me. We had to watch the coroner slice a body up in front of us. I'd been preparing for this, and I knew that, although I'd seen plenty of blood in my life, this would be different. From the canteen banter, I also realised that it was a bit of a test of sorts. The probationers that fainted or vomited were remembered with much glee. I knew I wouldn't be one of those, but I also hoped to be able to stay the course, and not have to excuse myself. We'd been told many times by Brian that it would be OK to leave the room if we wanted to, but he guessed correctly that I wouldn't. All eyes were on June.

I couldn't help but think that the corpse lying naked before me was a waxwork – it just didn't look human. The man had died in hospital a few days earlier, and now the Coroner needed to know why. I watched, transfixed, as the worst part of the procedure was carried out. If you got past what was about to happen, you usually stayed for the remainder.

Following a cut made along the back of the head, along the hairline, the man's scalp was gently peeled away from the back of his head and up over his face, exposing the skull. I braced myself as the Coroner switched on a small, spinning disc-saw. He carefully cut around the top of the man's skinless head, before putting the saw down. The silence after the saw was intense, as he gently prized the circular piece of skull off. I had to look away at that point, but the sucking noise as it finally came away was unavoidable. When I looked back, the man was holding a bowl-shaped piece of skull in his hand, the man's brain clearly visible. June bent over and wretched, before being led away by Brian. I stayed to the end, neither vomiting nor fainting, and, as the procedure continued, it became quite interesting from an investigative point of view.

I later questioned the need for such an experience, and was told that I might have to experience it if I am involved in a murder case. In reality, that happened just once in the next twelve years of service. I realise now that it was just to acclimatise the less experienced officers to the horrors of what they might have to deal with in public. My short twenty-four years had shown me worse horrors – living horrors – so this was a walk in the park. For the uninitiated, such as June, it must have been a horrific experience.

Once outside, the smell of the streets filled my lungs again. *My streets.* I had such a short time in which to tick off those forty-nine tasks, and I wanted to start immediately. The full afternoon post-mortem counted as just one tick.

One of the most difficult tasks to tick off was the simple task of issuing a ticket to somebody for not wearing a seat belt. It wasn't for lack of trying – dozens of people a day were guilty of this offence, and were easy to spot. We stopped them all, and I always left the car with determination, telling Brian 'OK, this time he/she is getting a ticket'.

It was just as before: I couldn't issue them a ticket as intended and required, for the simple reason that the offender was usually just too nice to prosecute. Brian called this the 'attitude test'. If somebody passed the attitude test, they were usually let on their way with a few firm words. For the following twelve years, I was to find it difficult to issue tickets for driving offences to genuinely nice people. Nice people were in the majority, and it was a scrote that we needed, so Brian found me one, although he didn't bother to tell me beforehand.

"Good afternoon, sir," I said to the driver in the most polite and professional manner I could muster. "The reason I stopped you is because you aren't wearing your seat belt. Is there a good reason why you don't have it on?"

"Wouldn't you be better off stopping rapists or fucking murders?" he instantly snapped back at me.

I was taken aback by the stranger's venom, but I quickly composed myself.

"I'm sorry," I said, kindly. "But do I know you?"

"No, of course not," he said, caught off guard by my unexpected response. I think he'd been expecting a bollocking.

"Then, to use your own words, sir, how do I know that *you* are not a rapist or fucking murderer?" I got my man, and the tick in my book.

Brian's patience and commitment paid off because, before the end of the module, it was confirmed that I had achieved a satisfactory level in all required skill areas, and the decision was made to send me out on solo patrol earlier than usual. I felt pretty much as I did many years later, when my flying instructor got out of the plane, telling me to fly my first solo, without *him!* On both occasions, I was silently crapping myself, unsure if I could do it or not. Yet, both times, my trust in the judgement of those men convinced me that I was, in fact, ready.

Of course, I was also eager to shake off the shackles of constantly being observed. But, could I actually do all of that on my own, without Brian there to fall back on if it all went horribly wrong? He was, after all, just the same as the pilot I would be accustomed to, sitting next to me, ready to grab the yoke from my hands, as we plummeted to earth.

There was only one way to find out, and the time for that had suddenly arrived.

COPS DON'T RUN Chapter Eleven

I WAS TO BE LET LOOSE, for the first time, on the unsuspecting streets of Cambridge, on night-duty week. A typical night began at 10.45pm with everybody being turned out mid-briefing for a fight or disturbance somewhere, with officers scrambling to find radios, then car keys, and finally the cars. The cars proved the most elusive, as the late-shift officers either still had the vehicles or were in the custody suite with a prisoner, the keys still in their pockets.

Once the fight had been dealt with, everybody ended up chasing their tails for the next three or four hours, with more urgent calls coming in than were officers available.

Back then, British pubs had to close at 11.30pm, the result being thousands of drunken revellers spilling out onto the city's streets, looking for somewhere to continue drinking, a place to eat a kebab or a curry or, often, a place to vomit. The police spent that time racing from one drunken incident to another, breaking up fights, catching drunks vandalising something on their way home, or attending to people covered in their own urine and vomit and completely incapable of looking after themselves. And it wasn't always men we found in that state.

Market Square was, statistically, a dangerous place for young men to be between 11.30pm and 3.30am on Friday and Saturday night. The crime reports for assaults proved this, with seventy percent of the city's violent incidents happening there between those times. Most people blamed it on the two kebab vans parked there, attracting the late-night crowd in search of food. Personally, I blamed the drink culture. Kebabs didn't cause fights; large queues of overly-drunk people waiting impatiently in line for them did.

After the initial pub-closing madness, things usually quietened down by 2.00am. But, at 2.30am all of the nightclubs in town closed, turfing out the revellers who had gone on to continue drinking, many of whom had been binge-drinking for the previous eight hours. Of course, the majority headed for the Market Square kebab vans.

For the next hour or so it was chaos, usually only going silent at about 4.00am, after most drunks had left the city centre in taxis, on foot, in shopping trolleys, or on stolen bikes. It was at this time that most officers tried to get back to the station for a bite to eat and a strong coffee. A few, incredibly, were known to park up in an out-of-the-way place on their beat, and take a nap. They were in the minority, but it did happen. The more committed would patrol the areas where burglaries were likely to happen at that time, and they were the ones most likely to bring in a quality arrest.

Incredibly for me, my first outing on my own was not only nights-week, but on a typically manic Friday night. Now, Friday night was special for all the wrong reasons: it was the last day of the working week and the first day when most people could get as drunk as was physically possible without dying, and stay in bed – feeling as though they *were* indeed dying – throughout the following day. So, from a police point of view, it was a very, very busy night indeed.

At 10.45pm we were briefed, and – predictably – half of the cars turned out mid-briefing to a report of a fight in progress. The rest of us stayed for the remainder of the briefing. There were just two officers walking in the town centre that night – myself and June. She was slightly senior to me in that she had been solo for the last five weeks. Despite the slight time difference between us, she seemed so much more experienced to me. That was what five weeks of patrolling did to a person.

We were both assigned the city centre. She got one half and I the other. Technically, we could only meet up on our adjacent boundaries, which happened to cut straight through the centre of the city where the nightclubs and food joints were. I knew she'd be there, a visible reassurance for me, despite her relative lack of experience too.

I tested and retested my radio battery, sought words of comfort from

Brian, as he got into his panda along with a Special Constable (a volunteer, unpaid cop) he'd been allocated in my absence. I just wanted to take up my usual seat next to him, but the over-sized SC was filling it up nicely.

"Got to go. Have fun!" said Brian, as he left on a blue-light shout to a pub fight, followed by the remaining police cars. As the car park fell silent, I felt envious, abandoned, irrelevant.

I stood in the darkness, took a deep breath, and walked out on my own. As I plodded along the lonely streets towards the throbbing city centre, I felt extremely alone and vulnerable. Everything before that point had been training, ably supported by Brian. But not that night. It was time to fly on my own, with no co-pilot to take over if I messed up.

That night, the real police work would begin.

Book Three in THE ROZZERS Series

ONE
for the
ROAD

A TRUE STORY by
DIEM BURDEN

This book is dedicated to each and every one of you who has single-handedly confronted a hardened criminal in the act of wrongdoing, despite your fears. You did what you did because you knew it was the right thing to do.

ONE for the ROAD Chapter One

Cambridge, March 1990

BEING A NEW COP IN A NEW CITY MAKES YOU DOUBLY disadvantaged. Not only do you have to quickly learn the street craft needed to survive as a uniformed cop out on Britain's violent streets, but you also have to learn to find your way around unaided. Unfortunately, patrolling on foot in police uniform whilst completely alone means there is far more urgency in learning the names of the roads than there is for the numerous tourists ambling around Cambridge. After all, they could just ask a policeman. But who can a cop ask?

The street called Parkside was easy enough for me to remember. Not only was it the name of the road that I was walking along but it was also the name of the police station: that's how I remembered it so easily. Parkside Police Station was on Parkside – I got that.

At the end of Parkside, I stopped dead. Parkside had finished and I was now standing in another street, and I had no idea of the name of it. It was unlikely, but, if I had needed help at that moment in time, I wouldn't have been able to state where I was. There was only one thing I could do: I walked back along Parkside searching for a street sign. Yes, I had a map in my pocket but one of the reasons I didn't want to walk along the road staring at a map is that it doesn't really fill the public with much confidence. Second, there was only one way to learn every street name in a city and that was to commit them to memory. Maps just made you lazy.

Drummer Street. I continued to walk along Drummer Street repeating the name aloud. I noticed the bus station that I had failed to direct a member of the public to during my first exhilarating venture outside in uniform.

At the end of Drummer Street came another junction. I looked for a street name, found it, and walked along the street, repeating the name over and over. I continued with this odd behaviour until I found myself in the centre of town on Market Hill. That was easy to remember: it was where the daily market was held, although – bizarrely – it lacked any evidence of a hill, not even the hint of a slight gradient.

That walk, despite being no more than three hundred yards long, had been quite momentous for me. I was in police uniform and, for the first time since joining the police, I was patrolling alone. I'd just walked from the relative safety of the police station to the heart of the troubles. If anything happened in front of me or if somebody needed help, I'd be expected to deal with it and to deal with it professionally, and without any guidance.

I needed to catch my breath, so I stepped into the shadows of the empty market stalls, becoming instantly invisible in my black uniform. There, I no longer felt every pair of eyes on me and I even managed to relax slightly.

It was 11.30pm on a busy Friday night and every pub in Cambridge was in the process of turfing out thousands of drunken revellers onto the streets. Back then, all pubs had to do this at that time. *Whose idea was that?* The place where I was would soon be thronging with people out to fill their bellies at the numerous fast food outlets in and around the square, before heading off home alone to sleep off their excesses.

On my way into town I'd noticed how small groups of drunks would suddenly become quiet once they saw my uniform walking towards them. It left me in no doubt that a visible police presence had an effect on the behaviour of late-night revellers. However, from my shadowy position, I was able to see the world behaving as if there were no cops around at all.

A noisy group of men were approaching my hidden position from an adjoining street, maybe six in total, late-teens, and clearly drunk. One was kicking a traffic cone along the road like a football. I could see them but, of course, they couldn't see me.

I stepped out of the shadows, appearing before them like some dark apparition. To say they were surprised was an understatement. The cone-kicker immediately forgot all about the cone and put his hands in his pockets and his head down, walking on as if nothing was amiss.

"A word, please," I said, in my best authoritative voice.

"Um, yeah, sorry," he said. "The cone. I'll put it back." His accent told me he was a super-educated young man, presumably studying at the university. A *Rodney*, as he'd have been called by my colleagues.

"Please be sure you do," I said, watching as he walked back along the road he had come from, the cone placed safely on his head so as not to lose it. His mates giggled at the absurdity of the scene.

I decided to walk along behind *Cone Man* for a while as encouragement, but soon realised that I didn't know the name of the street we were on. I stopped myself from asking the cone-kicker's mates who were loitering near the stalls, awaiting his return.

Fortunately, a name plaque was stuck to the side of the Guildhall: Peas Hill. I walked along Peas Hill, repeating the name to myself whilst wondering just how far the nearest hill actually was from the centre of the famously flat city of Cambridge.

Just around the corner were some roadworks where *Rodney* had reunited the stray cone with several others. He was dutifully realigning all of the cones into a tidy, straight line. I was glad he was doing as I'd instructed, but he really didn't need to put so much effort into it.

"Sorry, officer," he said, as he shuffled past me to re-join his mates.

I was pleased with the outcome. I was sure that he and his mates had sobered up considerably and were left with a positive image of the police. I was also aware that he'd probably committed some sort of an offence I could have reported him for – but what would that have achieved? I walked on, smiling.

I strolled in and out of the streets surrounding the market, committing the names to memory whilst keeping an eye on the ever-increasing number of drunks. I decided there and then that this was the most appropriate course of action for the night: identify and commit to memory some street names, step into the shadows for a breather now and again, and pop out when necessary. I could do that for a few hours and then head safely back to the station for something to eat at around 4.00am.

Then the radio buggered up my plan.

"Charlie 312, receiving?" This was repeated several times before I realised they were actually calling me.

"Yeah, go ahead," I said, fumbling with the radio set. What did they want with *me*?

"Yeah, can you go to Cinderella's Nightclub and speak to the doormen there. Apparently they've identified a male inside of the premises who's been stealing wallets from other customers. They have it all on CCTV."

I didn't know much about Cambridge but I did know about Cinderella's. It was the largest nightclub in Cambridge, and to get into it you had to pass a very long queue of drunken people waiting patiently outside.

I considered ignoring the message – the radios were notoriously unreliable – and guessed they'd just give the job to somebody else – somebody more capable, more experienced in dealing with such an incident. But, of course, if they couldn't contact me they'd start to get worried, and somebody would be tasked with tracking me down to see if I was OK. I didn't want to inconvenience anybody so I took a deep breath and clicked the transmit button, committing myself.

"Charlie 312, on way," I replied, stepping out of my comfort zone. I knew that I would be there within a minute or two, hardly giving me time to go over the various legalities that might apply. Can I search the suspect on private property? Do I need a complaint of theft before I arrest him? Should I view and seize the CCTV first? What if he kicks off?

I'd studied law at police college weeks ago but no two police jobs were ever the same; there were so many variables. I cursed the control room as I shuffled towards that enormous club. Why didn't they send June, the other foot-patrol officer who was more experienced than me? I'd also have to deal with the huge doormen, and they would be expecting a cop with experience and confidence. My nerves were threatening to get the better of me as I approached the dreaded staircase and the squeeze past the drunken queue waiting on it.

I loved Steve for what he did for me that night. Steve was one of the senior cops on the shift, and, because of this, he was driving the van. Always double-crewed, the van stayed central, ready to support any officer in need of assistance anywhere, offering both physical back-up as well as knowledge and experience. He'd heard the control room sending me to Cinderella's for a rather challenging first incident, and he knew they were asking too much of a first-night-out-probationer like me.

"Yeah, control, we'll take that job at Cinderella's. We're just outside now. If Eric can join us at the bottom of the steps?" Steve had decided that my name was Eric as he was a big fan of *Eric Burden and the Animals*. It didn't stick, but he always called me Eric and I never once argued with him as his was one of the calmest and most reasonable voices on the shift. *And* he looked out for the new guys like me.

It was reassuring to meet up with him at the van, and together we negotiated our way through the mass of bodies waiting on the stairs.

People generally aren't stupid when they are drunk and alone; it's when they are drunk and in company that they embarrass themselves. Accompanied drunks usually have to say something when they see a cop, and it's never anything original or even funny to a sober person. Still, it was a test of sorts, and something I'd have to do countless times in the future. Like all good cops, we ignored them and pushed our way to the front.

A mountain of a man let us through the front doors into the club foyer where another mountain towered over a wisp of a guy: the suspect. Accounts were quickly given by the bouncers whilst the suspect drunkenly denied all of the allegations. I thought perhaps we should consider viewing the CCTV evidence for clarification but Steve gave me an almost imperceptible nod.

That was all the advice I needed. I made a clumsy, training-school style arrest for theft – my first arrest whilst 'solo' – and spent the rest of the night in the warm comfort of the custody office trying to clarify which mountain of paperwork I needed to put in the file so that my prisoner could be dealt with in the morning.

It hadn't been a spectacular night by any standards, but it was a night I'll never forget – one full of apprehension, satisfaction, excitement, and resignation, as well as the inevitable boredom following arrest.

The next night, I returned to my city centre foot-patrol with eagerness and slightly more confidence than the night before. As I headed back into the city centre, I studiously recalled the names of the streets from the night before, doubling back and checking if I forgot any. I ventured off those streets to learn others, stopped in doorways, and stepped out when necessary.

Slowly the streets of central Cambridge became more and more familiar to me. As my knowledge of the city centre, police procedures and the law improved, my confidence grew ten-fold. As my confidence grew so did my arrest rate.

After a few weeks of solo patrol I was confident of the names of the city centre streets – so much so that I no longer needed to think about them; instead I began focusing on the *problems* of each particular street. I was also aching to get accepted by the shift, and the only real way for a cop to do that was to prove his worth – to get some 'quality' arrests in: something I was determined to do as soon as possible.

I began to study the intelligence reports. I learned which shops on my beat were getting hit, more or less who was probably doing it, and at what times. I went to the 'collator's' office and looked at the photos of the suspects. I also investigated the way the crooks got in and out of the buildings.

If the radio room could leave me alone for long enough I might just be able to put myself in a good position to catch a burglar: a quality, self-initiated arrest. Sod the drunks and petty hooligans: it was time to start proving myself and, with another week of nights coming around once more, I never felt more confident and ready. I was about to up the ante and make my mark.

Trust the Duty Sergeant to bugger up my plans.

ONE for the ROAD Chapter Two

I WAS EXTREMELY EXCITED ABOUT THE COMING WEEK of nights as I felt that I knew enough about the crimes on my patch to be able to make a dent in them. There was also the easy arrest of drink drivers (easy because the law was black and white: either they were over or they weren't, and the paperwork required after arrest was minimal). I discovered the best place to stand to spot motorists who were contravening traffic signs, and stopped them, sniffing their breath for any signs of alcohol whilst giving words of advice for the minor matter.

I'd also discovered several places where I could remove my headache-inducing helmet and get a stimulating mug of coffee. Cops were always made very welcome by the porters of Cambridge University, probably on account of the fact that when cops retire they become porters at the university. They loved to catch up on the gossip with a young recruit over a coffee.

With this knowledge under my hat, there was only one place left for me to explore in the early hours, and I was looking forward to it immensely.

The small area I was responsible for was a mixture of shops and department stores, with student accommodation crammed in above and behind them. I soon discovered how easy it was to access the rooftops of the city centre, which gave a great, unimpeded view of the streets below. The quiet period of any shift was a great time to go and explore, and I did so voraciously.

I memorised every rooftop access point, investigated shops and their vulnerabilities, and located vantage points to watch the deserted streets from. I avidly made notes at briefing of all the burglaries that had occurred in my area, and then went and looked at how the crooks had done it. I checked for patterns and possible suspects. I investigated, discovered, and prepared.

From the rooftops, I often saw my probationer colleague patrolling the streets alone below me; we never patrolled together. Every ten minutes or so she would ask for a Police National Computer (PNC) check of a vehicle or person over the radio. Her checks were made at random: a parked car here, a student heading home there. They rarely came back with anything of interest.

I had learned to ask the control room staff to print off a list of recent burglaries and other serious crimes on my patch. I was studying these avidly as the shift inspector walked in. We all stood up, as was the norm back then. Cars were duly allocated. June, as expected, got one of the city centre beats.

"Dave, can you do Beat Four tonight please? A nice change for you."

Beat Four? Where the hell was Beat Four? The centre was divided up into *three* beats, where was the *fourth*?

"Mill Road," whispered June, who had obviously clocked my confusion. I knew where Mill Road was – it was the place where we went for a box of mayonnaise-covered spicy potatoes at 4.00am every morning during nights.

As soon as the briefing was over I screwed up my burglary list and threw it in the bin. Brian asked if I was OK. I said I was just tired, and headed out along Mill Road, ready to start memorising street names once more. There was one positive: spicy potatoes. At least I wouldn't go hungry that night.

Now, there was nothing wrong with Mill Road. It was just that it wasn't in the centre – it was more of a trunk road out of the centre, stuffed full of late-night takeaways and student bedsits. But the worst part of patrolling this road was its geography. It was just one long, straight road just over a mile long. Once you got to the end – if you got to the end – you had to turn around and walk all the way back.

My old routine began again – enter street, check name, commit to memory, and move onto the next one. Mill Road was easy – it was a long straight road so its name never changed (or so I thought). It was the side streets that I had to remember but they were boring – a mix of either upper-class residences or terraced houses converted into student digs. There seemed very little for a foot-patrol officer to see or do there.

After exploring all the side streets up to about halfway along Mill Road and committing dozens of new names to memory, spicy potatoes began popping into my head. It was 4.00am and it had been a long, boring night. The food bars were only licensed to open until 2.00am but one or two got around this absurd restriction by spending several hours 'cleaning up' with the front door open, which meant that any late-night munchies could be quenched with a generous helping of spuds. They always gave visiting cops either a decent discount or an extra-large portion, which resulted in an expanded waistband after seven nights of such unhealthy eating.

I had been walking and exploring the linear beat away from the station for several hours, which meant it was about a mile walk back to the 'closed' food shop located very close to the police station. It was all-quiet on the radio and I'd heard several officers book in at the station, obviously preparing to tuck into their own potatoes. Now it was my turn and my stomach rumbled as I headed back.

After a few minutes of quiet walking, the boredom was interrupted by a voice on the radio. Cops quickly learn to detect the change in tone of radio operators, and you could usually tell the urgency of the call from the tone of the first couple of words. It is this skill that enables cops to get on with the routine of the day-to-day job whilst ignoring their police radio, but instantly picking up on matters of urgency.

"Any mobile available for a break-in-progress, Mill Road?" These were the words all cops loved to hear – a burglary (or a 'break' as we used to call them) *in progress*. It got the juices instantly fired up, banished any notion of tiredness, and instantly silenced a protesting stomach. A quality crime was in progress, somebody was witnessing it and calling the police, and we'd have the element of surprise if we could get there quickly enough, which often meant parking the police car a long way off so that the crook wasn't able to hear your screaming engine approaching. Good cops parked well away and ran to the scene in silence.

I knew that most officers were in the station eating, and therefore not far off, whilst others were presumably spread out around the city. The guys in the nick would no doubt be pushing their tats aside and running to their cars that would be parked no more than two miles away from the incident. They'd get there long before I could walk to the place, not that I had any idea where it was.

I thought quickly. A quality crime in progress in Mill Road. I was already in Mill Road but it was a ridiculously long road; what were the odds of it being anywhere near me? I made myself visible for any approaching panda in the hope that they would see me and stop, pick me up and race to the scene with me on board.

"Yeah, control, on our way from Arbury. Exact location please?" Steve in the van. Usually stayed pretty central in the city to be able to get everywhere quickly. Never napped.

"Yeah, information still coming in, we have the informant on the phone. Possibly Brown's Jewellers." A few seconds later she gave the street number as well.

"Number 48."

I knew the numbering started at the city end, and, as I was at the opposite end to the city, it was clear that not only was the incident a long way from me but that no panda car would be picking me up: they'd be stopping well before they got to me. I stamped my foot in frustration: there was no way I'd be able to get to this crime, even though it was on my beat.

"Isn't that on Broadway?" asked Steve.

I frowned. *Broadway? Where the hell was that?* I hadn't seen that name all night long.

"Yeah, confirmed: Brown's Jewellers, number 48 Broadway. Informant's at the rear, a house in *Coburn* Street." Again, a street name I'd never heard of.

Other units said they too were responding and I knew they'd stand a good chance of getting this guy as the streets were so quiet, and the cops knew exactly where this jeweller's shop was.

I cursed my lack of local knowledge and looked desperately at the shops around me. *If only I knew the city better!* No chance on this one Davey-boy. I stopped dead. Directly opposite me was a shuttered-up shop with a sign above it quietly declaring it to be 'Brown's Jewellers'. But this was on *Mill Road*, not *Broadway*. Surely there couldn't be two? I glanced at the side street that ran behind the premises: Cockburn Street. *Coburn*

Street! Of course, I'd read it as it was written, but obviously it had one of those absurd pronunciation quirks.

Bugger me. I was already on the scene, and there wasn't a police vehicle in hearing distance. I couldn't believe the situation I found myself in – surely Steve should have arrived by that time? Then I recalled that he said he was coming from Arbury. That was the name of the huge council estate in the north of the city: he was a long way off *and* nobody else had booked on the scene.

This burglar could be mine. My heart began beating and I fumbled with my radio.

"Yeah, control, Charlie C313, I'm standing in front of *a* Brown's Jewellers on Mill Road. Confirm there's only one?"

"Yeah, confirmed. There's only one. I'll book you at the scene. We have the witness on the phone still, says offender's still on the premises. Update *asap* please."

And that was it. I was now officially, and actually, the only officer at the scene of a break-in-progress with no sign of any back-up arriving, and the crook was still inside the building. I had to act – I had to quickly appraise the situation and update the control room who would in turn update the vehicles racing to the scene from across the city.

I was already there and I had the element of surprise. I ran across the road like a shadow and checked the security at the front of the premises. Disappointingly, it was very secure, completely boarded-up. *Was it the right shop?* I felt a bit uneasy. Surely I couldn't be at the right place at the right time and alone? Would I make a fool of myself by checking out a completely different place?

"Yeah, control. All secure at the front," I whispered.

"Yeah, the report is at the rear of the property. Repeat, at the rear. Man seen to smash a window and enter building from the rear."

Of course, she had said the witness was in Cockburn Street.

I ran down the side street and along a tiny, dark alley at the rear of the shops until I was directly behind where I believed the jeweller's to be. I had to guess, as the rear entrances of the premises all looked the same. I stood in the darkness and held my breath, waiting for my eyes to adjust. I listened for any sound. Nothing, not even the sounds of the distant cop cars racing here. I began to have doubts again.

"C313," crackled the radio too loudly. "Witness says she can see the offender standing in the rear passage as we speak."

I looked up and down the dark passage: there was nobody there but me. *The witness? Where the hell was she?* I looked back at the houses behind the shops and I saw the witness quickly duck her head back inside of a first-floor illuminated window, telephone clamped to her ear.

That told me two things: the fact that I *was* at the right place, and that it was me she was looking at, not the offender. I updated the control room and strained for the sound of approaching police cars. *Nothing.* The head cautiously reappeared at the window. *Turn off your bloody light!*

"Yeah, Dave, in that case she says the offender is probably still inside the property."

I knew that he couldn't exit through the front as it was boarded up with metal shutters. If he was still here, he'd be coming through me. Just me. *Where was that back-up?*

I entered the small rear garden. The shop had ground-floor windows, but these were all boarded-up and secure, just as the front was. The only possible access that I could see was on the first floor above a small flat roof extending out from the terraced building. I looked up – one of the windowpanes was broken.

"Control, I have a first-floor insecurity," I whispered into the radio. If he was still here, he was definitely going to be mine.

I climbed onto a fence and up onto the flat roof. I loved climbing, and it wasn't long before I earned the nickname 'the mountain goat'. There weren't many places in Cambridge I wouldn't climb into, over or up. I once climbed through a twelve-inch window located six feet up a bakery wall following a burglary alarm in Mill Road. The premises were empty, apart from row upon row of freshly baked cakes and pies. I was unable to climb back out again and had to wait inside for the key-holder to come and let me out. It took them an unreasonable forty-five minutes and, as it was about 4.30am, I was starving. I resisted the delicious smell of all of those freshly baked products – I never touched a thing in all that time I was stuck in there.

I told the key-holder this and he laughed, saying that I should have helped myself. He was so pleased that I'd climbed in through the window to check his property was secure that he told me to choose a tray to take away. I did and the shift had a bit of a feast that night. Of course, that sort of thing isn't tolerated in the service now.

From the flat roof at the rear of the jeweller's I had an excellent view of the broken rear window. I switched on my Maglite torch and inspected the scene. The windowpane had been broken at some time, but it was so dirty and dusty that it must have been broken ages ago. The window frame also seemed secure. Nobody could have climbed in through the small hole in the glass. If somebody had broken this window then they must have left quickly, as I was just the other side of the building and had arrived in seconds. I decided that the lady had been a tad overexcited – she'd even thought that I was the thief!

I heard a transit van screaming towards me and then stop suddenly on the other side of the building. Steve reassuringly booked at the scene over the radio. I knew that groggy officers were racing to this location from all over the place. That is when accidents happen. I shone my torch through the window onto a dirty, dusty backroom kitchen. It was more likely squatters than burglars, or a false alarm. We got many of these – well-intentioned calls, but a complete waste of time.

In my haste to slow the others down and reduce the risk of tired officers driving at speed, I made a quick decision. This was certainly no burglary-in-progress and I responsibly relayed this information to the control room and the other units who were en route. I was deflated: the high of my quality arrest had actually come to nothing.

"Yeah, control, slow everybody else down, there's no break here." It felt good to say it: I felt like a part of the shift. As I listened to the control room repeat my message to the other units I heard an unusual thudding noise, followed by a shuffle, coming from within the dark kitchen. I shone my torch back inside and stared as the kitchen door began to slowly move inwards, struggling to open through years of neglect. A man's upper body suddenly appeared in the small gap, carrying a large, black holdall. He seemed more surprised to see me than I was to see him, and he fled back inside the building. *Oh.*

"Yeah, control, cancel my last. Burglary-*in-progress*. Intruder still on premises. Can I have somebody else at the rear please?" I tried not to sound panicky. I looked down and saw Steve entering the overgrown back garden in the darkness. I swear he was smirking again.

"He's there, Eric," he said calmly, pointing to an upper window around the corner from me. Steve stayed where he was, indicating the direction I should be moving with a nod of his head. I swiftly dropped down into the garden and stepped around the corner of the extension. The swag-bag man was lifting the first-floor sash window and climbing out. He was hemmed in by the extension I'd just climbed off and the neighbouring fence. He had nowhere to go except into the garden and through me.

He chucked the holdall down and jumped out of the window. We stood facing each other in the darkness, neither quite sure what to do. He was about twenty-three years old, short, and slightly built. I felt confident in my own abilities: as long as he was unarmed, he didn't stand a chance against me.

"Well, get him then," prompted Steve, patiently. I stepped forward and the thief stepped back. He was cornered, his back to the boarded-up rear of the shop, a high fence to one side and the rear extension to the other. I was blocking his only means of escape, with Steve several yards behind me. A cornered rat. This is when they are at their most dangerous.

He opted to do the only thing he could do: he made a desperate run for it, straight at me. I grabbed him, slamming my full fourteen stone into his skinny frame, knocking the air out of him. He landed in a crumpled heap with me on top of him. He was going nowhere and put up little resistance. Steve joined me and together we handcuffed him.

My moment had come. This was a real burglar – a quality arrest.

"I am arresting you on suspicion of burglary. You do not have to say anything but anything you do say may be used in evidence against you." There was still a nagging doubt that this guy was possibly just a squatter, but I had said those magical words. Maybe later I'd have the piss taken out of me for nicking nothing more than a homeless guy trying to get his head down for the night.

"Let's see what's in the bag then, Eric, shall we?" said Steve. In all the excitement I'd forgotten about the bag he'd been carrying. Probably his worldly goods. Steve opened it up and shone his torch inside.

The reflection of precious metals made me smile. The bag was indeed a swag-bag. It contained nothing but jewellery – piles and piles of gold and silver and watches. I grinned the biggest grin I'd ever grinned.

"Nice one, Eric," said Steve, genuinely.

ONE for the ROAD Chapter Three

THE FOLLOWING NIGHT, ON ARRIVAL AT WORK, I went straight to the cell-block. I anxiously looked up the details of my previous night's arrest to see what the result was. He'd been charged with the offence of burglary to the value of several thousand pounds. When CID went to the scene, they discovered that he'd smashed a hole in the wall from the crummy upstairs apartment directly into the jeweller's shop, thereby bypassing the metal security shutters on the outside of the building.

Had I not been there just as he appeared at the window, he'd have most likely got away with his crime. A well-known local criminal and junkie, he was remanded in custody and eventually sentenced to eighteen months in prison for this crime. I later learnt that whilst in prison he took his own life. At just nineteen years of age, it was a sad ending.

My being in the right place at the right time was just a fortunate coincidence for me, and an unfortunate one for the criminal, but these sorts of coincidences always seemed to happen to me during my time in the police.

Needless to say, my confidence soared. During that week of nights I was on a buzz, eager to repeat my quality arrest. But, as much as I tried, I was unable to repeat my good fortune so soon afterwards. Slowly the nights turned into days, which turned into weeks. As the summer came to an end and the cold, dark nights began, foot-patrols got progressively more uncomfortable and the coffee-stops at the porters' lodges became life-savers.

Most nights I would get picked up by a caring colleague in a warm panda car to get me out of the poor weather. I'll always remain thankful to those who tracked me down for that purpose. Those unauthorised pick-ups were usually overlooked by the sergeants. Not only was I able to warm my feet, but occasionally I was able to go on a blue-light run that came up out of the city centre. One such call came in at 6.00am, when most officers were in the station finishing off paperwork related to an arrest, or were finally getting a bite to eat.

I was trying to dry out my soaking socks in the comfort of Steve's van, which was parked up in Market Square. Steve had come looking for me, located me, and then sat up in the centre, as we were the only unit out. Being central meant that we could reach any part of the city relatively quickly, and now he could justify having me on board, as we were double-crewed and available for anything.

We were casually watching an articulated lorry attempting the seemingly impossible task of reversing into the loading bay of Marks & Spencer's supermarket amongst the tiny medieval streets – as it did every morning.

"C810," said the radio, making us both jump. "Intruder alarm activation, The Yasume Club, Auckland Road." I had no idea what that club was or where in the city Auckland Road was, but Steve knew. He didn't need to be told twice and, as we were the only unit available to attend, off we went.

Such calls routinely came in at that hour of the morning as sleepy cleaners or staff opened up premises all over the city, but they rarely caused excitement amongst seasoned officers. Officers soon got to know which premises had faulty alarms or faulty staff, and which were likely to be genuine alarm calls, although we had to treat them all as genuine. Such alarms came through to the police 'silently' (meaning the alarm wasn't permitted to activate at the premises until after a predetermined amount of time). This was to give officers sufficient time to silently get into place, ready to catch the crooks, as the audible alarm caused them to flee the building into the arms of the waiting police.

"Interesting," said Steve, as we sped through the awakening streets. "This place has been hit a lot lately, and it's *always* a genuine alarm."

I later learnt that The Yasume Club was a run-down meeting hall for the survivors of Japanese prisoner-of-war camps. It backed onto

Midsummer Common, a huge field bordered by the River Cam, offering criminals an easy escape across the river and into the housing estate on the other side.

It was only a few hundred yards away from Market Square and, as Steve and I raced towards the scene, I heard other officers booking themselves en route, having abandoned their paperwork for that alarm. I heard the control room directing them to certain points away from the scene, ready to head off any runners from the premises. Adrenalin was high for this call.

Steve killed the blue lights early and parked up well away from the scene so as not to announce our arrival with our protesting, screaming Ford Transit engine. He ran down a quiet residential street, disturbing a milkman on his early morning rounds. If I'd lost Steve, I'd never have made it to the premises. I had no idea where we were going, so I just stuck to him.

He stopped at the front of a small, white, single-floor building set between residences. It looked like some kind of run-down community hall or scout hut. Steve quickly confirmed that the front door was secure, as he seemed to expect.

"Go that way," whispered Steve, indicating the left side of the building, as he vanished around to the right. I did as I was told and skirted down the left side, hugging the wall, knowing Steve would be doing the same on the right: a classic pincer movement.

At the back of the building was a small green area and, as I reached the rear corner, I saw four young lads sprinting away, presumably having spotted Steve creeping down the other side.

"Runners at the rear!" I screamed into my radio as I launched myself after them. It was probably the first and last time I *screamed* anything into the radio mouthpiece, as I later discovered that such overenthusiastic shouts usually came across the airwaves as distorted gibberish that was totally incomprehensible to everybody else. It was much better to say calmly, "Yes, we have runners at the rear". However, the scream was great for boosting the adrenalin.

As I ran headlong into the unknown, I looked back for Steve only to hear him confirming a break at the rear of the premises. I realised that he had to stay at the scene to ensure that no others were hiding there. I was now chasing four young burglars on my own, without a clue where we were going, and was expected to keep everyone updated as to their progress if we were to stand any chance of stopping them. It's fair to say that the offenders probably knew the area far better than I did at that time.

I was running at full pelt, the young criminals no more than thirty yards ahead, running faster than me, the gap widening. They were heading across the large common towards a footbridge over the River Cam, some two hundred yards away. I needed to tell the control room this, but all I managed to say was something like, "Towards footbridge over the Cam". I didn't know if this was enough, but I didn't know any roads in this area, not even the name of the housing estate on the opposite bank. In fact, it was the first time I'd seen that bridge.

From my initial glimpse as they had run past me at The Yasume Club, I guessed they were all about fourteen years of age. I didn't fear them, but I did fear that they might be able to outrun me. They were moving at an incredible speed towards that bridge, and I knew that if they did make it to the bridge, we'd most likely lose them. Once across it, they could vanish amongst the Victorian houses and gardens on the other side of the river. I also knew that we had no dog-handler in the city at that time.

They were no more than twenty yards from the safety of the bridge as my cold feet slammed heavily into the sodden turf of the common behind them. I knew my quality arrests were just out of my grasp – they'd get away from me in the next few seconds. They sensed it too, because, as they reached the start of the bridge, they slowed down. Then they stopped. Then they did the unexpected. Three took a sharp right turn and began running along the riverbank, leaving one panting at the steps to the bridge. They hadn't crossed the bridge!

I didn't understand it, but I smiled. Now, should I chase the three still running or go for the knackered one? My decision was soon made for me as two uniformed officers stepped into view from off the footbridge. They'd anticipated this escape route and cut the burglars off. Their sudden appearance had destroyed the will of the lead runner who had given himself up to the taller of the two cops.

I veered right and headed after the three runners, seriously reducing the distance between us as I cut across the common towards them. They were now running along the riverbank, with a great distance ahead of them to reach Elizabeth Road Bridge. This bridge, being one of only five city bridges across the Cam, was one road that I knew the name of. I happily updated the control room of the new direction of travel. I knew that a car would be directed to that bridge.

The spare cop from the bridge ran up to me and settled into a jog alongside me. I was a bit surprised at the ease with which he managed to catch me up, but then I had already sprinted far further than he had.

I was relieved to have additional support – it was now two of us against three of them. Mark was the new boy, being tutored by the other cop and on his first 'observation week'. I recalled my own baptism of fire, and, as *Jeremy The Axe* came into my mind, I realised that I was suddenly the senior cop on the scene, despite being a new boy too.

"What do I do? What do I do?" asked Mark, clearly excited but far from out of breath. Mark turned out to be one of the fittest cops I'd ever meet, and years later we worked together as formidable sergeants. As he spoke, I saw a panda car stop on the bridge ahead of us. Two cops got out and began to descend onto the common. The fleeing crooks saw this too, and abruptly changed direction. Two of them veered ninety degrees to the right and headed towards the back of what looked like a large community college. The other split off to the left and tried to make for a gap by the river under the bridge.

"See him?" I shouted at Mark, pointing. "Run him down and get a hold of him, then tell him he's nicked for burglary." I realised that Mark had had no legal training at that point but was expected to make the arrest, despite not knowing how to. As we ran along, I wanted to give him suitable advice so that he could effect a legal and safe arrest.

"Bring him back to me, and if he gives you any trouble, just smack him." It was sufficient advice, and well within a cop's remit. Mark flew off like a whippet and quickly closed the gap between him and the now tiring thief. I knew the crook stood no chance.

Two down, two to go. I focused my attention on the remaining two as they ran uphill and entered the college grounds. They were still a good twenty yards ahead of me, and the run up the slope finally reduced me to a walk. I heard Mark confirm his arrest. *Good boy.*

I cursed my luck as I entered the college grounds. They had managed to break my line of sight by vanishing into the red brick school buildings. I knew a car had stopped at the front of the college so they were pretty well cornered, but I needed to find them before they disappeared completely. I drew in as much oxygen as I could as I began the search, knowing that at any minute I might stumble upon them and have to begin another chase, or even a fight.

I had no idea where they had gone: it was a warren. I followed my instinct and turned the first corner. It was a dead end, and crouching against the wall of one of the far classrooms were two young teenagers, completely out of breath. They saw me and resigned themselves to their fate. There was no escape except through me, and they looked in a far worse state than I felt. I walked towards them, releasing my handcuffs as I did so.

"Here, share these between you," I said, as I flung the handcuffs at them. I was too tired to apply them myself. Incredibly, they obeyed and handcuffed themselves to each other.

I clicked the transmit button on my radio. "Last two in custody. No further assistance needed here," I said. I was surprised to hear a cheer come back from the radio room as the operator confirmed that all four burglars were now in custody with none outstanding.

I walked the fifteen-year-old burglars back onto the common where I saw Mark walking back to me with the other one. I smiled at Mark and he returned the smile. It was a good way to end the day, and Mark would have an interesting story to tell at police college the following week.

As for me, I'd been central to the arrests of all the burglars and was acknowledged by the whole shift, including some of the oncoming shift at 7.00am. My name was getting around, and that's how I wanted it to continue.

ONE for the ROAD Chapter Four

IT WAS DURING THE NEXT FEW WEEKS that I learnt of the term 'a purple patch'. It meant a run of luck, a good thing that was going to finish at some point. My purple patch certainly seemed to have arrived, but would it finish as quickly?

I was in the company of my first tutor from my observation week, Danny. I was double-crewing the van with him. It was about 10.00am one routine weekday morning and we were driving through heavy rush-hour traffic along Hills Road, a major route out of the city.

Of all of the cars clogging the road that day, one caught my eye. I have no idea why, but I double-checked the notes in my notebook that I had taken down at briefing that morning.

"Danny, a stolen Astra has just passed us," I said, looking in the rear view wing mirror as the stolen car struggled in the heavy traffic.

"What?" said Danny, doubting me. "Are you sure?"

"One hundred percent," I replied. I don't think he wanted to, but Danny was forced to attempt a U-turn in the heavy traffic, and to put the blue lights on to justify such driving. Everybody stopped and watched us, curious as to why we would be attempting such a manoeuvre. Danny didn't like it at all, and the driver of the stolen car clearly clocked us and vanished off down a side street. All the other pandas were miles off, and also stuck in traffic. The thieves vanished as quickly as they had arrived, but not before Danny had fortunately clocked the registration number and confirmed the vehicle had indeed been stolen. Would he have believed me if he hadn't see it?

Wherever I went my luck seemed to follow. Early one quiet Sunday morning, I decided to take a walk along the River Cam as it headed out of the city through several commons. It was, technically, part of my allocated city centre Beat Three, where the river sliced through the centre of the city. I was exploring the area and enjoying it – it was quite simply breathtaking.

The river was a peaceful place, the occasional university rowing-boat skimming the surface of the water as it raced past, as they did every morning regardless of the weather. I couldn't help but admire the determination of the students. Some mornings I'd watched as they broke the ice on the river before lowering their boats into it, such was their dedication.

It was a promising spring morning, and I was enjoying exploring the riverbanks as flocks of geese and ducks argued on the water, disturbed by the occasional boat. As I rounded a rather wide bend in the river, I noticed a bit of a commotion on the bank ahead of me. *Here we go, Sunday morning, in the middle of nowhere, and I've found something.*

As I approached, I saw people throwing a rope into the water in an attempt to lasso a horse that was mid-river, frantically swimming against the current. I soon discovered that these people lived on a boat on the river and had heard the horse enter the water. They explained that they had already got one horse out, but the other was panicking and in danger. I decided that we needed the help of the fire brigade and asked control to notify them. They had boats and methods for this kind of rescue – we didn't.

I began walking upriver and as I did so I saw a two-man boat in the distance, skimming out of the mist, towards the bend. I was worried about the horse in the water ahead of them, with only its head visible. The rowers were going really fast with a pointed canoe, their backs facing where they were going. They wouldn't see the horse ahead of them and risked injuring it if they hit it.

As they rounded the bend I called out to them. They both looked at me warily but continued rowing.

"Look out!" I called. "There's a horse ahead of you!" The river was about fifteen yards wide at that point, and few people were about, let alone animals.

"Yeah, right," one of them said dismissively, before putting his back even more determinedly into his stroke. They'd obviously heard such silliness numerous times.

"No, seriously! There is a horse in the water ahead of you – please be careful!" Both men chose to ignore me and rowed on, regardless. I have no idea who they thought I was or why I would warn them about a horse in the river if there wasn't one, as I was in full police uniform!

After a few more hard strokes the boat sliced by the side of the horse's head, missing it by inches. The sudden appearance of the boat and its speed panicked the horse. It splashed its legs down hard, rearing up until half of its body was above the water, nearly landing in the rowers' laps. The look of sheer horror on the faces of the two men was a sight to see, and it made my Sunday morning.

Thankfully, the fire brigade managed to get the unfortunate horse out of the water a short time later and before any more rowers ignored me.

If I could find something happening on a quiet Sunday morning on the river in the middle of a common, I could certainly find crime happening in the busy city centre. It didn't matter where I went or when, I found things that needed finding. Or they found me.

It was quietening down just after 2.00am and the centre of Cambridge belonged to me. Well, there was a group of Special Constables patrolling in a foursome, picking on cyclists, but I hadn't met them all night – it was easy to avoid such a large pack of Specials, and I didn't think they needed a *fifth* cop in the pack.

I had been enviously monitoring over the radio an ongoing incident on the large council estate in the north of the city. The whole of the shift was committed out on the ground, chasing down a couple of violent crooks. Everybody was involved except for me and the Specials: even June was there, having been double-crewed with one of the city cars as there were so many volunteer cops with us that night.

"C312," came the unexpected call. "Can you attend an intruder alarm at *Eaden Lilley's* department store, Market Street?" It wasn't a request. I was the only one who could attend. I knew the store: it was a large family-owned department store that had been burgled several times lately. Each time the crooks had entered via the rooftop.

I was there in seconds and quickly assessed the frontage: all doors and windows were secure, as I'd expected. I updated the control room, then used my growing knowledge of criminal activity in the centre and went to a street that ran behind the huge store. Green Street was a shopping street in its own right, although narrow and cobbled and more of a service road to the surrounding streets. Off Green Street was a small service yard with a metal staircase that ran up to student flats at the top of the building line, allowing easy access onto the rooftops for criminals and romantic students. If the store was being burgled, it'd be from the rooftops again, and I should be able to find the entrance point into the store up there.

As I ascended the noisy metal stairs I heard all four Specials say they were at the front of the store and that it was secure. I knew that: I'd radioed it in. Why were they even there? The control room duly sent them to Green Street to support me. They obviously didn't know about the stairs up to the rooftops, or where I was.

Once I reached the top, I discovered a new metal gateway had been erected, barring access to the rooftops unless you had a key. It was quite a secure gate, high and with very little in the way of footholds. I considered climbing it – I loved climbing – but it was very high and I was at the top of the building line. It was a long way down and wasn't worth the risk. Anyway, if *I* had doubts about climbing, probably the burglars had too. Everything was secure. I advised the control room and asked for a key-holder to attend so that I could enter the premises at ground level and check if everything was OK.

I returned to Green Street and met the pack of Specials standing in the road.

The Special Constabulary is a mixed bag of people. With full police powers and a uniform almost identical to regular police, they were the government's solution to increasing visible policing for very little cost. They had to attend several training days per year and were required to patrol for a certain number of hours. Some of them had failed police selection procedure, or were doing it to get a taste of police work before making a decision about joining full-time. Some just liked the uniform and the authority it brought them, whilst others should never have put the uniform on in the first place. If they joined the shift out on patrol, they might be allocated to a regular officer or required to patrol in twos in the city centre. Most times, it was a lottery whether you got somebody useful or a complete liability.

I didn't know them, but I was pleased for their support that night. Four uniforms in the dark looked like a considerable force to take on, even if they weren't 'the real thing'. The real thing were unavailable and out of their cars, chasing crooks. If I had needed them, it would have taken them ages to get back to their cars, and then at least eight minutes to travel across the city to help me. Fortunately they weren't needed, so I was happy to see these guys backing me up, however useful or not they might have been.

As the senior officer on the ground I decided to update them. I told them about the recent break-ins and of the rooftop access and the new gate. They told me the front was secure too, despite my initial call. I advised them that all we could do was to wait for the key-holder, and that it could take up to twenty minutes for one to arrive. One of the group quickly looked at her watch.

"Erm, we're due off at two-thirty. If it's all right with you, we'll head back." Of course, they all had day jobs to attend. I didn't want to keep them up late for nothing; I could deal with this matter myself now. Once the key-holder arrived, we'd check the alarm system to see if there had been a break. If not we'd reset it and I'd find a porter's lodge for a hot coffee. If yes we'd find the point of entry, secure it, and then reset the alarm.

I let them head back to the station and stood in the narrow street alone, glad of the solitude of the shadows. It was dark and the wind was blowing down the narrow road. I stepped back into the doorway opposite the service yard to avoid the cold wind while I waited for the key-holder to attend. I also loved the shadows.

Contrary to what is shown on the TV, a lot of police work can be extremely boring, and waiting for a key-holder to get out of bed and drive into town can be rather tedious, unless of course they arrived drunk. 'Well, *you* called *me!*'

Fortunately, that cold, dark wait was going to be filled with the antics of the shift getting lost on the same estate where Jeremy the Axe had chased me on my first outing. It was obvious they were close to giving up and heading back to their cars, if they could just remember where they had parked them. I shivered as I heard the Specials book into the station, into the embracing warmth and steaming mugs of coffee. Then I heard a strange metallic thud, followed quickly by another. What was *that*?

It sounded like something heavy, landing on metal. I carefully glanced up and down the road; nothing moved, although all of my senses were telling me something was seriously wrong. And then I recalled the fire escape up to the rooftops, with the high gate preventing access unless you were prepared to climb over it and drop down. Onto the stairs. *I should have climbed it!* I raised my radio to my mouth to speak just as three men appeared about five yards in front of me, from the service yard. I couldn't believe it.

Each man was struggling with a heavy, cumbersome holdall the size of a pregnant Shetland Pony. There was only one place they could have come from: the rooftops, and not *through* that gate, but *over* it. I knew I'd need help on this one.

"Assistance, please. Green Street," I said calmly and firmly into my radio, as I stepped out of my hiding place into full view. I knew the control room would work out what was happening, and send support urgently.

"Gentlemen," I boomed into the darkness, stopping the three men in their tracks. "A word, please." I still wasn't sure if they were students from the flats up top or burglars, although my hackles were seriously telling me they were scrotes. My sudden and close appearance, along with my best authoritarian voice, had the desired effect.

What happened next confirmed that I needed that assistance, and soon.

ONE for the ROAD Chapter Five

I KNEW I NEEDED TO KEEP THE INITIATIVE. They hadn't planned on me waiting for them. After spending so long in the building filling their immense bags, they'd assumed that they'd be away and out of danger once back down on street level, especially so far from the store they'd just ransacked. Sadly, they hadn't banked on my purple patch.

They weren't students – that much was clear: students generally took everything in their stride. I was a cop. Their body language showed me they knew that and that they were about to make a choice: fight or flight. I also knew that I had no support at all: it was me against the three of them. *Where were the bloody Specials when you needed them?*

As I approached them I could see what they had chosen: they were all moving slowly away from me, backing themselves into the service yard entrance. They sensed that they were about to trap themselves in there, and that there would be no escape if they did.

I'd got to within a few feet of the nearest thief before they decided to drop their monster bags and flee. I reacted instinctively, springing at the nearest scrote to me before he could get away. They'd chosen to flee, whereas I needed to fight, to apprehend at least one of them.

Fighting wasn't a problem for me; I'd always been well-built and capable. At police college I'd come second on the course in a self-defence competition. I was looking forward to using my skills to effect an arrest of somebody resisting.

I decided to use an arrest technique that eventually became my favourite and one I used many times: I landed on him like a fourteen-stone flying octopus might have done. He fell heavily to the floor and wriggled and writhed under my considerable weight. I was struggling to get a lock on him to secure him as he screamed after his mates.

"Don't leave me! Don't leave me! He's on his fucking own! Come back. He's alone!"

I looked up from floor level at the two silhouettes about one hundred yards down the cobbled street. They stopped, hesitated, and then turned back towards us. Slowly at first, then faster as their confidence returned. *Oh shit.*

I grabbed my radio and transmitted my first 10/16. *I need that assistance and I need it now!* I struggled to contain the thrashing man beneath me as his two mates approached. I could hear the urgency of the radio operator announcing 'urgent assistance required, Green Street. All units, please, to Green Street, urgent assistance'.

That call went out to every officer possible, over the city radio, the station tannoy, and the southern county radio, for any traffic units, dog units, or rural patrol cars. Everybody got the call and everybody broke their necks to get to you. You didn't yell 10/16 lightly.

I calculated how far away the nearest unit was to me. They would come – I knew that – but this would be all over before they got anywhere near me. No, I was on my own, and I needed to secure that squirming guy before the other two reached us, but, as I had nothing more than a wooden truncheon and old-style handcuffs, there was little I could have done apart from knock him out with my fist. I feared the repercussions of doing that, so I continued to struggle with him, whilst his two mates ran back to us.

I braced myself for a kicking and beating, expecting them to smash me off their mate, but they hesitated for some reason. *Good. Come on, Red Shift – get your frigging arses down here!*

I took the opportunity to hold the guy still beneath me.

"It's over, the cavalry are coming now," I said, trying to sound as confident as possible into the silence of the city night air. All I needed was one distant ambulance or fire engine siren, and I'm sure they'd have turned and fled again. Nothing. *How far off were they?*

Movement in the corner of my eye. I turned to look, just as one of the horse-sized bags was slammed into the side of my head. It certainly did the trick. I was knocked off the screaming man and rolled across the floor, stars in my eyes. My ear exploded.

My prisoner jumped up, and between the three of them, they grabbed the other two bags and sprinted off along Green Street.

Bastards! I was really angry: my prisoner was escaping, *and* they had the audacity to injure me to free him. I jumped up, carefully checking that my ear was still attached as I began to run after them. There was no way I was going to let them get away with that!

I spoke – not screamed – into the radio, updating my colleagues as to the route the scrotes (with me a short distance behind them) were fleeing. The bags were obviously going to slow them down considerably. They ran down Trinity Lane, a small lane with only two possible exits: towards the river, or back up into the city. They attempted to lighten the bags they were hauling by discarding computer games from them. Finally, they chucked the complete bags into a hedge.

At the bottom of the lane they had to make a choice: left or right. If they'd chosen left they'd have to run back into the city centre where they would surely be tracked down. They chose right, and I realised that that decision would be their eventual downfall. They were heading towards the river, along a narrow lane that ended on Queen's Road, several hundred yards away. There was nowhere else for them to go but Queen's Road and, unfortunately for them, my colleagues were that side of the river. And getting to Queen's Road would be much quicker for them than crossing the river into the city centre. I called it in, smiling.

I gave a calm running commentary as to where we were throughout the whole foot chase, including the disposal of stolen items along the route. The transmissions were recorded for evidential purposes, and my colleagues were also in need of my updates so as to place themselves in a position to assist me in the shortest possible time – on Queen's.

As the thieves sprinted along Garret Hostel Lane, they hit a steep, hump-backed bridge over the river. (During the daytime, this bridge was crowded with tourists taking pictures of the amazing river scenery below.) Despite its being a small bridge, the effort required to run to the top brought them to an instant crawl: they were burnt out. As I ascended the steep slope, I too ground to a walk, falling into step a few yards behind them. We descended the other side, completely out of breath from our fight and flight. I could hardly speak.

"Look guys, it's over," I said. *Just keep walking along this path like this, because my mates will be appearing anytime now just at the end of it.* I still couldn't see – or hear – any police cars, and I knew that the longer it took for us to reach the end of the lane, the more chance I had of getting some much needed back-up and of arresting these three before they got across Queen's Road. Walking was good.

About mid-way along the path I heard a car screaming along Queen's Road like a rally driver might have done, approaching from the north of the city. It could only have been a cop car, driving at that speed, and it was coming from the right direction. As a solitary blue light appeared, I guided the driver to the end of the lane over the radio. He duly stopped in the right place. Unless you've been in that situation you can't begin to imagine how that single cop's arrival could make you feel.

"See?" I said. "There's nowhere for you to go. Might as well give it up, now."

The long, dark path ended at a single flashing blue light, occasionally blocked out by a dark shape running towards us. He may have been just one cop, but I was so glad to see him.

The crooks, however, were being backed into another corner and were going to have to make another decision: continue ahead and take on a fresh cop, turn back and fight a tired but irritatingly persistent one, or stop where they were. Thankfully, they were in a worse state than I was and couldn't go forward or back. They gave up, collapsing onto the railings at the side of the path, panting deeply. I leaned on it too, alongside them, two yards away, willing my silhouetted colleague to arrive.

"That's it then – you're all nicked for burglary and assault on police." I arrested them at that point for two reasons: to help them realise that it was all over, and to ensure I was put down as the arresting officer before my assisting colleague nabbed my glory.

As my colleague got to within ten yards of us, one of the crooks came up with a fourth option. Without warning, he vaulted the railings, landing in a deep, stinking black channel on the other side. He waded through and out onto the manicured lawns of one of the colleges. I looked at the other two, and their body language said they weren't going to try the same. I wanted to go after the runner but wasn't sure if I had the strength to – nor did I want to leave my colleague alone with these two previously violent criminals. We'd got two of them, which was a result. I also knew that the police dog was on its way.

I smiled.

"These two are nicked for burglary and assault," I said to my colleague between breaths, as he handcuffed them together. Once they had been made secure, he took them along the lane to the rapidly arriving collection of blue lights whilst I updated the control room, staying at the place the runner had gone over so that I could direct the dog-handler to the right place.

"Two in custody, one outstanding having jumped into the grounds of King's College. He landed in a brook and is soaked through from the waist down – should be easy to spot. He'll also stink." I knew they would immediately put a cordon in place around the college to prevent his escape and notify the college porters who were mostly ex-cops.

I breathed deeply as I awaited the arrival of the dog-handler to point out the exact spot the man had fled across, in the hope that it would be another painful apprehension.

Little did I know that the British criminal justice system would cause me more pain than any criminal – or dog – was ever able to.

ONE for the ROAD Chapter Six

THERE WAS NO DOUBT THAT THE CAVALRY had truly arrived. The mass of flashing police lights at the end of the lane illuminated the darkened college grounds with an intermittent cool blue hue. I was overjoyed to see them all, but none more so than The Exocet. I watched as its gangly silhouette of a handler was dragged along the path towards me by the four-legged beast.

The dog-handler checked if I was OK before throwing the beast across the railings then hopping in after him, both landing in the fetid black water below.

I watched the man as he was dragged off into the darkness and looked around me. I was alone on the walkway. After the surprise arrival of the criminals, the fight, and the assault, followed by the sprint through the city, and the arrival of the whole city police force, it all suddenly seemed so very quiet.

I looked back after the dog and his handler. They'd vanished into the college grounds. I considered following them over – I wanted to follow them over. The jump and the foul water wasn't a problem – it was that creature. I really didn't want to be stumbling around in that darkened field with that animal on the loose. Would I have been expected to go over with them? I didn't know, but what I did know was that I needed to be back at the station with the prisoners. As the arresting officer, it was my job to tell the custody sergeant why I had arrested them, and before long he'd be demanding my attendance over the radio.

Everything seemed to be under control. They had a full description, a clear scent to follow across the empty gardens, and officers covering all points out of the college. A half-wet, out of breath, stinking scrote would be easy to spot.

Another officer had been allocated to collect the evidence that had been discarded along the route, so I decided to walk back to the station, retracing my steps to meet up with him and point him in the right direction. I found Steve picking up various computer games consoles such as Game Boys. I looked into the huge bag he was carrying – it was full: there were hundreds of them.

"Big job this, Eric," said Steve. "Good work, seriously." Steve was a quietly spoken and well-regarded member of the team. I beamed and basked in his praise before heading off back to the station. I heard over the radio that the key-holder had arrived at the store, but refused to enter without an officer present. He was advised to wait until the outstanding crook had been caught and an officer would join him.

On arrival at the station I went straight to the custody suite and updated the sergeant. I related to him the full circumstances of the incident and subsequent arrest. When I got to the part where they had slammed the bag into the side of my head I remembered my ear. I touched it and recoiled. Ouch, it stung.

The sergeant examined it and nodded, then made some notes on the custody record. I was then spoken to by Night Crime, which was the name given to the CID officer on duty at night. He was there to ensure that all relevant actions and paperwork were completed, and to prepare a full handover package for the morning CID shift so they'd be able to deal with the prisoners.

From there I went down to the radio room to update them. I entered as a hero. It was such a great feeling answering their questions and receiving their praise. I was then sent to get a coffee in the back kitchen and write up my statement of the event. This took the remainder of the night, and naturally I was happy to be interrupted by the rest of the shift as they came in and caught up with me. The only negative was that the dog had failed to pick up a trail in the college, meaning that the third offender had managed to avoid arrest – and a bite.

By 7.00am everything was ready and I was able to go home, satisfied with my night's work. I silently entered the house, slipped into bed alongside my wife, and closed my eyes.

Unless you have worked a night shift you'll never understand what it is like to climb into bed as the sun rises and everybody else is waking up and starting the new day. During the summer you have to sleep with the windows open and try to ignore your neighbours mowing the lawn or putting up shelves. For most people it is difficult. Not for me. I once slept all morning with all my bedroom windows open and woke up to discover that my neighbour had cut my front lawn beneath my windows with an antique petrol mower. I'd slept right through it.

That day, I slept like a baby, although I wasn't able to sleep on my right ear. I awoke, as usual, at 3.00pm and couldn't wait to get back to work to find out what had happened.

At 10.45pm I arrived at work and did what all officers do after a quality arrest: I went directly to the custody office. I was overjoyed to discover that the third outstanding burglar had been arrested at home during the morning. It hadn't taken CID long to find out who he was from the two we had in custody. All three had been charged with burglary to the value of approximately £20,000, and Actual Bodily Harm to me. By all accounts, it was an amazing arrest and I was praised for my persistence in not letting go of them. My determination and my doggedness in pursuit of the criminal was something that was to stay with me throughout my police career. It was something that was noted in the letter of commendation I later received for these arrests.

Six months later I was required to go to Crown Court for the trial. On arrival I discovered it was a trial just for the third offender – the other two had admitted the charges at the (lower) Magistrates' Court. (They were hardly in a position to deny them.) Crook Three had elected trial by jury at the higher court.

I sat in a back room until I was called in to give my evidence. It was the first and only time I gave evidence at Crown Court and it was quite an interesting experience, far better than at Magistrates' Court. Here, the judge was clearly in charge and knew what he was doing. Once I'd given my evidence I sat at the back of the court and watched proceedings. Before long, he was found guilty on both counts. I sat forward, anticipating this next bit.

"You have been found guilty not only of a serious burglary in this city, but of a very serious attack on one of this city's police officers in the lawful execution of his duties. Only through this officer's exemplary tenacity and the subsequent investigation was it possible for you to be brought to account. I must warn you now that any person who appears before me for attacking one of our officers in such a way can expect a custodial sentence, and a lengthy one at that …"

The defence council stood up. "Begging your pardon, Your Honour."

"Yes, what is it?" asked the judge, annoyed at being interrupted mid-flow.

"His two co-defendants were dealt with at Magistrates' Court, each receiving a conditional discharge and a fine of … £120 each." A conditional discharge meant they were free to walk out of the court, no further action.

"What?" spluttered the judge.

The judge had just been given an insight into the British criminal justice system that police officers have to deal with on a daily basis. All criminal cases go first to the Magistrates' Court, but the maximum sentence they can impose is six months in prison. If a case merits a greater sentence, then it is passed up the line to the Crown Court for sentencing. Ninety-five percent of cases are dealt with at Magistrates' Court, meaning only the really serious ones reach Crown Court.

That is not the only problem: as well as that, the magistrates are unqualified civilians drafted in to do the job. They are usually middle- or upper-class people, which means they have absolutely no idea of what *real* life is actually like. They've never seen a fight at the kebab van, never been threatened by a drunk, and have absolutely no idea what they should be doing as a magistrate. They have a clerk who is trained and advises them in court, but the decisions are theirs to make, and therein lies the problem.

I often had to do the job of gaoler at the Magistrates' Court. My job was to take prisoners up, stand with them during the procedure, and bring them down again. I took one sixteen-year-old serial offender up. He had been breaking into houses since he was twelve, stealing cars and robbing people at knife-point. He was a one-man crime wave and, after weeks of knowing he was behind the crimes being committed each night, my colleagues finally caught him in the act again and locked him up. For one night, people could sleep peacefully in their beds in Cambridge.

The following morning, he was charged with dozens of offences to add to his sixty previous convictions, and, as he was already on court bail and breaching those bail conditions each night, he was sent directly back to court. This scrote was breaking into numerous houses each night – some with people sleeping in – and ransacking them. I'd had to deal with the distraught occupants in the mornings, people who no longer felt safe in their own homes. The only way to stop him was to lock him up, and preferably to throw away the key.

He wasn't stupid: he knew the law could do little against a juvenile offender such as him, even one with a list of previous convictions as long as his. He'd admitted the offences, so the magistrate decided to deal with it immediately.

She put on her half-moon glasses and stared sternly at him over the top of them. She glanced down at his list of previous convictions and shook her head slowly before looking back at him. For effect, she removed her glasses before speaking. (I guessed she was a head-teacher at some private school in Cambridge. Those kinds of actions would probably have scared her eight-year-old pupils, but what was she doing here, with recidivist offenders? *Ninety-five percent of cases?*)

"Let me tell you now, young man, this is your very, very, *very* last chance. And I'm going to *give* you that chance and I think you should take it before it's too late."

I tried not to roll my eyes. *Oh, here we go ...*

"You have a conditional discharge for a period of twelve months." What she meant was that he was about to walk out of court a free man, but if he was a naughty boy again during the next twelve months he'd have to come back to court where he'd face resentencing. Surely she'd just been privy to the police report stating that he was a one-man Cambridge crime wave and would continue to commit serious crimes if allowed back out onto the streets. But she hadn't finished there. "If you put so much as one tiny toenail over the line (which she emphasised with her little fingers) then you'll be for it. Do you understand?" She raised her voice at the end.

I think he was more surprised than I was. He looked from her to me, then back at her.

"Er, yeah, whatever," he said, smiling.

"Good," she said. She nodded to me, indicating that proceedings were over and that I could take him back down and release him on the population of Cambridge once more. As the door closed behind us and we descended the steps, I looked at him. He smiled back at me.

"I bet you crapped your pants up there, didn't you?"

He laughed. "What was that all about? Is she for real?" Sadly, we both knew she was, and we both knew that he would be out and about that night, breaking into the homes of innocent people once more. It was his vocation, and it was my job to catch him. There was nothing personal in it – that's how it worked. During such times as that, we had a friendly, professional relationship.

"Well," said the Crown Court judge to my third man. "I can't even begin to explain what happened at Magistrates' Court but it does rather tie my hands somewhat." He looked at the scrote. "Very well, you have a Conditional Discharge and a fine of £350 plus £150 court costs, and £150 compensation to the officer for his injuries. You are free to go."

The judge was unhappy that he couldn't punish the violent burglar appropriately, and that his two co-defendants had also got away with it. They should have been sent up to this judge for sentencing together, where they would have all been sent to prison.

Me? In such a short time, I learned that criminals usually laughed at the punishments handed out to them. There was no deterrent, and these types of people would only stop committing crime when it was physically impossible for them to do so, such as when they were banged up in prison. Sadly, prison was usually a last resort, after all other 'last chances' had been used up, and they got a hell of a lot of last chances.

I still slept like a baby that night and went to work the next day, ready to do my best once again.

ONE for the ROAD Chapter Seven

I WASN'T THE ONLY OFFICER WALKING BRITAIN'S STREETS who occasionally got pummelled by the common criminal. And just like all the others, I shrugged and accepted it as a part of the job. It wasn't personal, it wasn't a problem; I could handle violence directed against me and not lose sleep over it. What really hurt was the government's attitude to people like me, and never more so than in 1992 when the police service was totally destroyed by the government of the time.

Kenneth Clarke QC MP was a man who'd been appointed Health Secretary by the Conservative government in 1988 and subsequently shook the National Health Service to its very foundations with his drastic financial reforms. He was then moved across to Education and did the same there. In 1992 he became Home Secretary, and the police service let out a collective sigh at his appointment: we knew what was coming.

He immediately commissioned an enquiry into 'Police Responsibilities and Rewards', and appointed Sir Patrick Sheehy to chair it. The report was to become known as The Sheehy Report. Sir Patrick was chairman of *British American Tobacco (BAT)*, the second largest tobacco company in the world, by sales. I agree – what did *he* know about policing, and why was he chosen to chair the report? Well, just by chance, Clarke was Deputy Chairman and a director of BAT and therefore an associate of Sheehy. The whole farcical waste of money was dismissed by the police service and

Clarke's successor, Michael Howard. However, it was a sign of the beginning of the end of the police service as we knew it.

At around this time, I heard of a 'report', which stated that an officer on foot-patrol was only ever likely to discover a crime occurring *once* in every eight years of walking, and was therefore a waste of money. Not only was this completely absurd, but it was highly insulting to those officers walking the beat each day and putting themselves in danger, and getting results. Did that researcher ever walk the beat? Not with me he didn't. Maybe if my mum walked the beat, she'd never find anything, but a keen cop with access to crime patterns and a thorough knowledge of the criminals suspected of committing the crimes would, and did. Often. I have been unable to trace the author of the report, and it may be that it is just one of those apocryphal stories that gets dredged up and used as fact, time and time again.

Police officers learn quickly to ignore the constant crap thrown at them by successive governments and the people they serve so valiantly. In fact, they just dismiss it as a minor irritation and get on with the job they are paid to do, as best as they can. As a new recruit, you wanted to prove them all wrong.

The intensity of those first few months is difficult to explain to somebody who never went through it. New recruits who joined five or ten weeks after me saw me as a seasoned cop, just as I'd viewed those before me. Nobody learned faster than a new cop – you had no choice. Police life takes you over completely, and, even when off-duty, you could easily get involved in police action. In fact, you positively relished jumping in when the chance arose.

I'd been in Cambridge shopping and took the bus home to Girton, a village just outside of the city. As I stepped off the bus, intending to cross a major trunk road called Huntingdon Road, I was looking forward to getting home and relaxing.

It was raining lightly and, as usual, a constant stream of traffic was coming into the city. There were two teenage girls behind me, also attempting to cross the road. I saw a gap in the traffic and reacted quickly and positively, as was my nature. I was across the road before the car reached me. Unfortunately, the two girls behind me had decided to follow, but then hesitated mid-crossing. This caused the approaching car to slow down and wave them across, so as not to leave them in the middle of the road in danger. Sadly, they hesitated yet again. The car was now committed to stopping to let them cross, rather than risk continuing and hitting the girls.

As I walked past the stationary car, I noted the elderly, patient driver casually waving the girls across. Further up the road a large coach was approaching. It was several hundred yards away but was travelling quite fast in the 40mph limit, and hadn't begun to brake, despite the stationary car just ahead. I looked back and saw the girls were finally reaching the pavement and that the car was just about to continue its journey. I looked back at the coach. It still hadn't adjusted its speed and the roads were very wet. I realised that it was not going to stop in time.

Before I could do anything more the wheels on the coach locked up and it skidded past me, making an awful noise as its tyres failed to get any grip on the slippery surface. I covered my head with my arms and turned away as the coach slammed into the back of the stationary car alongside me. The noise of the impact was deafening.

The car was thrown forward and came to an untidy stop thirty yards further up the road, half on the pavement and half on the road. The two girls had only just passed across the front of the car and were safely on the pavement, having initiated the sequence of events that caused the crash.

In the awful silence that followed, I reacted quickly. I ran to the car and saw that there were two elderly men in the front and two elderly ladies in the back. I helped the men out of the car but couldn't open the rear doors – they had been concertinaed shut by the impact. The two ladies were trapped in the rear of the vehicle and covered in broken glass. They were clearly very shocked and in distress. I needed help.

As chance would have it I looked up and saw my wife's car, stationary on the other side of the road. She had seen me walking along the pavement just prior to the accident and had stopped to say hello to me. I told her to go back home and call for Fire and Rescue to attend. She was home in two minutes and made the call.

In the UK we pay a lot of tax. People often bemoan this fact and wish they could pay less. I did once, many years later, when I was showing my new foreign wife the emergency response to an accident in Cambridge where a car had rolled over, trapping somebody inside. We happened to be passing. She watched in amazement at the huge response and the professionalism of the rescue teams that attended. Coming from Brazil, she'd never seen anything like it. She asked me if I'd be willing to 'give all that up' and pay less tax. She had a good point.

The response that came to my assistance that day was just as unbelievable. Within one minute of my wife making the call, I heard a siren approaching, coming from our village. I thought it must have been the local policeman. It wasn't. It was a civilian BMW coupé with a bar of green lights flashing on top.

Magpas had arrived. The *Mid-Anglia General Practitioner Accident Service* was a charity founded in 1972 by a local doctor who voluntarily attended serious accidents in his own time. The service evolved into a state-of-the-art medical response team, which could be relied on to provide a rapid, highly qualified response to any accident in the Mid-Anglia region. It's difficult to express how I felt when I saw those green lights arriving at a serious accident – they truly are life-savers, and it's all funded by donations.

Once the ambulance service received my wife's call with the report of 'persons trapped', they activated the Magpas alert. A message was sent to the nearest doctor or paramedic available to attend. The doctor lived just around the corner and had recently returned home. His response time was truly amazing.

The old ladies were still stuck in the back of the crumpled car, in shock and a little panicky. They feared that the car was about to go up in flames, with them inside it. That's what Hollywood does for you. To reassure them that that would not happen and they were safe, I climbed in through the shattered window and sat with them, ensuring they were comfortable, and putting them at ease. As I saw the doctor's BMW arrive, I told them that they were in the best of hands but that I needed to talk to the doctor.

I climbed out, briefed him, and watched as he leaned in through the window, checking the vital signs of the two ladies, and fitting surgical collars. I spoke to the two elderly men who were anxiously standing by. I looked up as more sirens approached from the city side. A fire tender and the emergency equipment rescue vehicle arrived, completely blocking the road. I briefed the senior fire officer and left them to their magic. I finally briefed the two traffic cops who arrived just before the ambulance pulled up.

It didn't take long to get the old ladies out and into the ambulance, along with their husbands. They were all taken off to hospital for check ups. The traffic officers interviewed the coach driver, and the doctor attended to a passenger who had smacked his nose on the seat in front during the impact. I gave my name to the traffic cops, then went home to bore my wife with the tale.

It was great being a cop.

ONE for the ROAD Chapter Eight

DID YOU KNOW THAT BRITISH COPS have to buy their own footwear? I was surprised when I first found out but I didn't mind the extra expense because it meant I could choose what I put on my feet, within reason.

I remember the first pair of boots the army had given me back in 1982 – I don't think my feet (or knees) have ever been the same since. So, it was with great joy that I splashed out on a gleaming new pair of Doc Martin's shoes. They weren't cheap, but they were amazingly comfortable and they looked 'official'. What really attracted me to them was the fact that the sole of the shoe contained an air cushion, which softened the step and made walking for miles a doddle. They were also slip- and oil-resistant, which meant they were safe too.

The alarm call to the locked building was on my patch and, despite walking there, I arrived within minutes. The front all seemed secure but I couldn't see into their rear yard area, which was most vulnerable to burglaries. The only option was to ask for a key-holder and sit out front until one arrived, which could take anything up to thirty minutes. I didn't like that – if it was being burgled, the crooks would be long gone before the key-holder turned up.

Being a tenacious (some said relentless) cop meant that I didn't give up that easily. I was not one to sit idly by and wait until the responsible person had finished their dinner, got dressed, found their keys and the alarm code and come out to the property.

From the street I could see that the rear yard was overlooked by an adjacent pizza restaurant. I realised that the view from their dining-room window would be great for when the alarm finally sounded.

The waiter was very kind and understanding and took me up to the first-floor restaurant. It was early evening and several couples looked up as a uniformed cop entered and went across to the windows behind them.

"Do these open?" I asked the waiter. He was quick to help and soon had the sash window up. I leaned out and scanned the yard and the doors and windows of the shop, aware of the numerous eyes on my back. All was quiet below and appeared secure. Still, the audible hadn't activated yet and there still might be a thief down there somewhere.

Just below the window was a metal fence, separating the pizzeria from the adjoining yard. I handed my helmet to the amazed waiter as I gingerly climbed out through the window. I carefully stepped onto a metal fence post and tested to see if it would take my weight – all fourteen stone of me. It held firm. I swung my other leg out and put it on the fence too. Although I was about three yards up, I knew that if I could just turn around on the fence I'd be able to drop down into the yard with ease. Then, once the audible activated, I'd be in a great position to surprise any fleeing baddies. All of this was, of course, entertainment for the restaurant customers.

I was mid-twist on the insecure fence when the audible alarm suddenly activated, surprising both me and the waiter. The fence wobbled beneath my shifting mass, which, along with the shock of the alarm, caused me to lose my balance. My instinctive reaction was the right one: I grabbed the concrete firmness of the windowsill and pushed myself up and off the unsafe fence in one smooth, fluid movement, landing on the sill with aplomb, and climbing back inside.

Unfortunately, the post I had stood on had a rather sharp metal point on it. As I had pressed all of my fourteen stone down onto this single post and pushed upwards, the spike had pierced my beloved shoe with its air bubble, along with the bottom of my foot. I grimaced as I landed back inside of the restaurant, noticing the numerous stunned faces of the customers staring at me. Not only had a cop just climbed out of and back in through their window, but a deafening siren had also just activated.

"Well, everything seems to be in order, thank you," I said, brushing my hands together. I took my helmet off the amazed waiter, glanced back to check that nobody was running from the shop, and forced myself to smile a relaxed smiled. I walked as straight as I could until I left the restaurant and vanished from sight.

I sat in the doorway of the alarmed premises and inspected the sole of my shoe. There was a one-inch slice in the centre, and my foot was screaming in pain.

"C312 update," said the radio. "You can resume if all seems in order; we can't contact the key-holder."

I limped back to the station and had my foot checked out. It hurt me for about three weeks and my shoes had to be thrown away – after all, one had a puncture. I'm sure the diners that night had an anecdote that they used for years afterwards, but for me it was just another day, albeit an expensive one.

I wasn't always walking alone in the city centre, sniffing out trouble. Sometimes I was double-crewed in one of the panda cars to get a taste of other parts of the city, as well as different types of work. Attending to road traffic accidents (RTAs) wasn't something you often did on foot. It was only the cars that were sent to them. so it was important that new recruits experienced as much of the job as possible.

I'd been double-crewed with Steve all evening to help him deal with a series of domestic burglaries he'd been getting on his patch recently. The idea was that we'd park up and get out and walk around the residential streets, listening and watching out for the criminals. Now, Steve was a big old boy, a quietly spoken stereotypical farmer who also happened to be quite high up in some martial art. In other words, he was handy to have around in a fight.

After a rather quiet walk around the estate he decided it was time to go back to the car and head in for handover. Shortly before reaching the car, a young couple were rather surprised to find two cops walking along their middle-class road in the dark. They were slightly drunk but very glad to see us.

"Just the people to help us out," said the man. He explained his problem and within a few minutes we arrived at their first-floor apartment door. After a quick check of the exterior of the building we told them that there was no way into their flat without the key, which is the one thing that they had lost.

"But, you *must* be able to get us inside – you are the police, after all …" It's amazing what Joe Public thinks the police are capable of. No, we weren't able to pick locks, and no, we didn't have skeleton keys.

"The only thing we can do," said Steve, "is to force the door open for you." Steve carefully explained that, from his experience, if he forced the door open, the wooden frame around the lock would shatter, and that it'd be easy to secure it again once inside, and that to get it fixed the following day would be quite cheap. After a quick consultation between the couple, the man gave Steve the nod.

Steve used his radio to check that they actually lived in the flat, then asked the man to sign his Police Notebook giving him permission to force his way into his home, which he did. I filed both actions away should I need to do this in the future.

Throughout all of this, I was just a spectator; I had no idea were permitted to do this, or even that it was possible. I stood back and held Steve's cap as he prepared to force his way in. I expected him to karate kick the door or something, but what happened next surprised everybody, including Steve.

From about a yard away he ran at the door, slamming his huge shoulder into the centre of it. The lock unexpectedly held firm, but something had to give under such brute force. A large circular hole, about eighteen inches in diameter, appeared in the centre of the flimsy wooden door, the circle falling onto the floor inside with a plop.

The silence that followed seemed like an eternity. I looked at the man, expecting him to protest, but his face was frozen in shock, as was the woman's. Steve quickly took the initiative.

"Oh," he said, as he reached an arm through the hole and unlocked the door from inside, "that dunt normally happen." He opened the door and waved the couple through.

"But at least you're in now, heh? Goodnight," he said, as he turned and silently walked away.

"Always get them to sign your notebook giving you permission beforehand, if you ever have to do something like that."

I just stared at him.

ONE for the ROAD Chapter Nine

THE RANK OF SUPERINTENDENT IS A HIGH RANK, equivalent to the rank of major in the military. The man who held that position at Cambridge ran the operational side of policing the city. In other words, he was my top boss in the city. Superintendent 'Rocky' Nubell was also very different from the bosses of today. It was rumoured that he often put his uniform on and partnered up with an officer walking the beat in the city centre on a Friday night.

And so it was, shortly after the briefing on Friday lates, that I was told 'Rocky' was going to patrol with me that night. I didn't believe it, of course. Wind-ups of new recruits were quite common back then, and I was well overdue mine.

They'd got June a corker a few weeks earlier. June had started five weeks ahead of me, and she'd been called in to help deal with a 'special incident'. It was due to the eagerness of new recruits and their desire to be accepted that made them so gullible for such tricks. She was made to dress in a white paper scene-of-crime suit 'for protection', taken to a local park, and told to crawl across the field to the local kiddies' pool, take a sample of water and crawl back, as it was believed that somebody had poured a dangerous chemical into it. The water would then be taken away for analysis and the appropriate response determined. She fell for it, apparently, and I missed it. Now mine was well due.

I laughed about it with one of the other officers as I clipped my radio to my belt. I turned around and came face-to-face with the operations manager, Superintendent 'Rocky' Nubell, a larger-than-life character who was on a par with God to us new recruits. I froze.

He smiled broadly and introduced himself. "Looks like you're lumbered with me this evening, David."

"Yes, Sir," was all I could say in response.

And so it was that the greenest officer on the shift was walking the streets with the highest-ranking cop in the station, on a typical Friday night. As we headed downtown, he chatted to me in a very relaxed way, putting me at my ease. He explained that he might be a bit rusty on a few things and would let me take the lead, but that I could call on him for anything I needed. I just had to *tell* him what I wanted of him. I hoped that nothing was going to happen and that I wouldn't have to tell *him* to do anything.

After walking for about forty minutes, I heard a disturbance in the street just ahead of us. I could see a young man throwing a cycle across the street and shouting. I instinctively sprang into action.

"Come on," I said, tapping the boss on his chest with the back of my hand without thinking. I ran forward and cornered a small group of youths. They clearly hadn't expected a police officer to appear out of the darkness in this back street. Or two. I checked, and Rocky was right there with me, and I realised that I was about to deal with something in full view of the boss.

"OK," I said. "Which one of you threw this bike across the street then?" Naturally, they all denied any knowledge. "So from that, I can take it the bike doesn't belong to any of you?" Again, they all shook their heads. It was obvious that they were students and had had too much to drink.

"Sir, could you bring me the bike over, please?" Rocky trotted off and duly brought the bike from the centre of the road. It was chained up and the back wheel was badly damaged. I looked around the street and noticed hundreds of bikes locked up in the cycle racks.

"I guess one of you found it not locked to anything, and decided it'd be a good idea to throw it across the road?" No response. "One of you is guilty of that, the other three are innocent. Can I suggest that the guilty one be man enough to put his hand up to it, so that I don't have to arrest all four of you on suspicion of Criminal Damage, thereby saving your mates a night in the cells?" There was some awkward shuffling and eyes cast downwards, none willing to admit their mistake.

"Very well. Sir, can you request the van to this location, please?"

"OK, OK, it was me, sorry," said one of the lads.

"Good, now we're getting somewhere." In view of the fact that I didn't know whose bicycle it was he had damaged, or even if the damage hadn't been caused before he threw it around, and the high improbability of ever locating the owner of the bike and therefore a complaint, I decided to take the lad's details down. They had also sobered up very quickly and were showing remorse.

"Now, if the owner of this bike comes into the police station tomorrow to complain of this damage, you'll be reported for the offence, do you understand?" I officially cautioned him.

"Yes, I'm really sorry. I'll pay for any damage, of course." He looked like he might start crying. I knew that he would stay awake all night praying that nobody reported the damage. I also knew that it wouldn't happen, but it was fair punishment – make him sweat a bit longer. To finish off, I made him pick the bike up and put it back where he'd found it. He attempted to straighten the wheel out a bit, too.

As we turned and walked away I suddenly remembered who was with me. What would he say to me? Should I have arrested him?

"That was bloody excellent, David," he said. "No point in wasting resources arresting him. He was certainly contrite enough and no doubt really respects you for what you did. Well done."

I smiled.

"And it was rather funny watching him trying to straighten that buggered wheel …"

By about 2.00am I was alone again. Rocky had an important function to attend the following day and would like to have stayed out longer with me. And I believed him. From that day onwards I respected Superintendent Rocky Nubell as a police officer and a boss. Whenever our paths crossed again – which was often – I always felt that I could say what was on my mind to him. And he always remembered my first name.

ONE for the ROAD Chapter Ten

AT AROUND THE NINE-MONTH MARK I had become a fairly competent officer, yet not an essential one, as I didn't have a permit to drive a panda car. As a 'walker', I was actually surplus to requirements – I could be used to deal with a prisoner, double-crew a vehicle, or walk a particular beat, but I couldn't fill the driving seat of one of the cars. For most city shifts, having a spare bod like me was a luxury. It was officers with a driving permit who were essential, and it was because of this that all recruits aspired to being a police driver as soon as possible. Only then had you truly made it.

Unfortunately, it cost the force money to train you, and it would mean that you were away from shift for five days whilst you took your driving course. As a result, getting a permit wasn't easy. However, they tended to come along towards the end of your first year in the job.

Another option that came the way of the recruit at this stage was to be trained up to work in the radio room. Drivers were needed to drive the cars, so walkers were ideal for the radio room. Each shift had to provide one police officer to be a radio operator alongside the civilian staff, so pressure was put on new recruits to do the course and get in there. I had heard that, once qualified, you never saw the light of day again. However, that didn't stop me from applying. As a squaddy, I had been familiar with professional radio networks and considered myself suitable for the job. I also thought that it would add another string to my bow and get me off the streets when it was cold.

After a week at Force Head Quarters, I returned as a fully qualified radio operator, and didn't see the light of day for the next six months. I mean literally: the city radio room was located in a basement room with no windows in it and therefore no natural light.

I was to spend a lot of time, on and off, working in this tiny room over the next few years. It wasn't unusual in winter to drive to work at 6.30am in the dark, start work in the basement at 7.00am, and not come back out until end of shift at 3.00pm, when it was dark again. For seven days in a row, every three weeks, I never saw the light of day.

The civilian staff were highly capable, and I started out in a supporting role, sitting next to the radio operator, taking phone calls, updating the command and control computer system, and doing any computer checks they needed. During quiet periods, I would take over the city radio.

Before long, I was as adept as the others and began to enjoy my new role, although I never knew until briefing if I would be inside or out, which was rather frustrating. My civilian colleague was actually the force radio trainer, and he began to make recordings of certain incidents I dealt with to use as training examples. He told me that they were examples of good use, and I had no reason to doubt him. I learnt a lot of tricks from that man.

Located just behind the radio operator's seat was a small closet of a room, containing a space-aged looking piece of equipment. I was told it was the central government's nuclear attack warning device, and that if that alarm ever activated, we would have just three minutes warning, and that I should just grab the best-looking girl I could find. For months afterwards I kept glancing back at the strange, silent device and checking out who was in the room.

The control room was the centre of police life. All patrol and non-patrol officers came in to speak to us or update us, to ask for jobs, or just to see if anything was going on. As a small, crucial team, it was important that we got on well with each other and were able to deal with a sudden, high workload, which could come at us anytime. We could spend hours with nothing but dull, brain-numbing routine and then something would wake us all up.

It might come from an officer shouting for support over the radio, or giving out a 10/16 urgent assistance call. If they did, it was essential that we – the control room team – knew exactly where they were and sent back-up to them immediately. This close-knit camaraderie was lost years later when they centralised the control rooms into one large room at Huntingdon, twenty miles away.

Another source of work was the ABC alarm system machine. This was like a cash-point machine on the wall behind us that received instant alarms over a dedicated phone line. They would come in the form of intruder or personal attack alarms. The machine would beep on receipt of an activation, and display a six-figure number followed by the type of alarm. By entering that number on the command and control computer we had an instant address of the alarm location along with details of the premises (high value, notable occupant, best means of approach, etc.). The audible alarm at the premises would remain silent for a predetermined period of time, allowing us to get officers to the scene before it sounded. These alarms were highly regarded, as they were often genuine, and always instant.

Our bank of white phone lights was accompanied by a single blue light. If this blue-light phone rang, it was a central station alarm calling. The caller gave you a six-figure number and the process was as for the ABC alarms. They weren't as reliable as the ABC system because the alarm company (which could have been in Birmingham, Manchester, or even India) would often have a list of alarm activations from all over the country and the operator would have to call each police force in turn, giving the details. The lag from the actual activation to the local police notification was always unknown and varied from almost instant up to twenty minutes delay. Years later, I attended a personal attack alarm at a local building society, and, despite being no more than a two-minute walk away from the place and attending within seconds of receipt of the call, the bank manager's first words to me were, "Where the hell have you been? We've been robbed at gunpoint and I hit the personal attack alarm ten minutes ago!" I advised him to speak to his central station alarm company re the time lag.

Other urgent jobs came through on the 999 system, the calls being directed to the central control room at Force Head Quarters. The incident was created in seconds and pinged down to us at Cambridge via computer. If needed, a voice would boom down over a radio link directly, advising the radio operator instantly of the incident in progress, who would then despatch officers accordingly. If this happened, you knew it was serious, and I dealt with numerous armed robberies notified to me in this way.

The final instigators of adrenalin were known as jackpot alarms, and I grew to love these. Jackpots were portable alarm systems that were temporarily installed at vulnerable premises by the police. If we had intelligence that a place was going to get hit, or we had grounds to believe that it might, any officer could request the installation of such an alarm at any premises. Sadly, as there were so few of them, they only went to the most likely. Once it had been installed, the officer would write up a plan of attack, and the details would be handed out at briefing. Officers would then quietly check out the premises so as to be prepared should an alarm activate. They very rarely failed. Once activated, the alarm would instantly transmit a short series of bleeps over our radio system. By counting the beeps, officers on the ground and in the control room could identify which premises were being attacked, and all officers attended according to the plan. Naturally, all was silent at the target premises as the police raced towards them, which often resulted in intruders being caught on the premises.

Months later, I attended a jackpot activation listed as 'The mobile garage, Coldham's Lane'. I had no idea what the 'mobile garage' was and intended to visit and check it out as soon as I was informed of the new installation. Unfortunately, one afternoon the alarm activated before I had had a chance to visit, and I raced to the scene alone as the control room guided me in. On arrival, I could see no sign of any *mobile* garage that might be the subject of a burglary so I stopped on the forecourt of a petrol station and got out of my car scratching my head. As I did so, I saw two men inside the garage shop and considered going inside to ask them. Surprisingly, when they saw the police car parked outside the window and the cop looking at them, they ran and dived through a broken window I hadn't seen, at the side of the garage, and legged it down the road. Naturally, I ran after them, calling it in on the radio. As I looked back at the garage behind me, I realised that it was the *Mobil* Garage – a brand name. The officer who had installed it had foolishly added an extra 'e' to the word and changed its meaning completely. As the two burglars jumped a wall from the road into an industrial estate I cursed the illiteracy of the cop.

Sprinting after two desperate criminals and giving a running commentary on a police radio takes a great deal of skill and fitness. The commentary is necessary for the control room to direct officers to the scene in an attempt to cut off the fleeing crooks. If you don't give it, you'll end up alone with the crooks. If you don't keep up with the crooks, you'll end up alone with the police. The idea was that your colleagues found you and your prey simultaneously. In this case, the nearest car was sent into the industrial estate that the thieves had just fled into.

Fortunately, most crooks are not very fit and even an average cop can keep up with them. As for me, I was super-fit by then and relished such a chase. I very rarely lost my man. The two men were about fifty yards ahead of me and running through the busy industrial estate. I could hear a police siren some distance over to my left as it entered the estate. They could hear it too.

In an attempt to avoid the impending arrest, one of the men dived into a five-foot high industrial dustbin as his mate kept running. He was directly in my line of sight, so it wasn't such a great move. As I reached the dustbin, the panda car appeared just in front of me. The cop quickly spotted me and I pointed out the runner ahead. He went straight after him and I stopped running, leaning against the bin to catch my breath. Once I was ready, I called out to the crook hiding in the filth, who must have started to believe he'd got away from me.

"OK, mate. Nice try but now it's time to climb out and join me." Unsurprisingly, he did just that and cooperated fully with me, as many crooks did when spoken to fairly. Both men were arrested by me for burglary of the Mobil Garage shop – just two of numerous burglars I nicked after a 'fun run'.

Sadly, whilst being in the control room during such an incident was enjoyable, being outside was always infinitely better. There was possibly only one time in the control room that beat anything that happened outside.

It was about 4.00am and the city was quiet. Most officers had booked in at the station to get something to eat or to do some paperwork. That time of the day is always the coldest as the body slows down and wants to sleep. Unfortunately, the air-conditioning unit in the control room was working at full blast and several people were complaining about how cold it was. As there was no sergeant with us, I was the senior officer of the three in there, as well as the civilian staff. Efforts were made to locate the air-conditioning off-switch, which was proving to be elusive. Eventually, all guesses were on a lone switch in the middle of the wall in front of the radio positions. It could only be for that, couldn't it? It had no markings or labels on it and stood alone in the centre of the wall, just below the air vent.

I gave the nod and the young WPC hit the switch, plunging the control room into absolute blackness. I couldn't see my hand in front of my face: all of the computers died, as did the phone lines, and the radios stopped working.

"Shit! Turn it back on, quick!" I shouted.

"I have, I have, but nothing's happening!" came back the reply out of the darkness.

We were totally incommunicado, in perfect darkness, and completely alone. It took ten minutes for one of us to crawl along the walls to the first floor, only to shout back down that the whole station was in complete darkness. That little, inconsequential switch had killed everything: the whole divisional HQ had been deactivated. If the crooks had found out!

We managed to find a working phone and called the main control room who sent traffic cars into the city on a different radio channel, whilst also phoning an unhappy caretaker to come out and find the switch to get us back on line. This whole process took about ninety minutes during which time the whole city was vulnerable.

A week later that switch quietly vanished.

ONE for the ROAD Chapter Eleven

POLICE DRIVING PERMITS WERE GRADED from one down to five. A grade five permit could be obtained by an officer who'd had an hour's drive with one of the police driving instructors. Unless you killed somebody, you usually got your grade five permit allowing you to drive a panda car within the speed limit, i.e. you were not allowed to respond to emergencies or contravene red lights, but could drive sedately to an enquiry. In practice, if you were out and about in your general enquiry panda car and somebody shouted for help, or a serious crime was in progress nearby, you usually put your single blue light on and broke the speed limit. Human compassion and professionalism pay scant regard to ill-considered regulations. These pandas did not have any audible warning devices (sirens) fitted, so dodging through the traffic often took greater skill than a better-qualified driver racing along with the benefit of sirens.

A grade one permit was the highest level available, and was only afforded to traffic officers who attended a long and comprehensive driving course. Grade one UK police drivers are highly sought after all over the world as drivers for high profile people. Any traffic driver who couldn't obtain the highly acclaimed grade one was given a grade two permit. That left the grades three and four for non-traffic officers. These were the grades given to officers who needed a higher driving qualification than a grade five permit. Unfortunately, it also meant a relatively long course to learn how to drive at speed with 'blues and twos', or sirens and lights. As city panda drivers 'didn't respond to urgent calls' – calls that were taken on by grade one or two traffic drivers – we only needed a grade five to attend routine crime reports and enquiries.

Of course, it was nothing like that. Traffic officers were few and far between and were rarely seen in the city. Their patrol areas were the county's motorways and principle roads, often backing up lonely rural officers far from the city. In reality, the emergency calls in the city were always attended by the panda drivers, drivers who had had nothing more than a cursory check-ride to see if they could in fact drive, and certainly no training in how to drive at higher speed. We had to learn on the job.

Ask Joe Public and he'd have told you that all police drivers were highly trained individuals, obviously. It was not like that at all. Once a driver got his grade five he would be allocated a panda and advised he was only to attend routine enquiries within the speed limits, but then the job would take over and he'd drive at speed to emergencies, haring about like a maniac with no training whatsoever. If he'd had an accident, he would have been prosecuted, and many of them were. If we complained about the situation, we were told the traffic cars were to respond to emergencies, but we were supposed to attend to crime reports within the speed limits. Whilst the management espoused the drive-within-the-limits mantra, it was down to the grade-fivers to respond to the city's emergencies – otherwise nobody would.

As probationers without driving permits, we didn't know any of this. We just wanted to get permits, but, due to costs, they were like gold dust. They were difficult to come by and yet they would mean you were highly valued drivers and not just spare foot-patrol officers. A permit took you out of the city centre and further afield, to more interesting incidents and blue-light runs. There was nothing more exciting than an unqualified driver activating an almost invisible, revolving blue light and breaking the speed limit with no police siren in an attempt to catch a criminal in the act, or to save life and limb. The fact that you weren't 'allowed to' just made it even more exciting.

Although I was needed in the control room it was also time for me to get my driving permit. A day came when I took a driving instructor for a spin around the city (well, in truth I'd just left the station, driven along

East Road in rush hour negotiating rush-hour traffic when he told me I might as well go back to the station as he could see I not only could drive, but drove well). The 'test' took just five minutes.

With a shortage of experienced and qualified officers, it wasn't long before I was put in a panda car 'for general enquiries'. Common sense ensured that I was given the city centre beat (which I'd been walking around for the last eight months and therefore knew well) which also included the attached 'village' of Newnham, an up-market area of the city for me to discover. I loved it.

In came the emergencies, on went the blue light, and off raced the grade five driver to all manner of incidents. It took great skill to negotiate the narrow city streets at speed, especially when drivers couldn't hear you coming. I'd picked up the habit I'd seen other police drivers do and used my car horn as a kind of siren when needed, hitting it rhythmically to get people's attention.

Not only did I begin to learn the streets of Beat One, but I often had to attend emergencies right across town. These were long, challenging, and highly rewarding drives. It didn't help that I had to use a map to get there, but such was the intensity of policing Cambridge with so few officers that you soon got to know most parts of the city.

I loved the driving, but felt so frustrated at the lack of equipment we had. A single revolving blue light on the roof – that became invisible if the sun came out – and no siren to move traffic aside, just didn't seem right. I was constantly told that if a siren were fitted we would all have to get a grade four permit, which the force couldn't afford. It made no sense to me at all, as the transit van had a siren fitted, and it was driven by officers like me (but only the most senior on shift, because that vehicle was sent as back-up to all violent incidents and was used to collect arrested people). The experience and knowledge of those two senior officers were invaluable at any incident, but they had no higher driving grade than I had.

A good example of the stupidity of the system and the commitment of the officers working in such a mess was as follows. I was parked up in Market Square one morning, having just been to a shop-lifting incident. I was writing up my crime report when a high-priority call came over the radio. A woman in Newnham was reporting an intruder in her rear garden. The suspect was obviously up to no good, potentially a burglar.

The lady needed police help and quickly. It was my beat and I was probably the closest, being only a couple of streets away. I immediately threw the crime report aside and prepared to race to the scene, with the van offering to back me up but from a long way away. There was nobody else available.

The first thing I did after firing the engine was to switch on the car's headlights – they are often the first thing people see, even before the blue light. I then hit the blue light whilst making a mental note of the shortest route to the scene. Then came my problems.

It was about 11.00am and the city centre streets were crowded with shoppers. The road I was on was a pedestrian zone and remained so for several more streets. Only once I was safely out of the pedestrian zone would I be able to increase my speed. Then came an update: the man was attempting to force his way into the house!

I had a choice: to drive there sedately and within the guidelines and risk the man getting into the house and possibly harming the occupant or, using all means available to me, to get there and help her. I didn't think twice, I just had to get to her aid.

I drove through the pedestrian zone in low gear, honking my horn intermittently, the sound of the high-revving engine giving pedestrians an indication of the urgency of the driver. It worked. The hordes milling about on the road ahead looked back at the unusual, approaching noise, saw my headlights, heard the screaming whine of the engine, and got out of the way quickly. I drove all the way through the pedestrian zone like this, perfectly safely and relatively quickly, considering. Once clear of the *ped* zone, I left the horn alone and carefully jumped several sets of lights as I raced to the scene, arriving within a minute or two of the initial call.

I screeched to a halt on the lady's drive, jumped out of the car, and was greeted at the door by a hysterical, middle-aged, upper-class lady. I ran through the house, through the back door and into the back garden. There was nothing there and no sign of any intruder or damage to the premises. A false alarm.

I immediately cancelled the van, which was still two-toning its way across the city to back me up. (If we could lessen the chance of an accident occurring, we did.) There was no intruder. Police time had been wasted, and lives put at risk, for nothing. The lady was tactfully advised, and I continued on my way.

The following day I was walking past the office of the chief inspector, the man in charge of city operations. He saw me and called me in by my first name.

"Dave, hi – have you got a moment?" I had – he was the boss. I stepped into his office.

"I was in town yesterday with the wife, doing some shopping, and I saw you driving through the pedestrian zone rather quickly, sounding your horn intermittently."

"Er, yes. That must have been about eleven?" He nodded. "Yes, Sir, I was en route to a break-in-progress in a house in Newnham with a female occupant."

"Ah, yes. I guessed it must have been something important. It's just that, it looked so unprofessional, driving along with your car horn blasting out like that."

Tell me about it! Of course it did. Every officer who was forced to drive that way knew. The public knew, too.

"Well, Sir," I replied without hesitation. "Of course it does. Give us the tools to do the job and we'll use them. Until then, I'll get to a lady in danger as quickly as I can using what I have, without worrying about how it looks." I didn't regret my response, I was totally right and we needed the tools.

"You mean *sirens*?" he said, quietly.

"Yes, Sir, sirens. It would not only look more professional, but also I'd get to the complainant faster, and more safely too."

"Well, yes," he said. "I agree with you, but there are cost implications."

"Then we have to accept how unprofessional we look, Sir, if we are to respond promptly."

He was quiet for a second. "Yes, I guess you're right. We have been looking into it, but I suppose it's about time. Thank you. Good work yesterday – well done. Did you catch him?"

"No, Sir, I was too late," I lied.

Had I realised then that having sirens would mean I'd get to extremely dangerous situations much faster, often alone and without any protection other than a wooden truncheon and my wits, I might have opted to stay on foot-patrol in the city centre. But I was – like so many others still are – young, eager, and fearless. I was also a very fast driver.

And, for that, I came extremely close to being shot.

Book Four in THE ROZZERS Series

THIEF
TAKER

A TRUE STORY by
DIEM BURDEN

This book is dedicated to the volunteers of Magpas (Mid Anglia General Practitioner Accident Service). As a cop, I recall the relief of seeing you promptly arrive at injury incidents I was dealing with. For the casualty, you must be living angels. Thank you for everything you have done, are doing and will do. You are amazing.

THIEF TAKER Chapter One
Cambridge, circa 1991–1997

I'D FINALLY MADE IT ONTO PANDA CARS and I no longer felt like the new kid on the team. Being able to drive also meant that I went to where the action was, so I needn't miss out on anything. It elevated me too: I was essential now – the cars and the van were always staffed first, and anything that was left over was a bonus. I was no longer that spare.

Unfortunately, nobody told me about the negative aspect of police driving; or if they did I wasn't listening. With so much adrenalin kicking around, it took months before the downside hit me. The greatest irritant was the constantly interrupted or missed meal break – it was par for the course. We were professionals and we never ignored an emergency call, no matter what. In fact, the kitchen staff were marvellous to us: whenever an officer dropped his fork and ran out of the station, they'd quickly collect your meal and have it ready for you if and when you came back for it. There aren't many professions where an eight- or ten-hour day without food would be tolerated, but policing is certainly one of them.

Safety was another issue. Being on foot-patrol meant you were walking the city centre, which was conveniently central should you shout for help. Being in a car was very different. Cambridge was divided up into four quarters (or beats), with one panda car assigned to each beat. These cars were mostly single-crewed, which meant that you were usually out on your beat completely alone.

So the four cars (or the four officers) were responsible for any jobs that came in on their respective beats. A van, usually double-crewed with experienced officers, was used as back-up to these officers and for the collection and transportation of any arrested people. To ensure the van crew was able to offer back-up in a timely fashion, it was fitted with two-tones and lights. Naturally, everybody wanted to drive the van just for the siren, but only the more experienced officers got to do it. They generally stayed away from long, bureaucratic jobs so that they were readily available should their help be needed. The van generally went to where the trouble was, so, if you were sent to a potentially violent situation on your beat, you automatically listened out for and judged the timing of the arrival of the van at your location. The two extra staff were always a physical reassurance, but the fact that they were generally the guys with the most experience on the shift meant that they could be relied on in any tricky or new situations. They always knew what to do, and it was great to know that they would be there for you. If they were available.

Staff numbers permitting, a fifth panda car was often used as a general enquiry car. This was usually given to the newest officer and had no assigned beat – it was a wandering, citywide car. The officer was generally given the lengthy enquiries to do, and left to get on with it. It could go anywhere in the city, and if the van wasn't able to back you up, then this car usually would. If not, a colleague from a neighbouring beat would come across to your aid.

So, apart from being hungry on a daily basis, being a driver also made you feel very alone. Attending a violent incident on the northern edge of the city, on some sprawling housing estate, knowing that your nearest back-up is coming to you as fast as they can, but often through heavy traffic from the other side of the city, is not for the faint-hearted. When the van was committed elsewhere, and a colleague was coming to your aid from their beat and without sirens, it was often quite worrying. Yet, such work was routine to us.

Occasionally, support might come from other departments. Home Beat Officers, who were foot- or cycle-patrol staff, might be out in their respective neighbourhoods doing their jobs. If they were close enough to you, they could walk or cycle there. Traffic officers didn't work the city, but they were based in the central police station with us. If they were travelling through the city to the motorways, or in the city on enquiries, they could also back you up, but they were few in number.

Hunger and isolation were the principal changes newly qualified drivers had to learn to contend with, as well as the variation in the type of job they were expected to handle. RTAs – or Road Traffic Accidents – tended not to get allocated to foot-patrol officers, for obvious reasons. Once in a car though, that all changed – you could easily get sent to several accidents in a day.

I hated them – there was so much to deal with on arrival: securing the scene, identifying witnesses, gathering evidence, securing personal property, ensuring traffic flow, *and* possible injuries (blood!). Imagine having to do all that alone! Furthermore, accidents are rarely accidents: usually somebody is at fault, so there might be follow-up prosecutions *and* the dreaded civil claims, etc. As I hated them, and as there were so many, especially during the rush hours or when it snowed or rained, I realised I couldn't do my job well by avoiding such incidents. So I told the control room staff that I would volunteer for every RTA that came in. And I did. I did so many that, before long, I thought nothing of dealing with accidents. In doing so I not only became very adept at RTAs but also rapidly developed my people skills.

During one 7.00am briefing I was introduced to a new probationer who was on his observation week with us. I recalled *my* first day, roughly a year earlier, and how I had been chased by Jeremy the Axe. It had taken less than a year on shift and I was considered capable and experienced enough to take out a new lad. Kevin looked awkward in his new uniform, and fiddled continuously with his radio set. He was a rather large, middle-aged guy, and instantly likeable. I was glad to have another officer to patrol with me, even if he had no legal knowledge or the slightest idea of what he would be doing. The public wouldn't know that, and, to me, he was a big guy with maturity, somebody who knew a bit about life.

"Dave, can you turn out for an RTA on your patch?" It was always said as a question, but there was no way I would have said no. "It's a head-on collision on The Fen Causeway roundabout."

The head-on bit worried me. Even if both cars had been driving at the mandatory 30mph, the collision speed between the two vehicles would have been 60mph. That usually hurts people. From experience, I knew that most people drove at 45mph in the city, giving a coming-together speed of 90mph. That usually *kills* people. Yet most drivers will whine like buggery if you pull them up for driving at over 40mph in a 30mph area. Such drivers don't get to see what cops see, day in day out.

The fact that it was on a roundabout pleased me, as it would mean lower speeds and hopefully no blood, but I couldn't help wondering how it could be head-on on a roundabout. Maybe the information was incorrect – often it was.

I steered Kevin out of the briefing room and into our car. I let him hit the blue lights and, within minutes, we arrived at the scene – a head-on collision between two cars on a roundabout at 7.00am, just as stated.

"Stick with me, Kevin," I said, as I threw a reflective jacket at him and put mine on. "Don't say anything, do as I say without question, and watch, and try to enjoy it," I told him, as we approached a man and woman standing by a low wall near the scene. My car was left parked at an angle behind the accident to protect it, and the roundabout was blocked. Traffic was light, but rush hour would be building soon, and this was a major trunk road into the city.

A quick glance at the vehicles told me what had happened. One of the cars had inexplicably entered the roundabout against the flow of traffic and hit the other car head-on.

The couple were arguing. The lady was middle-aged and middle-class, the male a young lad of about nineteen years. The woman was berating him heavily as he was counter-arguing.

"Are you two the drivers involved?" I said, in a commanding voice that cut through their argument, stopping it dead.

"Yes, he–" said the lady, pointing at the young guy, clearly agitated and wanting to get the first word in.

I wanted to show Kevin the first rule of RTAs: take total control. Drivers couldn't see the bigger picture, had their own agendas, and were often in shock. Start as you mean to go on.

"Is anybody injured?" I cut in, setting my priorities before the recriminations started again. The two suddenly considered the question, and then looked at each other and at the cars.

"Well, no …"

"Good. In that case, I want you both to take a breath, sit on that wall, stop talking for a moment, and think about what happened. My colleague and I are going to put some chalk on the road to mark the cars' positions before moving them off the roundabout; it's coming into rush hour and we must get the road cleared. Then I will come back and talk to you both to see what happened. I want you to know that it isn't necessary to have a prosecution to apportion blame; insurance companies are very good at sorting that out for you. However, it is clear that one of you is to blame here, but the good news is nobody is injured!" I gave them my brightest smile and quickly set to work. Within a few minutes, and with Kev's help, both cars were pushed off the road, and I returned to the two silent drivers.

"OK. Feeling better?" I asked.

"I must say, officer," said the previously irate female, "you have an amazing ability to calm everyone down."

I thanked her, and, within a few questions, the male driver had admitted he was on his way home from work after working all night, and 'must have dozed off at the wheel' as he entered the roundabout. Instead of following the curve of the entry road to the left, the car had continued straight on and entered the exit lane for traffic coming into the city. He had collided with the lady. He took the full blame and was reported for driving without due care and attention. Both cars were towed away and, as I drove back to station, Kevin looked at me.

"That was bloody amazing! Do you think I'll be able to do that one day?"

"Oh yes, sooner than you think, matey." I wasn't joking – the intensity of the work was immense and there was never time to stop and reflect on what had just happened: you just raced off to the next job.

Drivers were first-responders. That is, as a single-crewed car, you often arrived first at a dangerous incident, all alone, with only a vague awareness of how long it'd be before the next officer arrived. As professionals, we attempted to get to emergencies as quickly as possible and as safely as possible, regardless of the type of incident, including armed incidents.

Obviously, British patrol officers don't routinely carry firearms. Back then, we didn't even carry batons or any type of gas. All we had to immediately defend ourselves with was a wooden truncheon. If we were attending a firearm incident, we could – if we wished – make use of something which was usually buried underneath all the police signs and equipment in the boot of the car: an extremely heavy, black ballistic shield disguised as a clipboard. It was masquerading as a clipboard for the ridiculous reason that we didn't want the public to know what it was, as we tried to get two fourteen-stone officers concealed behind the clipboard-sized shield if and when somebody began shooting at us. It also weighed a ton. Naturally, it remained buried and never saw the light of day. They are possibly still hidden and forgotten about, in the back of police cars today.

"Useless clipboard, this is, innit? It weighs a bleeding ton!"

You're probably thinking that the words 'guns and Cambridge' couldn't appear in the same sentence. So did I. Yet during one summer I recall at least one armed robbery per week occurring in the city centre, and the officers who were sent in, tyres screeching, to catch the offender in the act, were poor, cleverly disguised clipboard-carriers. But for some reason we never grumbled – we just got on with it, despite the obvious dangers.

It was a sunny morning about 11.00am and the radio was relatively quiet. I'd been on the go since 7.00am and desperately needed caffeine. I was alone and covering the north half of the city and decided to drop in on my then wife's place of work for a coffee, as it was on my patch. As I pulled up she came to the door of her shop, recognising the distinctive panda car and correctly guessing what I had come for.

The urgency in the voice over the radio caused me to raise my hand to stop my wife as I bent down to listen to the radio.

"All mobiles stand by, stand by." The operators rarely used the harsh tone of voice: this was serious. Something was happening somewhere in the city and we were about to find out what. "Armed robbery in progress, Arbury Court – all units to attend, please." There was that 'please' again.

Arbury Court was a small, rectangular collection of shops with flats above, located in the centre of the large housing estate in the north of the city – my responsibility that day. It didn't really matter whose patch it was on – everybody dropped what they were doing and headed directly there. The fact that it was on my beat would probably mean I'd be first to the scene, as I was the closest.

"Sorry, got to go!" I called out apologetically to my wife as I ran back to the car, fired the engine, and dramatically raced off with the blue light activated. It was important to look important in front of those you knew. I vanished around the corner at speed whilst mentally preparing the quickest route in, and waiting for a gap in the radio traffic, to let the radio operator know I was en route.

"C512 en route. Two minutes," I managed to interject. That short message told them who I was, that I was alone in the car and that I would arrive at the scene of the armed robbery in less than 120 seconds. During those two minutes the only updates I recall receiving were that it was at the rear of the post office, that a security van was being attacked, and that numerous calls were coming in re this. But that was enough. Common sense should have told me to slow down, to back off a little and wait. Why? Because the 'numerous calls' indicated that this was genuine and not some hoax or confused caller. The 'security van' told me it was likely to be a professional job with professional criminals, and the initial report was 'armed' robbery. Somebody had a gun, apparently, and I didn't, and I'd be there in seconds.

I turned into the rear service yard of Arbury Court in less than the stated two minutes – it had been one hell of a thrilling drive – and came to a dead stop behind a security van.

"C512 on scene," I transmitted as I scanned the area intuitively: the rear doors of the security van were open, there was a man sitting down on the road behind it, and another standing over him. They both had some kind of uniform on. There were crowds of onlookers all around, including on the balconies of the flats above the shops, and everybody was now looking at me – a lone, unarmed cop with little more than a year's service under his belt.

I jumped out of the vehicle, eyes darting everywhere to take in as much the scene as possible and to locate any danger, completely forgetting the useless ballistic clipboard in the boot of the panda; it would not be coming out to play today.

A constant, high-pitched scream assailed my ears. It was the security van alarm and it was awful, deafening. I covered my ears and approached the two men, who were both wearing the uniforms of security guards.

"What happened?" I yelled, trying to be heard. Their response was yelled back at me but, despite their proximity, the screaming security alarm was deafening me. I couldn't hear a thing, and I knew the next few seconds were crucial: I needed an instant update to pass to the control room who would then adapt the police response based on what I said. I needed to think fast.

I pointed at the suitcase-sized box on the floor that was emitting the 200 decibel scream, and made a throat-slashing gesture with my hand at the standing guard: *kill the damned thing!*

"I can't," he mimed back at me. "Impossible."

Jesus. I needed to think; a lot was depending on my prompt update. The guard on the floor was holding his knee and was clearly in pain, but I could do nothing until the alarm was silenced; I couldn't even speak to the control room with that thing blaring.

I tapped the guard on the shoulder, pointed at the alarm and then to a distant corner of the field behind the shops. He hesitated.

"Now"! I screamed at him. *Total control.* He got the message and took the damned thing away at a trot.

As the sound receded and my hearing returned I looked down at the security guard on the floor. I needed to establish some facts, and soon. If these men were armed, I needed to know how many, what with, and what car they had left in. Assuming they had left …

"What happened to you?" I asked, hoping to glean some information from the witness as I rubbed my ears.

"What d'you frigging think happened to me?" he replied, sarcastically, and a tad angrily, as he removed his hands from his knee. "I've been fucking shot, ain't I?"

The blood spreading out around the material of his uniform suggested he had indeed been shot in the area of the knee, and I was sure he would know if he had been shot or not.

"Ambulance required, gunshot wound to the leg of a security guard," I transmitted, automatically. This was the first update I had given, and it told the control room a lot: it confirmed the reports of guns being used; the level of violence the offenders were prepared to go to; that I needed help at the scene; and that the offenders had left (as I would have said something if they had still been there). It also told them that this was an extremely serious incident and to mobilise all necessary resources. I was still alone at that time.

"OK," I said to the guard. "An ambulance is en route, and it looks like you're going to be OK." I was crouching down inspecting his injury. The entry wound was above the knee. "Sore but not too serious. Just clamp your hands back on it to stem the blood flow, would you?" He co-operated fully. "That's it. Great. Listen, the next few minutes are essential if we are to stand any chance of catching these bastards who shot you – understand?"

He nodded and winced as he clamped his own injury.

"Can you tell me how many, what weapons were used, and how they left the scene?"

"You mean you *didn't see* them?" He was very surprised.

"What? How?

"When you pulled up they'd only just left – seconds, mate. You must 'ave seen 'em pulling away as you turned in? *No?* Well, if you'd 'ave been thirty seconds faster you'd 'ave got 'ere whilst they were still bloody shooting, mate. Seriously, you *didn't fucking see* 'em?"

I stared back at my humble panda parked across the entrance, with its lonely blue light revolving, barely visible in the bright sunlight. *C512 en route, two minutes.* How close had I been to this? I racked my brains. I couldn't recall any car pulling out or speeding away from the scene. I learned later to transmit to the control room the registration of any vehicle going in the opposite direction to me as I approached the scene. I hadn't done this on that occasion, but it wouldn't have mattered in the end.

"They even shot at the witnesses on the balcony!" said the guard. "And threatened me, threatened to shoot me if I didn't do what they said. I was co-operating fully but then they just shot me in the leg anyway, for no reason, the bastards! There was no need to shoot me. I was doing everything they asked."

I understood why he was so angry. I relayed all of the information I was able to get from him and his colleague (who soon returned minus the scream-box): getaway vehicle colour and make, direction of travel, description of men and weapons used. And I seriously hoped none of my colleagues would find these shooters.

As I'd approached the scene and turned left into the service yard, they had just left the same yard and turned left, heading off up the road in front of me. I hadn't seen them, of course, missed them by seconds, but I was so glad I did.

When I returned home that night, I saw my wife, and remembered the last time I had seen her. I had smiled and waved and showed off a bit as I raced off to an armed robbery. *Oh the glamour of being a cop.* If I had been thirty seconds faster I might have arrived when those bastards chose to shoot that young guard who had been fully co-operating with them.

There is no doubt in my mind that they would have shot me too, and no ballistic clipboard in the boot of the car would have prevented it. I'd have been shot.

It might have been the last time my wife saw me – gladly racing off to the scene, unarmed.

So why didn't I stop and hold off? Because I was a cop, and it was my beat, where a serious crime was being committed. People were in need of help, and that was my job. I felt responsible, and I wanted to be there. The fear gets buried in the adrenalin, and you go and do what you are paid to do, as best as you can, even without the coffee.

THIEF TAKER Chapter Two

I'D NEVER MET NICK BEFORE THAT DAY, but we ended up working together for many years to come in Cambridge.

I remember Nick well because, as I stood next to him in the corridor, I figured that he must have had a tougher journey than I'd had. Whereas I was relaxed – bored even – he was overjoyed, shaking his fist repeatedly in triumph, and completely incapable of containing his joy, even from the stranger standing at his side.

I couldn't actually comprehend his joy because, for me, it was just a rubber stamp from the boss: arrogant as it might sound, I had never doubted that I'd get to that day, and now that it had arrived, I just wanted to get it over and done with so that I could get back to the streets of Cambridge.

For the past two years, I – like everybody else at the start of their police careers – had been a 'probationer'. A probationer was not a full-fledged cop: we were closely monitored. And dismissal from the force was easy during the probationary period, and some officers never made it to that all-important day – confirmation. Confirmation was the moment the Chief Constable contracted you as a trained cop, changing you instantly from an easy-to-fire probationer to a full-blown cop.

I found it inconvenient, archaic, and unnecessarily bureaucratic. I'd had to leave Cambridge in the morning and drive the half-hour to Huntingdon Police Headquarters, hang around a few hours until the boss was ready, then drive back to Cambridge. It was taking me away from the job I was doing day-in day-out and a job that I loved. I didn't see the point at all – I just wanted to get back to Cambridge as soon as possible. As far as I was concerned I was already a cop: two years at the sharp end in Cambridge made you so.

I don't recall anything of what actually happened in that office with the Chief Constable. It was so unimportant to me that I have no recollection of events on that auspicious day.

Despite the confirmation taking no more than thirty minutes of the Chief Constable's valuable time, and Cambridge only being thirty minutes' drive away, it still took me away from my job for more than half of my shift. When I eventually returned to Cambridge, Karen (a colleague) remembered where I'd been and congratulated me on my confirmation.

I then went out on patrol again, exactly the same but different. I didn't have a new badge to wear, I didn't have an extraordinary increase in salary, and I certainly didn't feel any different. I was just like the rest of the team: a uniformed cop doing the job to the best of his abilities every day. Maybe the only difference I recall is looking at the new recruits joining the shift and thinking how different we were after just two years of intense police work. They still had so much to learn.

Even after confirmation, a cop is still learning – you never stopped learning. Most officers made mistakes, especially when dealing with something new and unusual, and most of the errors went completely unnoticed due to the autonomous style of the police officer's job. Occasionally, however, a mistake was made which stayed with you for life.

Possibly the only time that an officer got to switch his radio off and be completely alone was whilst dealing with a sudden death. Grieving relatives just don't need a police radio intruding on their thoughts and feelings, and so it was that I advised the control room that I was switching mine off.

It was maybe the third sudden death I had dealt with alone, the others had all been pretty much routine. I didn't like dealing with them, but I felt confident in this area. If I needed advice, I could always make a call from the phone at the house.

The ambulance crew had been and gone. They'd call us when there was nothing more they could do. That's when it became a police responsibility. When police attend sudden deaths they always give the incident priority attendance for two reasons: the first is that you never know if it is an actual crime scene, and you have to keep this in mind no matter how routine the death seems. And, second, you just can't keep relatives waiting around with a deceased loved one lying in the house.

I entered the family home to find the elderly father lying on the lounge floor on his back, with his arms across his chest. Somebody had placed a white bed sheet over the body up to the neck, and a sofa cushion behind his head. He could have been sleeping.

The family were gathered in the adjoining room at the back of the house, off the kitchen, and now had to contend with a cop prying into their lives.

It is important for officers to put the next of kin at ease as soon as possible. They don't understand the system, and why the police are suddenly in their home. They often feel under investigation, which makes the whole event even more stressful for them. I always explained that, if a doctor was unwilling or unable to issue a death certificate, it fell to the coroner to establish the cause of death. As the coroner cannot possibly attend all sudden deaths, a police officer acts on his behalf. I was only there to establish the background and events leading up to the death, so that the coroner, with the help of the medical examination – I never said 'autopsy' or 'post-mortem', as that was often just too much information for them to cope with – would hopefully establish the reason for the death. I would never mention the crime scene aspect of our job unless that became relevant.

The atmosphere in that room was one of tearful shock and hushed voices. Present were the widow, three adult children, and the son-in-law, who was the guy who had let me in. He was the only one who seemed to have some control over himself; the others were clearly devastated by events.

I knew that this day would stay with them forever. They would also remember 'the policeman who came' and what I said, and did, and how I dealt with them. Everything I was about to do would probably remain with them for the rest of their lives.

I had to get it right: be professional and genuine with them – helpful and informative, yet sensitive to their grief. It might seem a big ask for a cop just out of his probation, but it wasn't. It was just a part of the job that I had to get right, each and every time. Mistakes could be made elsewhere and laughed off, but this was too serious not to be done right.

I took out my insensitive sudden death form, which had to be filled out for the coroner. Some of the questions on it were uncomfortable to read, but still had to be asked. It was down to the individual officer to phrase them appropriately, and the whole report needed deft handling. This report would accompany the body to the mortuary and be the only thing that the coroner had to read before he started his post-mortem. It was important that we put as much information on it as possible.

People react differently to the death of a loved one, and no training course or book can prepare you for every eventuality. Few courses actually consider the feelings or knowledge of the officer in attendance.

I took my time explaining the process that would come next, and obtained the details needed for the awkward form. This took at least an hour, as I had to think of how to phrase the questions for the information needed, and answer their myriad questions with care. When it came to the part where I told them their father would be taken to the hospital and be examined by the coroner to determine cause of death, the widow become very upset.

"I don't want him put in a fridge on his own. This is his home – can't he stay here tonight?" She looked at me, pleading. "Just this last time, please?"

Her request made perfect sense to me. *If I were in her shoes …* I'm a very sensitive guy and I blame this sensitivity for overriding my professionalism that day. Or was it just the fact that I was still relatively new at this game, and cut off from advice, having turned the radio off?

"Well, I'm not sure …"

The whole group then decided to support the mother's request. I had five people begging me for a bit of humanity in their moment of need. The couple had been together for over fifty years, and suddenly he was gone, leaving her alone. What harm was there in just one more night?

My sensitivity shoved professionalism aside and beckoned in practicality.

"Well, we can't leave him where he is." He was lying in the front room, which gave access to the front door and the upstairs bedrooms. To pass from the kitchen and dining room or to go upstairs to bed one had to practically step over the body. He couldn't stay where he was.

"We could put him in here," said the wife, helpfully. "He'd be comfortable in here and … out of the way." What she said made perfect sense; it was possibly the only room in the house where he'd be 'out of the way'.

"OK – but I won't be able to move him by myself," I said. I'd handled bodies before, and they were always extremely heavy. I also found it unpleasant to touch one.

"I could help you," volunteered the son-in-law. I looked at him and realised he was the only person in the room up to the task. He was also a very brave man. I nodded at him.

"OK – but you'll all need to leave." I knew it was going to be a difficult task and didn't want anybody to witness us struggling with his corpse.

I shepherded them all past the body and up the stairs. I then nodded at my assistant.

He took the old man's hands whilst I grasped his ankles. We half dragged the body the two yards towards the adjoining door. As expected, it was extremely difficult to move him. Bodies multiply in weight after death. A large sob burst out from upstairs. I realised that they could hear us struggling with the body.

My able assistant managed to open the door and manoeuvre the body towards it. Then we came to a stop. The door was tight up against the wall, and then the second door leading to the back room was very close. We could have taken him into the kitchen easily but needed to make a sharp turn to the right. The only way to do it was to bend the body almost into a 'U' shape. We were at the point of no return, so we bravely battled on.

It took about twenty minutes to move him the four or five yards, and as we laid him out on the backroom floor with his arms across his chest, gently covering him in the bed sheet, we stood and caught our breath. Sweat was pouring down both of our faces and we nodded at each other.

"Thanks," was all I could say. It was an awkward situation for two strangers to be in. "I'd better just call this in, let them know what's happening."

He took me to the telephone and I called the sergeant in the control room.

"You did what?!" he almost shouted. "You can't do that. The body belongs to the coroner now. We have to take the bodies in for security. Anything could happen to them if we leave the bodies at the scene. I'll call the mortuary team."

I hung up slowly and looked at my assistant. "They're coming to collect the body. Now. Sorry."

THIEF TAKER Chapter Three

From a police point of view it was an unfortunate mistake and just part of the learning curve. There was no comeback on me. The sergeant I'd spoken to clarified the point about the body belonging to the coroner – and it made perfect sense to me. But at the time …

Despite this, I went home unhappy. Mistakes that cause other people to do something unpleasant and unnecessary cause me personal stress. I was really disappointed that I'd put that man and the family through such an ordeal. I should have known better. They would remember that day – and me – for the rest of their lives.

Other mistakes might simply be put down to being half asleep …

I was turned out of the briefing at 7.00am to attend another sudden death. I was barely awake as I took the incident printout from the control room and scanned it. 'Wife just woke up to find husband dead. Nothing suspicious. GP confirmed'.

I arrived at the semi-detached house within ten minutes of the message, grabbed my unpleasant paperwork, took a deep breath, and rang the doorbell. A middle-aged woman greeted me at the door still wearing her nightdress and dressing gown.

"Thank you for coming so quickly, officer," she said, pleasantly and quietly. "We'd better go through to the kitchen to talk." She pushed open the door to the lounge and hurried through to the kitchen at the rear. I closed the front door and followed her, surprised to see an elderly man just inside the lounge, having breakfast at the table.

He had his head down over a bowl of cereal and a spoon in his hand, and didn't look up. I nodded at him and walked through to the kitchen to join the lady. I spoke to her quietly, so as not to disturb the old man, and managed to get some background leading up to the death. As she slowly related the events of the night to me, one thing started to become apparent. I glanced at the old man still sitting at the table, and realised he hadn't moved since I'd arrived.

"So, your husband got up in the middle of the night and complained of being hungry? You heard him come down to the kitchen and rummage around, and then you fell back to sleep. In the morning you woke up and realised that he still hadn't come back to bed. You went downstairs and found him like that, at the dining room table?"

She nodded.

I realised what a dreadful thing it was for her to have come downstairs and found him like that – dead at the table. She too must have initially thought he was alive and well.

I realised my mistake. "Oh, I'm sorry, I ..."

She shrugged it off as if she understood the mistake, and indicated for me to go through.

Every sudden death I'd attended before that time had been after the medical services had been and gone, attempted to resuscitate the deceased, and confirmed death. That meant that the body was clearly a body, usually prone on their back, with evidence of the attempt to revive. They had never resembled a living, upright person having breakfast.

What I hadn't registered before attendance were the two words at the end of the printed message: 'GP confirmed'. Their own doctor had attended and quickly confirmed death without disturbing the body, but, as he couldn't establish the cause of death, he'd told her before he left to call the police. I put it down to a lack of attention so early in the morning, and learned to read all of the details on the incident reports thereafter.

These events are the reason officers learn so quickly and are able to cope with most incidents the job has to throw at them. Afterwards, you go home, think about how you could have done it better, seldom talk to anybody about what happened, and then file it for future reference. Tomorrow is another day.

Sometimes, officers are thrown into the complete unknown in dreadful situations with very little information to go on, and they have to adapt to the changing circumstances and think on their feet – again, usually alone. Perhaps one of the worst such incidents I had to deal with started, once again, with an innocuous slip of paper at the 7.00am briefing. It also involved the death of a loved one.

A car had crashed on an isolated road in the north of the county in the early hours. The only occupant – a young blonde female – had died instantly and horrifically: she'd been decapitated in the crash. She had no identification with her, and the car was registered to a company on my beat in Cambridge. I was tasked with making 'tentative enquiries' at the company, to see if we could identify the driver and get somebody around to her house quickly to notify her next of kin. That was all the information I had to go on: that and the car details.

I parked up opposite the company entrance at about 8.30am, looking for evidence of staff. The company was a small business located on the first floor above a video shop. While I waited, I read and re-read that message to see if I'd missed anything. At around 9.00am a solitary male unlocked the office door and went inside. I took a deep breath and followed.

I had no idea who I was talking to: for all I knew it could have been the victim's husband or father. He wore a shirt and tie, was in his mid-30s, and very comfortable in his surroundings. He was also very friendly to me.

"How can I help you, officer?" he asked, smiling.

Here goes … "A car which is registered to this company was involved in an incident last night and I'm trying to identify the driver. I wonder if you can help me?" What I said was the truth, and I must have said it in a matter-of-fact way, for the man suspected nothing out of the ordinary at that point.

"Sure," he beamed. "I'm the MD and owner. The name's Mike. Please, take a seat." I sat heavily in the indicated seat as he sat behind his unassuming desk. "So, what's the vehicle?"

I gave him details of the make, colour, and registration of the car.

"Yep, that's our car all right. In fact, it's used by Sonia, our company secretary." I noted the name down.

"Sonia?" I noted the surname he gave me too. "Is she blonde?"

"Yes – yes, she is. I wonder if I might ask what kind of incident she was involved in?" I'd expected that question.

"I'm not really able to say anything at the moment," I replied, uncomfortably.

"Oh, OK. Do you need her address, too?" That was just what I needed, and as I opened my mouth to say yes, the phone rang.

"Oh, excuse me." Mike picked up the phone and, professionally, announced the name of the company, and identified himself. He then broke into a broad grin. "Hi, Pete, how are you? ... Yes, great, really great, and you? ... Really? Oh, that's odd ... No, she didn't stop at ours ..." He glanced across at me. "Actually, I've got the police here now asking about her car. Do you want to speak to the officer?"

He spoke quietly off-phone to me. "It's Pete, Sonia's husband. Apparently, she didn't arrive home last night."

Did I want to speak to the husband of the deceased lady on the phone? No, I didn't. I wanted to disappear, to vanish. I wanted to throw my police uniform off, and run all the way home, and scream and hide.

"No! No – tell him I'll call him back," I whispered, urgently, trying to show professional calm.

"Pete, they'll call you back in a minute. OK?" he said in a monotone. "Yeah, speak soon, OK – bye." He hung up and looked at me.

"Something is wrong, right? I mean *seriously* wrong ..."

Yes, there was something seriously wrong, and I had to act quickly before the husband called back. I didn't want to have to tell him over the phone, and now I had to make a judgement call, and hope I was right.

"This car was involved in an accident last night – a fatal accident. The sole female occupant was killed instantly. We didn't know who she was. I'm sorry."

The news hit him hard; they had obviously been close. He stared at me in silence, his eyes questioning me, unable to take the news in.

"Listen, I need Pete's address quickly before he calls back. I need to send an officer to tell him personally. Can you provide me with that?"

Practicalities usually distract people from the awful reality of the situation. He soon passed me the dead girl's address and her partner's full name. I relayed it over the radio and explained to them that the next of kin had just called the office and got a hint that something was wrong. The message was quickly passed up to the car that covered the address. My heart went out to Pete: his life was about to be irreparably changed. I also felt sorry for the officer who was required to tell him this awful news.

"Oh, God. No – not Sonia," said Mike. He was devastated, motionless, lost. "Excuse me," he whispered as he picked up the phone and relayed the horror of the situation to the person on the other end before hanging up. "That's my wife. We're all good friends here. Small company. Sonia's been with us from the start," he explained, almost apologetically.

I just sat there, feeling completely inept. I didn't know what to do or say, so I just let him speak.

"We all went out for dinner last night. It was a lovely evening, we were celebrating … Well, I don't suppose that's important now. She'd had a few glasses of wine, nothing much. I offered her our sofa – she'd done it before, but she said she was OK." He looked out of the window. "I guess I should have insisted." He sobbed slightly, but held it together until his wife arrived a few minutes later.

I sat in my car for five minutes in an attempt to gather myself. I'd got five long hours of work ahead of me. It'd take Mike and his wife much longer to get over today, and maybe Peter would never be able to deal with that morning's news.

A personal attack alarm came in at a nearby bank, and, grateful of the distraction, I activated my blue light.

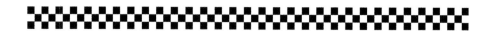

THIEF TAKER Chapter Four

KEITH WAS TEN WEEKS BEHIND ME as a recruit. He certainly couldn't be faulted for his eagerness, especially when it came to driving. Now that he'd gained a grade five general enquiry permit, all he wanted to do was take a car out – for anything, even though a grade five meant no response work!

One cold and wet evening when very little was happening (rain is a great crime preventer), Keith was summoned from walking his city centre beat to attend the custody office for a quick 'transport job'. I'm not sure where in the centre he was exactly, but I'm sure he ran all the way back to the station before somebody else took the job.

"Keith," said the custody sergeant with a straight face. "We need you to take a car to A&E (Accident and Emergencies at the hospital) and collect some stuff for a prisoner. It's quite urgent, so can you go find a car and get back to me, and I'll give you the details?"

Whilst Keith ran around looking for a spare car, a call was quietly made to reception at A&E. They were fully briefed by the time Keith – now proudly dangling a set of keys in front of his face – returned to the custody office.

"Right, Keith, I need you to go to A&E and ask for Staff Nurse Hayward. Ask him to give you the Fallopian Tubes he has prepared for us, and bring them straight back here as quickly as you can. OK?" Keith scribbled the name down and nodded eagerly.

"What are you collecting?" asked the sergeant, still straight-faced.

"Fallopian Tubes, from Staff Nurse Hayward," replied Keith.

"Good, and don't dally: a prisoner needs them urgently. But drive at the speed limit. And no blue lights!"

Thirty minutes later, having been sent from ward to ward looking for Staff Nurse Hayward and his Fallopian Tubes, Keith returned to the station and booked in over the radio. Because of this, we all knew he was about to enter the custody office, following his urgent transport job.

The whole shift was hiding in one of the interview rooms as he walked in clutching a handful of beige rubber medical tubes.

"Sorry it took so long, Sarge, but nobody knew where Nurse Hayward was. It took me ages to find him! But I've got them now …"

As he handed them over to the sergeant, the tightly packed officers fell out of the interview room laughing hysterically.

Keith couldn't understand what the joke was until it was explained to him.

Laughter was necessary in such a highly demanding job. Officers faced so many different types of emotions whilst at work, and none more so than a police driver – the one role Keith aspired to: driving at high speeds; a continuous stream of updates coming over your radio; and mentally preparing your fastest route across town whilst having to deal with that idiot in front of you who decided that the best way of dealing with the approaching police car was to slam his brakes on at the narrowest part of the road, thus preventing you from passing. The temptation to gesticulate at such idiots wasn't always overcome.

Naturally, accidents happen. And, due to the speeds involved, they can be serious. Nobody wants to cause an accident, and officers certainly don't. The first thing an accident means to an officer is that you will not be attending that urgent incident you were en route to. Plus – you have let those people down, and your colleagues, who now have to cover for you. Second, you have to request an officer of a rank above the driver to attend and investigate the accident. It might seem strange to some – officers investigating colleagues – but, believe me, nobody prosecutes a police driver as aggressively as the police service does. The third thing that happens is your police driving permit is instantly pulled, regardless of the investigation, which means you can no longer drive police vehicles until it is reinstated. This is normally done several weeks or even months later (depending on the seriousness and any charges that may follow) by means of a 'check-ride' with a police driving instructor.

For many officers, the lack of driving is a throwback to early probation, whilst for others it is a pleasant break from the manic job-to-job life as a police driver. There's actually nothing like a pleasant walk in the city, listening to your colleagues being run ragged in their cars.

It amazes me to this day that the public (and tabloids) have so much to say when there is a police car accident. In reality, there should be so many more such accidents, considering the amount of hours officers spend each day racing from incident to incident, often under extreme pressure. Perhaps the number is so low because the quality of the driving instruction is superb, and refresher courses are held annually. Whatever the reason, the public should acknowledge the low number of accidents rather than expecting none.

I was involved in one police accident and a very near miss in my twelve years of driving as a cop. I would say, considering how often I was on an urgent call, that that ratio was extremely good.

A year or so after my bollocking for driving through the city centre on a blue light whilst sounding my car horn, a decision was made at the top level to equip all police cars with bar lights and sirens. I don't think there was any connection with that and my pointless 'words of advice', as it had been hinted to me that it was already being considered at the time of my bollocking. However, the day did come and officer morale rocketed. There is nothing like being given the tools to do your job, and, as driving at speed meant danger, we were really relieved that finally we had something we could work with.

I was responding to an alarm call one bright afternoon: driving back into the city along Milton Road – a major trunk road – at about 45mph with my blue strobe lights on and siren sounding. The limit was 30mph but I judged the speed to be appropriate for the conditions and the type of call. I was approaching major cross roads and the light was against me, and I knew the junction to be quite blind.

Just before I reached the crossing two things happened simultaneously that would have been given no consideration in any subsequent enquiry: the lights changed to green and the control room cancelled my attendance as the call was a false alarm. I immediately eased off, began decelerating, and killed the siren. I decided to leave the blue light on until I was back to the speed limit, which would be just after the junction.

As I crossed the junction on a green light, speed at about 38mph and slowing, a cyclist appeared directly in my path from the left junction. In the split second that I saw him I registered that he had clearly jumped a red light; that he was looking away from me to his left, towards the oncoming traffic; and that the impact was going to put him in hospital.

My quick braking and swerve probably saved his life. I came to a stop at an angle on the exit of the crossroads and looked back at the cyclist. *Had I missed him?*

He had stopped just beyond the junction and was looking back at me, as if he was confused as to where I had come from and what part I had just played in his life.

The relief at not hitting him was mixed with the anger at his stupidity. Not only had he needlessly put his own life at risk but he had also nearly cost me my permit, if not my licence. I was furious.

As I was stationary, at a funny angle across the junction with a blue light on, all other traffic had come to a stop, waiting to see what happened next. I decided to take the opportunity to have words with the cyclist and manoeuvred, pulling up in front of him.

He was in his early twenties and was listening to music through his headphones.

"You bloody idiot," I said, strongly. "What on earth do you think you were doing, jumping a red light like that?"

"Oh yeah, sorry," he admitted, sheepishly. "But I did look!" he added, suddenly brightening.

"Look!? Look!? Yeah, you looked all right: you looked *down* Milton Road but you didn't bother to look *up* Milton Road, did you? If you had, you'd have seen me, with my blue lights on, wouldn't you?!"

"Oh yeah, that's true. I only looked left. Sorry."

I should have prosecuted him but he didn't seem fully there, and anyway, I'd been so angry I'd already given him a good bollocking instead.

Years later, I was driving down exactly the same road for the exact same reason but at 4.00am, with no traffic anywhere. I was in a marked police car, and two colleagues were following me in an unmarked police car. We'd been looking for car thieves in the north of the city when an alarm activation came in.

It was always a good alarm, this one: the sports clothing shop on Mitchum's Corner was routinely hit, and thousands of pounds of ski clothing stolen each time. The crime was highly professional and was always over in a matter of minutes, so getting there quickly was essential.

The roads were deserted, nobody was about, and it had been raining all evening; even the criminals hated the rain.

I went first because I had blue lights, but my siren remained silent so as not to warn the criminals we were coming. I was driving at a considerably higher speed than the previous near miss, and, within one minute of the call coming in, I was fast approaching Mitchum's Corner. It was looking good.

Just ahead of me, walking away from the scene and on the other side of the road, was a man. I quickly calculated his distance from the shop in relation to the time since the call and realised he could quite possibly have broken the window on his way past. He had to be eliminated as a suspect.

The road at this point was very wide and wet, so I needed to bleed off speed before attempting to swerve across the deserted lanes to stop next to him; not doing so would have been reckless. No doubt Tony in the car behind me would brake hard and cross the road too, effectively sandwiching the guy had he chosen to run.

I braked hard, reduced my speed to about 40mph and swerved across the road, confident of keeping control of the vehicle as the tyres fought against the wet surface. I assumed Tony was doing the same but I hadn't considered one thing – that Tony might not have seen the suspect.

Tony hadn't. He saw me braking hard and had no idea why, so he decided to overtake me to continue to the scene. The front left side of his car slammed into my front right wheel at about 50mph, putting my car into a full spin. I spun two or three times in slow motion. The sound of the impact in the deathly quiet night was immense, and my left knee had been struck heavily by the gear lever in the impact, causing considerably bruising and pain.

Once the car had come to a stop, I staggered out, checked for further injuries, and soon realised what had happened. I then asked if Tony and his colleague were OK. Thankfully they were, so I approached the suspect who was standing on the pavement staring at me.

I asked the control room to send a supervisor due to the '*PolAcc*', which was the dreaded term we used for a police accident, and confirmed that others would be attending the alarm in our place. I then spoke to the suspect, checked his details through the Police National Computer (PNC), and searched him.

Everything seemed to be in order with the man – he just happened to be in the wrong place at the wrong time – so I turned my attention to the two mangled police cars in the middle of the road, blue lights still flashing. I knew that this would be investigated and that this man was now an important witness.

"So," I said. "About the accident?"

"Accident? What accident?" he asked, seriously. It was my turn to stare at him. I pointed to the two cars littering the road. "Oh, that accident …"

Both cars were written off in the impact. I was advised that it had been fortunate that the other car had struck my car's wheel, which meant it and the axle took most of the force. Had it been slightly further back, I would have been seriously hurt, particularly my legs. Luckily, I was just bruised … and very, very sore.

The sergeant investigating the accident did the right thing: she interviewed both drivers under caution, then told us we would both be reported for driving without due care and attention. Tony and I both lost our driving permits, and enjoyed our quiet walks in the city for several months.

In fact, the 'break' was so beneficial that I never chased up the situation with the prosecution, as I didn't want my permit back for a while longer. As the six-month mark passed, I made a point of asking, as I knew that a traffic prosecution had a time limit of six months. So what was happening with my case?

"Oh that?" I was told. "The CPS (Crown Prosecution Service) dropped that prosecution months ago – insufficient evidence." Had I been a member of the public, you can be sure that I'd have been informed of this fact. As a cop, you sometimes felt like a second-rate citizen.

Shortly after my asking, our driving permits were reinstated, and Tony and I were back out on the pandas again.

THIEF TAKER Chapter Five

DESPITE MY RELAXING TIME WALKING the city, having full lunch breaks and feeling sorry for my colleagues racing from job to job, I was pleased to be back in a panda car. I was a good driver and I loved driving. I knew the risks involved – having just faced the prospect of going to court and possibly losing my own driving licence for doing the job I loved – but I still wanted to chase after the bad guys. And, because of my driving skills, I often got there early and caught the bad guys in the act. It was where I belonged.

Unlike police colleagues in many other countries, British police didn't, and still don't, have 'partners' to patrol with. Back then, you generally patrolled alone. Luck was with you if you were given a co-pilot to work with.

Double-crewing, as it was called, had many benefits: from an evidential point of view, you had the word of two officers, and not just one cop against the suspect (and his mates). Physically, two officers were a deterrent whereas many people were happy to try it on with just one cop. Confidence was much higher with a partner at your side, and you'd get involved more, whereas being single-crewed might cause certain officers to hold back for safety reasons; and who could blame them?

The arguments against double-crewing were numerous, including that it wasn't efficient use of officers. We needed visible policing, and two cops in two cars were more visible than two cops in one car. Also, a co-pilot could easily spend the shift being chauffeured around, doing very little.

The management were against double-crewing, despite the obvious safety advantages, whereas the staff were *for* it. So, most of the time, I was – in common with all of my colleagues – alone in the car.

There was one possible advantage of single-crewing cars that nobody ever mentioned, and that was the weight difference. I weighed fourteen stones, and if you sat me in the passenger seat next to another heavyweight cop (and there were quite a few), it was bound to affect the performance of the car, especially if that car was a Ford Escort with a flat 1.6 diesel engine. No turbo, nothing.

With the boot groaning under the weight of all that police equipment – not to mention the heavy ballistic clipboard – with two heavy cops up front, the car was possibly the worst idea of a police car you could ever come up with. And this could only happen in the UK.

The idea, apparently, was to save money on fuel: diesels were cheaper to run than petrol – according to our *civilian* fleet manager, who obviously believed they were still driven at the speed limit. However, when driven like racing cars, diesels are not economical.

With such a camel for a panda car, if you took one large cop out, there was bound to be a slight difference in performance, and it was this difference that was crucial in an urgent call – despite the obvious dangers – faced by a single cop arriving too quickly at the scene of an ugly incident.

The first time I realised just what a real camel I was driving was one quiet afternoon cruising the local hot-spots in the north of the city. A Ford Fiesta XR2 approached me, going in the opposite direction. It was a sporty car (high insurance costs), and contained four very young faces, all staring at me. Each forehead had 'shit, a cop' written across it in wide-eyed white.

As the car passed me, I transmitted the index plate twice across the radio from memory without any preamble to the controller, ensuring I got the plate right, knowing that the switched-on team in the control room – who I'd worked with on many occasions – would scribble the number down on a piece of paper.

Then, as I turned my car around as quickly and nonchalantly as I could, I asked for a PNC vehicle check. I didn't need the reply from the control room because, as soon as I'd begun the turn, the XR2 reacted by throwing itself into the nearest junction, vanishing from sight.

I floored the throttle in second gear and prayed that I'd get to the corner before the car reached the next one. I knew if I missed it turning into an earlier junction, I'd lose it, not knowing which route it had taken.

The appalling response of my flat diesel was mitigated by the other driver's poor decisions: instead of turning off at an earlier junction causing me to lose sight of them, he drove the full length of the road and was still visible as I turned in after it. All I needed to do was close in on it, which seemed highly unlikely under the circumstances.

By then I'd called in that the car was failing to stop, hoping that a traffic car might be in the city or on the nearby A14 and able to respond – I stood no chance against an XR2 with my flat 1.6D. My shift colleagues would also start making their way to me, but I had to keep the target car in sight until they got to me – and they were driving the same crappy cars as me.

One of the most difficult aspects of police pursuits – which we weren't supposed to be doing – was the running commentary over the radio. It wasn't sufficient to say 'a car making off' then fall silent: colleagues needed to know where the car was heading and at what speed. This meant juggling the car controls with the radio button, knowing precisely where you were, including the names of every street you are racing through or towards, as well as driving safely whilst moving at high speed. You also had to make sense when you spoke, bearing in mind the car siren would be blaring across the radio as well, and try to remember to avoid shouting or screaming.

Everything you said was recorded and could be used in evidence, so what you did say had to be clear in its meaning, and you had to remain professional at all times – the recording of the pursuit may well be played out in court, many months later. You also had to take in everything being said over the radio – updates, other units joining, locations, etc. – for obvious reasons. Over all of this, you had to remain calm, avoiding any 'red mist', and ensuring you, and everybody else, went home in one piece that night. You didn't really give a toss for the thieves – they had made their choice.

I knew the area like the back of my hand, and part of the secret of policing is second-guessing what the driver of a (presumed) stolen car might do on that particular street, driving in that direction. I was able to give my colleagues the precise location the car was heading to, and they could anticipate more or less where he would go from there.

Before the car had got to the end of the road it was on, the radio room came back to say they had just spoken to the owner of the car, and he'd confirmed that the car wasn't where he'd left it. It had only just been stolen. The confirmation was rewarding: I'd located more car thieves. But it didn't change the fact that I had to get my hands on them first, and preferably without anybody getting hurt. More interesting than the control room report, however, was the sound of a *Zulu* call-sign calling up to attend from the station: a police dog-handler was also en route.

Back then, it seemed that anybody with a screwdriver could steal a car in a matter of seconds. Vauxhall Astras were the favourites, although most cars were easy pickings. And steal them they did, especially 'hot hatches'. It wasn't unheard of for ten or fifteen cars to be stolen from Cambridge city in a typical day, and, with a bit of thinking, luck and time, it wasn't too difficult to find them.

Time was on their side though. I was far from the city centre, on the northern edge of the city, driving through a large council estate. Even on a clear drive, it was several minutes from the other beat areas to get there, including the dog-handler from the station.

I prayed for a traffic car to be nearby. I heard the shout go out over the force radio and a reply come back from a traffic car deep in Newmarket. They were on their way, but I knew it'd be over long before they managed to get here, no matter how good the driver.

I was well aware that my diesel was useless at acceleration, so when I slowed down for a junction, it took me ages to build up speed again, whereas the XR2 had great acceleration. My only hope was to try to maintain the speed through the junctions, so this I did, where it was safe to do so. As many corners on that northern council estate had wide green areas, I was able to gain slightly on the car, surprising even myself.

My running commentary faltered when the car drove down a road I couldn't name or explain. It was a small tarmacked service track that served the rear of rows of houses. The gardens on either side were narrow and long, and I recall seeing people look up from their allotment chores as the XR2 sped down the narrow track, followed by a police car with lights and siren blaring. The cat on the track was startled too, and miraculously managed to avoid the wheels of the fleeing XR2.

Unfortunately, the poor creature hadn't expected a second car to be bearing down on it at such speed. Despite it trying to dive out of the way at the last minute, I knew that the dull thud on the chassis of my car meant that somebody's family pet was now dead.

"You bastards!" I yelled. I love animals. I considered calling off the pursuit at this point: this was dangerous. We don't drive down such back alleys at this kind of speed, and it could have been a kid back there.

Two streets later, and with back-up still a long way off, I was just about to let them go when the driver made another ridiculously novice-like error: he turned into a dead end.

This action caused my heart rate to go into extra-overdrive. Either he'd turn around and drive straight back at me, or they'd all decamp from the car and run off. Either way, the next few seconds promised to be full of a certain type of fun and action that few other jobs can offer.

I knew there were at least four thieves in the car, and it was just me against them. They were young teens, and I knew they would just want to get away from me and not face me down. So I was fast approaching the culmination of this pursuit, and I had to choose my target wisely. I also made sure my back-up knew what was coming and where. It was great to be able to rely on such a team as they were.

The first man you wanted was the driver: passengers can just say they were picked up by the guy a few minutes earlier, and didn't know the driver, and certainly didn't know the car was stolen. The driver could hardly say the car was his, especially with a screwdriver dangling from the ripped out ignition. He also faced extra charges of dangerous driving, driving with no insurance or licence, etc.

At the end of the road was a small green, ringed with concrete bollards to stop cars driving across it. The car smashed into one of those beautiful bollards and came to an abrupt stop. Both doors instantly flew open and four young lads made a starburst decamp from the car. I screeched to a stop right behind them and exited the car just as quickly, having released my seat belt on approach. I left the siren blaring – it would have been time-consuming to kill it, and every second counted. The position of my car would prevent anybody getting back into the stolen car and driving off, although my car was unlocked (no central locking) and could easily have been moved with a calm head.

"Decamp, decamp, decamp!" I transmitted over the radio, followed by my precise location. These words are probably more exciting than 'failing to stop', as a foot chase was now in progress, meaning the odds had changed in our favour: police human engines were generally faster than the criminals' human engine. I also gave a brief description and direction of travel of the three youths I wasn't chasing. They were the ones my colleagues would be looking for as I latched onto the driver. I had to do all of this whilst at full sprint. It certainly tests you ...

My target fled straight ahead and I did my best to keep him in sight. I have short legs and I'm not particularly fast; I'm more of a workhorse than a racehorse, but I usually manage to maintain a gap to anybody who wanted to run from me. They would usually collapse before I did.

After several hundred yards of running, the driver had had enough and chose to dive behind a hedge and into the front gardens of a row of houses. By the time I reached his vanishing point he could have doubled back or continued onward. He might also have slipped down a side passage to the rear of the houses and escaped.

Damn! I had to choose and choose quickly or I'd lose him.

"Zulu 412 on Campkin Road. Where is Dave, please?"

I turned and saw the police dog van blue-lighting its way down the road towards me. My running commentary, even during the foot chase, had brought him to me. I don't know which commentary was more difficult – the one during the high-speed drive or when sprinting flat-out after a crook. I answered the dog-handler over the radio and with my waving arms. I was pleased to see the van alter course and drive directly at me.

"Look, mate," I called out into the shrubbery. "It's all over. Either come out now or the police dog will come in and find you." I had no idea if that would work or not, or even if he was still there, but I wanted to arrest him myself, to have my name on his arrest sheet. I deserved that much.

Silence.

As the van came to a sudden stop and the handler went to the rear doors and prepped his barking beast, I kept my eyes on the front gardens in case the car thief made a move, but saw nothing but still gardens. He must have escaped down one of the many side-passages. I pointed to the last point I'd seen the driver and smiled as The Exocet was brought out of the van, almost slipping on his own saliva.

I stood well back as he dragged the handler up the path of the nearest garden. Within twenty seconds there was a sudden bark and a high-pitched scream. I was pleased. We had him.

The dog had dived into a beautiful purple Buddleia bush and latched onto something. I remember it well, as I had the same bush in my back garden, and it was always covered in butterflies. I couldn't see any on this bush, but smiled as another scream pierced the quiet gardens.

I admired the strength of the handler as he pulled out the beast, which was now attached to a young man who didn't want to come out. I say attached: the dog had bitten into the guy's stomach and was rather enjoying it. Once the handler realised he had got my man, he attempted to get The Exocet to release his victim.

Alas, he didn't want to. No matter how many times the handler tried to pull the dog off, whilst simultaneously shouting 'Release!', the beast just refused to comply.

The dog, up on his hind legs and with his teeth sunk into the lad's flabby abs, was like a German Shepherd with a Kong full of biscuits. He was having none of it.

Every time the cop pulled on the dog's lead, the lad's hips and guts did an involuntary movement forward. Arms flung skyward, the victim stared down in horror at the beast with his fangs sunk into his stomach, the dog's eyes wild, its mouth snarling. I was expecting the dog to shake his head from side to side, as they do, and he did. I was amazed that there wasn't more blood.

"Release!" screamed the cop, repeatedly – resisting smacking the beast through fear of being attacked himself – as the dog and crook continued in their bizarre dance of give and take.

After about five or six pulls on the dog's collar, which in turn pulled on the lad's abs, the dog finally decided to release its prey. The lad fell to his knees, clutching his stomach whilst staring down at it. I couldn't help but think he looked like he was in deep prayer. Even during my formal words of arrest he never took his eyes off his stomach and the small stain of blood slowly seeping through his T-shirt.

I truly felt sorry for the youngster: he was in real shock, and clearly injured.

"Should have bloody come out when I told you to, dickhead," I said. "Come on, you're nicked."

As I arranged for his transportation to hospital, I was pleased to hear over the radio my colleagues tracking down and arresting his three co-accused. All four of the thieving little buggers were now in custody. I was well-pleased: I'd spotted the stolen car, managed to keep it in sight despite the difference in vehicles, got resources to it prior to decamp, and, despite back-up being so far away, we'd managed to get them all.

The following day, I was back at the garden alley attempting to identify the owners of the cat so that I could explain what had happened. I wasn't able to locate the owners, but one of the gardeners told me that the father of the fourteen-year-old driver had been gleefully boasting in the local pub that his son had outrun the cops the night before.

I asked him if he had told everybody that the cop was in a useless 1.6 diesel whilst his son had been driving an XR2, and had he mentioned the fact that his son had actually been arrested, so he couldn't have run *that* far? The guy was very pleased with the information, and I knew it would be all around the estate by the morning.

I grew to love these car chases, which, because we weren't qualified response drivers, we weren't supposed to do. But seriously, who else was there to do it?

To see a good example of a Cambridge police pursuit on my old beat, using the police helicopter and local units, with the full recording of officers involved, visit http://tiny.cc/PoliceChase.

The commentary of the pursuing traffic officer is difficult to hear over the car's siren, but he initially states 'vehicle failing to stop', which seriously gets the juices flowing of most cops (in cars). The female voice is the control room operator, and the police helicopter picks up the transmissions (and tone of voice), and, from the pursuing car's commentary, soon arrives overhead of the fleeing car.

The pursuing officer clearly states 'we are staying back, not putting him under any pressure' for evidential reasons.

'VB' is Victor Bravo, the control room, and Quebec Hotel 88 (QH88) is the helicopter. The helicopter commentary is actually from one of my old bosses, who I still dislike to this day (even his tone on this occasion is one of total irritation with the pursuing officers).

At 4.28, the traffic officer requests city units to assist, as he knows this is going to end soon and he'd like some more officers to help out when it does, as they are now deep in my old city beat. He's preparing for a decamp.

At 6.26, the control room advises the traffic cop that 'tactical contact' has been authorised. This is the bureaucracy that ruins our police. The highly experienced pursuing officer has had many opportunities to safely nudge the car off the road, bringing it to a stop before it kills somebody. Sadly, he has had to wait for the delayed authorisation from a boss in the Force Control Room, some twenty miles away in another city.

Give the authority to the officer on the ground!

Eventually the officers do 'make contact' and manage to stop the car safely. You can see the vehicle is fully boxed-in and officers are smashing their way in through the windows as the dog-handler gets his dog out for any runners.

It's interesting to hear the pursuing officer's main concern during the conclusion: it's for the road being blocked by police cars, and that they don't want any more to the scene, just the (city) van.

THIEF TAKER Chapter Six

I HATE 6.00AM. WELL, ACTUALLY I HATE BEING *UP* at 6.00am. Unfortunately, I'd spent most of my working life in two jobs that often meant I was either getting up at 6.00am or I was still up at 6.00am from the night before. I still don't know which was worse.

After working through the night, often non-stop from 11.00pm, and with just one hour to go, we were usually dead on our feet and looking forward to going home. It was also quiet time, a chance to get some paperwork done. However, criminals usually do shift-work too, and officers should never switch off to their activities, no matter what the time.

From what I could ascertain over the radio, I was the only car out and I was single-crewed; everybody else was at the station completing paperwork or preparing to hand over prisoners to the morning shift. As was often the case, a single officer was out responding to incidents in the whole city, whilst other officers were monitoring and would turn out if needed.

The Astra GTE passed me in exactly the same place that the XR2 had previously, and continued heading along Histon Road towards the city. The five young faces in such a powerful car, and the uniform turning of their heads towards me, instantly told me it was stolen. I called it in and turned around as quickly as I could. There was no point in trying to hide this from them – I knew they would be speeding up already and I needed to stay with them.

By the time we hit the 30mph city limit, we were doing 70mph and still accelerating. Fortunately, the streets were deserted at that time apart from the occasional milkman. As the car continued on in a straight line, I was able to build up momentum and keep them in my sights until they hit the brakes for a 90-degree right-hand turn. I'd been expecting this turn, as they had been heading directly towards the centre of the city where any of my colleagues might be. They needed to turn off and away from there, and this was really their last opportunity.

The concertina effect of the turn allowed me to close in enough to read off their number plate, as well as put pressure on them. Because of their turn and my continued acceleration, I looked to be gaining on them. I really wanted this pressure at that time as they had just turned into a road with a very new 'pinch-point' – a traffic calming measure that allowed a car to pass through a tight barrier, leaving just a few inches either side of the vehicle.

As hoped for, the driver was caught off-guard by this tight squeeze, although I'd discovered it when it had been installed at the start of the week and had practised driving through it in ever-increasing speeds during the quieter hours of the past week.

He slammed his brakes on as soon as he became aware of it, almost losing control of the car in the process. He had no choice but to enter the gap, and went through it, clumsily losing the passenger wing mirror in the process.

Having just navigated the earlier turn I was by then building up my diesel's speed again when I sped through the barrier with confidence (although I did hold my breath for an instant!). The result was that I managed to close within fifteen yards of them at the next critical point. I knew what was going to happen next and this made me smile, although I cursed at not having a partner in the car.

I could see three little white faces staring back at me out of the rear window, urging the driver to lose me. The driver did just what I had anticipated and accelerated hard away from me, completely missing the last left turn up onto Huntingdon Road, a trunk road out of the city and possible freedom. By the time he realised his mistake it was too late. He was accelerating hard down a dead-end road to nowhere.

I knew that most if not all of my colleagues, maybe even traffic and a dog van, would be on their way to me as fast as they were able to. I wouldn't be on my own for long.

"Stand by for decamp, stand by for decamp," I called over the radio, giving the exact location. I still love those words, nothing got you more excited than knowing that a group of car thieves, who had put other people's lives at risk, were just about to leap from a car and try to run away from justice. That morning, *I* was that justice, and I'd have the driver at the very minimum.

As I raced towards the end of the road, I had my siren and blue lights on. In about three hundred yards they would run out of road, and there was no way back: the road was too narrow. The middle-class neighbourhood consisted of semi-detached Victorian houses, with large agricultural fields at the end of the road. And I knew those fields extremely well: it was where I walked my dog each day.

As the stolen car came to a screeching halt in the middle of the road, I released my seat belt and jumped out of the panda car even before it had come to a full stop, ensuring my car was blocking any possible escape of theirs. That car was going nowhere.

The Astra sat on the tarmac, engine still running, faces inside looking back at me. No decamp.

What were they up to?

I walked quickly up to the driver's door and made sure he couldn't open it by pressing my thigh hard against it: I didn't want the driver to escape, even if the others did. I was confident of being able to direct my colleagues in across the fields to intercept the others if they did run off, but – oddly – they just sat there.

The driver looked up at me, the surprise clear in his eyes. "What's up?" asked the cocky fifteen-year-old, whose face I instantly recognised.

I glanced from him down to the ripped-out ignition. It was definitely a stolen car, yet nobody was running from me. Seeing as there were five of them in the vehicle, *not* running was a good thing (for me, not them). I decided to play their game to allow my colleagues the chance to get there.

"Driving a bit fast, weren't you?" I said, stating the obvious, whilst glancing back along the length of the dark and deserted street for any sign of support. *Come on ...*

"Yeah, we're late for work."

I knew that this driver hadn't done a day's work in his life.

"Oh, OK," I said. "Can you turn the engine off then; the residents look like they are still sleeping?"

He struggled a bit here, but, after fiddling with the wires, the engine did die and the silence closed in. *Still no distant sirens.* I think they must have believed that they were dealing with the stupidest cop on the planet, and that they might actually get away with this.

I looked back along the road. The place was deserted, curtains drawn, the only sound being the clink of the milk bottles being delivered by the approaching milkman, and the twitter of stirring birds. Residents were peacefully sleeping, oblivious to the stench of the twenty-four hour crime that permeated the city all around them. It was an ideal English street scene where nothing seemed out of place, except for the flashing strobes on top of my police vehicle, parked diagonally across the end of the road.

In the distance I could hear the strain of a protesting diesel engine trying to get somewhere fast. It was growing louder. *Not long now …*

"So, what happened to your keys then?" I asked, nodding at the dangling wires.

"Ha, yeah, you know …" he mumbled, smiling. Did he really think I was that stupid?

"Come on, boys. It's over. You're all nicked, as you've probably guessed by now. The dog van is nearly here, so he who runs first gets bitten first. Fair enough?"

"Fair enough," said the driver. They seemed resigned to their fate.

As the driver stepped out I handcuffed him, still expecting the front-seat passenger to make a run for it, but he didn't. He stepped out and lifted the seat for the three in the back. Out they stepped, and stood quietly at the side of the car.

Before I could update the control room and my colleagues, we all turned at the sound of the police van approaching: it looked impressive with its flashing grill-lights and roof strobes, engine straining at maximum. They were making haste as they'd not received any transmission from me since the stop, but there was no need for the siren as there was no other traffic around. Sometimes, the siren is used to let the crooks know that support is only seconds away, just in case they are attacking the officer. The crooks would stop and leg it on hearing the noise, possibly saving the officer from further injury.

Even the milkman stopped to admire the approaching vehicle.

The van was immediately followed by two pandas driven in similar fashion. As other cars came to a stop behind those two, the whole street seeming to fill up with police cars and flashing lights, I couldn't help but be reminded of a scene from *The Blues Brothers*.

"Come on then, lads," I said. "No silly business, OK?" I led them all to the back of the van and updated the crew that I had already arrested them. With their help, the five were searched and placed into the cage in the back. As the door was closed and locked, Kevin, the van driver, turned to me and laughed.

"How the hell do you do it, Dave?"

I had no idea, of course. I just shrugged my shoulders and smiled.

"Just luck, I guess."

The following day I was advised that the group of fifteen-year-olds had stolen the car to get up to Norwich Crown Court, ninety minutes' drive away, where they were facing charges of car theft. Naturally, they never made the court case that day.

Life in the police wasn't always so easy, or such fun. After such a shift it wasn't unusual to go home and pick up a copy of the Cambridge Evening News and see members of the public writing in and criticising the local police for just about anything. Who knows, maybe one of the residents who had been sleeping peacefully in that dead-end street might complain that he had been woken up by so many police vehicles?

Nobody did complain, but there was a complaint from another part of the city. From that contributor's description, I was able to identify the exact house he lived in; it wasn't cheap – the previous public toilets had been converted into an expensive town house close to the city centre and I knew how much the place had sold for. The occupant was a man of money.

His complaint? During the previous morning rush hour, when the streets around his house were – as usual – at a crawl, he'd spotted a panda car waiting in the queue at a side street. After a five-minute wait, the police car had activated his lights and siren and raced through the junction, 'obviously unwilling to wait like normal people have to'. There was no evidence to say what the cops were doing – just his observation and possible unhappiness at being disturbed by a police siren whilst in his lounge.

In my twelve years of policing the streets of Cambridge, I think I activated my lights just once without justification, and that was because I was late for a coroner's inquest (some might say that was justifiable, but I don't), and I felt really bad for doing so. I'd never witnessed anybody else doing it, or even considering it. What I knew from experience was that officers would patiently sit in the horrendous Cambridge traffic queues in an attempt to get to the next routine job, but would willingly attend to any emergency calls that came in. Yes, sometimes it was a relief to be able to do this and push through the traffic, but only because we had to.

Maybe if the writer's burglar alarm activated in rush hour, he'd be annoyed if the cops attending did so by waiting in the traffic jam instead of using the equipment designed to help them do their job better?

The world is full of professional police complainers and professional police officers. Sadly, the press only give space to the former, whilst the latter rarely respond to such ignorance, which gives a very one-sided view of police work and the officers who do it.

Another stupid complaint followed an urgent call I attended. I was turned out from the 3.00pm briefing to a report of a 'violent eviction' from a squat on my patch. I knew the squat well. Nick, my 'confirmation colleague', was turned out to support me in his own car.

The house in question was set back from the road on a sharp bend, the road being a semi-dead-end. To park outside of the house meant obstructing the road and possibly causing danger to other road users on the bend, despite the fact that few used the road. Parking legally meant parking several hundred yards away. However, the information we received en route was that baseball bats had been used against the squatters (who, whatever we think of them, should not have to suffer such violence).

I raced to the scene and stopped in front of the house, parking half on the pavement and half on the road so as not to obstruct any passing car or pedestrian, and left my blue lights on to indicate the emergency. Nick, who was always second on the scene if I was sent, parked behind me in the same manner.

We dealt with the violent eviction and went on our way.

The following day, Nick and I were called into the Chief Inspector's office. He'd had a complaint from a 'concerned member of the public' that we'd parked on a bend, half on the pavement, which was illegal, obstructive and possibly dangerous, and a bad example for the police to be giving. How much police effort had been put into finding out which two officers had done this I can only guess at.

Despite instantly admitting and justifying what we'd done, the CI went on to tell us that he'd deal with the matter 'by way of informal resolution'. I knew what this meant: the complainant would be told that the two officers involved would have been given 'words of advice' and the matter settled.

I was not happy with this, and felt comfortable enough with this senior officer to state my point of view. He was the same man who had spoken to me for using my car horn in place of a siren.

"I'm sorry, sir, but I refuse to accept an 'informal resolution'. What we did was perfectly legal under the circumstances. We made a judgement call, we had no real alternative, and the law is on our side. We are exempt from parking restrictions under these conditions. If I get sent to the same call today, I'll do exactly the same again. Words of advice will change nothing. We did nothing wrong and he needs to be told that."

Thankfully, Nick immediately backed me up. The CI seemed at a loss as to how to proceed. We left his office with apparent 'words of advice' that we were not prepared to listen to or accept. What a farce. I'm certain that the complainant was told we'd been given those words of advice, and would have been thanked for bringing this matter to the boss's attention. He no doubt went away satisfied that he'd done his bit.

Sometimes, police management need to stand up for the organisation and tell the public some truth, and not be so acquiescent. Unfortunately, there are too many people looking for their next promotion that don't want to rock the boat. Maybe the police should introduce a manager whose job it is to defend the police against such stupidity?

I remembered the toilet dweller's complaint a while later when I discovered a suspicious Astra parked up on his street, no more than fifty yards from his house. It was parked in a pay-and-display bay alongside other cars, but for some reason it had caught my attention. I checked it out and discovered that it had had its ignition ripped out, and the engine was still warm. It was parked up correctly and not abandoned by the thieves in the normal manner: it was clear to me that they were coming back for this car.

It was mid-afternoon and unusually quiet so I sought permission to sit up on it and watch for a while to see if they came back. Authorisation was given and I requested an unmarked car if possible because I was in a very clearly marked police car, and nobody would come back to the stolen one if this vehicle was in view.

Mark said he was in the station and would try to find one. A short time later, he arrived on the scene in a plain red Ford Escort. I quickly briefed him and drove my car to another side street and parked it up. I walked back and climbed into the passenger seat of Mark's car.

Mark had parked about three yards from the stolen car, at 90 degrees to it, and facing it. We were in a tightly packed corner where there was a bit of a concentration of cars – visible to an observant person, but most criminals are very dim.

So we sat down in our seats and we waited for stupid.

THIEF TAKER Chapter Seven

AFTER ABOUT AN HOUR AND A HALF the workload began to increase as the afternoon passed into evening. Two officers sitting up doing nothing was a big strain on the rest of the shift who had to cover their absence.

"Shall we call it a day?" I asked Mark. "Doesn't look like they're coming back, does it?"

He agreed and I called the control room to arrange for a vehicle to come and recover the stolen car. As I was doing this, Mark pulled our car out of the line of parked cars and parked right next to the stolen car.

And then we saw them. The driver of the previous stolen Astra and another well-known car thief were walking directly towards the stolen car – and us. I was still talking to the control room, my radio up to my face and in clear view. The thieves were just four yards away from the front of our car.

"Stand by. Stand by!" I transmitted, very quietly. The control now knew it was 'game on' and began directing resources towards us.

"Mark, they're here, they're bloody here!" I said, laughing, as I shrank as low as I could into my seat, Mark following suit.

Either the thieves would see us and walk away, in which case we'd have a hard time proving any connection between them and the car – unless the car contained something to connect them to it. Or they'd get into the car and the case would be proven, which was more preferable, yet more risky – we didn't want a car chase on our hands, or for them to get away with the car, which we had in all truth already recovered. That would mean red faces all round and possible neglect of duty.

Still, they'd see us. They'd have to be blind not to.

With just our eyebrows above the dashboard, we watched as the two lads happily chatted away and walked straight past our awkwardly parked car, located right in front of their stolen one. They sat in the car, the driver reaching down to connect the wires. That was enough. That was our signal.

We both sat up as Mark fired the engine and jolted the car forward to block off the vehicle's exit. There was no way they could leave in the car now.

The two thieves looked at us in irritation as first, not fully comprehending what was happening, until I shouted, "Go, go, go!" over the police radio, telling any nearby units to go straight to the scene for the arrest.

Simultaneously, Mark and I exited the vehicle, as the crooks – who'd finally twigged we were police – exited theirs. Mark dropped the ignition keys in the footwell as he went – it could prove really embarrassing if he left them in the ignition and a thief managed to steal the cop car. Also, it would have been really easy to lose them in what was about to happen …

I raced around the side of our car towards the driver in theirs. Mark was closest to the passenger as he decamped, and he naturally went for him.

"Decamp! Decamp! Decamp!" I yelled into the radio. *Foot-chase on.*

I'd known this full-time crook since he was about nine years of age, when he'd started staying out all night and getting into trouble. But by the time of this incident he was a gangly young teen who sprinted off up the road like a March hare. He was taller than I was – he'd grown a lot recently. I bet his grandmother was proud of him.

I did my best to keep up with him, but I was no sprinter. Mark was, and he disappeared down a different road after the passenger. We then had two foot-pursuits in progress, with two officers trying to transmit conflicting accounts of where they were, which all added to the general confusion.

My suspect turned left and ran headlong down the centre of the street. It was clear he was a lot faster than me and would soon be out of my sight. I could hear on the radio that cars were coming, but they were still too far off to make a difference. I also noted that a police dog was en route. The Exocet ...

As the suspect vanished around the next corner I just caught sight of him diving into the tiny garden of a town house, disappearing behind a large privet hedge. He was trapped here, but if he were to get past me again, he'd be gone, so I reached for my CS spray. We hadn't been issued with the horrible stuff for long and I'd never used it before. I'd been dying to try it out and this seemed like a good time to do so.

As I entered the garden I glimpsed a shape vanishing through the opposite privet hedge. He was doubling back on himself, and I was annoyed that he might be about to escape for good. He glanced back at me as he went through the hedge.

I released the spray directly at his face, hoping to disable him enough to stop him from running so fast, to give me the advantage. He was no more than a yard away from me – how could I miss?

I saw the spray hit the leaves just above his head and bounce back towards my face. I instinctively closed my eyes but it was too late: I was semi-blinded by the spray. *Shit!*

I ran out of the garden and caught sight of the thief jumping the wall into the grounds of the college opposite. I ran across to the spot and looked over the wall. He'd disappeared into the grounds.

I called it in, and the arriving officers were directed to form a cordon around the small college. And, of course, the dog was nearby. I had no idea where Mark was or how he was faring, but I had total confidence in him. He was a lot faster than me, and he always got his man.

The dog-handler arrived, went into the college with The Exocet and searched for the lad, but found nothing. Most of the time the dogs were infallible, but occasionally they got nothing. I was of no help to him: I was still trying to get the CS out of my eyes.

After it was agreed that he had indeed got away, I went back to the stolen car. Mark was there and he'd got his boy, and my boy was arrested days later, having clearly been identified by Mark and I.

We didn't always get our man, but we usually did. It was rare that crooks got away. I found them hiding in dustbins, in gardens, under cars, and on flat rooftops. I never liked giving up: it made me feel like I'd failed and that an idiot had got the better of me. I cursed using the CS: it would have probably been a different outcome had I not used it. These kids do run fast, but they have no stamina, which is something I always had. I put it down to experience and carried on.

An example of my persistence was a call that came in about 4.00am. It was a good time for burglaries to happen from a police point of view. Bars and clubs had long been closed, and the drunken violence that followed those events had generally finished by that time. It was usually quiet time for us, a chance to get something to eat and catch up with paperwork. Traffic was also scarce, so getting anywhere quickly wasn't too difficult. I loved 4.00am.

"Neighbour can hear some scraping coming from the side of her house. There is a shop next to her and she thinks somebody is trying to break into the shop."

I knew the row of shops in question but wasn't exactly sure which one she meant. I was also aware that the sound of my diesel engine racing to the scene would alert any criminal of impending police presence, and I didn't want to do that: I wanted to catch the person in the act.

I parked up a good two hundred yards short of the scene and ran forward as quietly as possible, almost invisible in the darkness. I reached the end of a row of houses and stopped. There was a lane running between the last house and the first shop, and it was in complete darkness. I wasn't sure if this was the right place or not, so I held my breath and listened.

There it was, a scraping noise coming from up the alley, more or less at the side of the shop, as the witness had described. It was just twenty yards along the alley, but I couldn't see what it was due to the darkness. I needed my eyes to get their night vision so I stared into the void, willing them to adjust to the darkness. All the time, the scraping noise continued.

After a few seconds I began to see a dark shape moving at the side of the shop, roughly the size and shape of a man crouched down. The fact that a man was in this dark alley at 4.00am, and the noise was coming from him, told me he *was* trying to break into that shop. I pressed my transmit to whisper 'burglary in progress', but, before I could do so, a diesel engine came racing up the street and swung a left into the alley, illuminating the whole scene with its high beam headlights.

Despite being startled at the intrusion, I saw the suspect in all his glory. He was holding a shovel, which was jammed into the side of the door of the shop, as he tried to force the door open. He froze for a second in the unexpected glare, then dropped the shovel and ran off down the lane in the opposite direction.

I swore as I ran after him at a twenty-yard disadvantage. The car was an unmarked police car being driven by one of the more experienced officers on shift, who should have known better. All of my careful approach and good work had been blown away in an instant of thoughtlessness. I didn't even call it in as I ran – he could do it: I was in full sprint after the thief.

The police car flashed past me and came to an abrupt stop at the end of the lane. I ran past it as the officer struggled to release his seat belt and get out of the car. It was clear he was totally unprepared for this incident, and had presumably initially dismissed the call as a false alarm.

At the rear of the shops was a green area leading to a small, insignificant housing estate I hardly knew. There was one road in and out, and it was bordered by older houses and their back gardens. The thief had vanished into there somewhere. I began a quick search to see if I could sniff him out, whilst the other cop did the same. Cars were being placed in a cordon around the scene, and there was no dog available. The runner couldn't have got far and was probably hiding up in there somewhere.

After an initial search of the obvious places to hide on the estate I decide to do a more thorough search. This is where a dog was essential. The other officer went back to the scene and confirmed an attempted burglary and asked for the key-holder to attend so that he could complete the paperwork. That was the least he could do.

My second search also revealed nothing, but I was beginning to learn the lay of the land. An officer was parked up at the entrance to the estate; he confirmed that he had been in position when the other officer had yelled that there was a 'runner at the rear', and that nobody had passed him. That meant that the thief hadn't been able to escape the obvious way. With the cop there, he'd have had to find an alternative way out or just lay low.

OK, without a dog to do what dogs do best, I'd have to do what I could. I checked in all of the back gardens surrounding the estate and they seemed to have secure gates preventing anybody from passing through to the front of the houses.

By 5.30am everybody had given up and gone back to their paperwork, except for the officer parked on the entrance to the estate and, of course, myself. I was beginning to feel the cold, but, as there was nothing else happening, I decided to keep on looking. I knew he was there somewhere: all I had to do was keep looking. Oh for a dog's nose …

By 6.00am I was beginning to think he might have somehow escaped. I was freezing cold and thought it'd be a good time to call it quits and go in for a coffee. I didn't want to – I felt like a failure. But I also desperately felt the need for a pee.

As it was still fairly dark I decide to take a pee up against a tree at the edge of a small parking area, out of sight. As I did so, I clicked the transmit button and told the operator I was giving up on the suspect. I was now beginning to get angry – that officer's amateur actions had cost me a good arrest.

I don't know if it has something to do with when men pee, but as I did so, I looked up, glancing around me. On the other side of the parking area, on a flat garage roof, something moved in the shadows and caught my attention. I stared at it and saw the soles of two feet sticking up. Then the thing that had moved reappeared – it was a face staring down between two feet, looking directly at me. As I turned my head casually, as if looking around me, the face vanished from view again, leaving the two soles of his feet visible. *He was lying on his back on the garage roof!*

"Yeah, control, cancel my last – I've got him. Can the other unit join me here, please?"

I zipped up and nonchalantly walked towards the garage. Within seconds the other officer joined me.

"Where is he? Where is he?" he asked, excited, if a little amazed. I was pleased he hadn't given up on me and had stayed long after the others had left. He believed in me and now his belief was being proved right.

I pointed up towards the garage roof.

"Up there. Go that side, I'll cover here," I said quietly. We stood either side of the roof. There was no escape. "Ready?"

He nodded at me and we both screamed at the top of the voices that he was under arrest and that he had better come down off the roof now or I'd come up to get him and pull him down.

The noise of two shouting officers clearly woke up several residents, as bedroom lights began illuminating the quiet estate.

The crook stood up slowly and painfully and showed me his palms in submission.

"OK. OK. I'm coming down. Seriously, I'm fucking freezing." The man had been lying there, motionless, for the last two hours, and it was a very cold night. He struggled to get off the roof, but when he did I immediately handcuffed him.

"Yeah control, one in custody," I said, quietly, smiling at my probationary colleague.

As the operator transmitted her 'well done' back to me, she was drowned out by a huge cheer from numerous staff in the control room. That was reward enough.

It had taken stealth to get to the scene. Then my colleague had blundered in like a novice and blown it. Refusing to give up, perseverance and self-belief took me through the coldest part of the day looking for him, even after everybody else but one had left. An understanding of the area and an investigation of possible exit routes had led me to believe he was still there.

And, finally, I answered the call of nature in just the right place at just the right time. This was what being a cop was all about and I loved it!

THIEF TAKER Chapter Eight

IT WASN'T EVERY SHIFT THAT I GOT TO GO OUT on patrol: I was still a radio room operator, and an experienced and capable one at that. I loved doing both jobs and working with both teams, and I did these equally to the best of my ability.

Sooner or later it must have got to the point of being a difficult decision for the sergeants: put me in the radio room where I was efficient and unflappable, or out in a car where I was a rather good thief-taker? I obviously preferred the chase more, although the radio room also had its advantages, especially in deepest winter.

After several years of doing this I decided to add another skill to my police CV: I volunteered to become a PSU officer. A Police Support Unit (which is never referred to as 'the riot squad' in the police) is so-called because they rarely have to deal with riots. Their primary role is supporting other officers, sorting out all manner of aggressive situations where putting a 'standard' bobby in would be far too risky. The type of job that might require a PSU intervention would be – among other things – entering confined spaces (i.e. a house or a police cell), or dealing with a violent, armed and dangerous thug. Maybe a prisoner in the cell had somehow produced a sharp or pointed object and was threatening to stab the first officer through the door. That would be a call for a PSU. A house siege? PSU again.

At Cambridge, any officer could volunteer to be a PSU officer. You didn't get paid more for it, although overtime could be available for such jobs. Provided you passed the initial training, you continued doing the job you always did, but you were also given a large bag of specialist equipment that could be dragged out at a moment's notice to equip you up to the necessary safety standard. All that was needed were six PSU officers to make up a 'serial', plus a PSU sergeant in charge of the serial.

Training was a paltry couple of days at most, once a year, on some disused airfield somewhere. Two things stand out from those infrequent but fun training days.

The first is the feeling of being totally engulfed in flames as a well-meaning colleague petrol-bombed you. Being completely on fire is unnatural, exhilarating, and essential training for any PSU officer; and having to stand still and wait for a colleague to put you out promoted close teamwork. It also gave you the much-needed confidence in the flame proofing of your PSU suit, although you'd think they'd have invented fireproof bootlaces too.

My second memory was the terror of a visiting, police mounted unit cantering towards us as we jeered and heckled them. Acting as hooligans for the mounted unit training session was a unique experience: those horses are big, they are scary, and they hurt like hell if you don't get out of the way quick enough, as one overly cocky officer was soon to find out. You don't shoulder-barge a horse of that size at that speed and walk away from it!

Outside of those jolly training days, the reality of being a PSU officer meant weeks and weeks of forgetting that you actually were such an officer. There were pre-planned PSU events, which proved to be extremely boring, when we spent hours just sitting around in the back of a van and waiting for something to kick off. And then there was the occasional intense burst of dangerous fun that randomly cropped up, which just managed to keep you interested.

One such burst of dangerous fun occurred shortly after a new shift pattern had been introduced in the city, which had resulted in an overlap of officers on duty, meaning we had lots of officers on duty at peak times and fewer on at 'quiet times'. Having worked a variety of different shift patterns over the years, I knew this one was the only one that worked. Suddenly, because we had the right amount of officers to cope when it counted, we hammered the criminals, and our morale was sky-high.

Naturally, the powers-that-be soon dropped it for something less radical. We were never told why, but suspected that it made us look too successful, and that it might result in the Home Office giving us less officers in the future. Yeah, I know – ridiculous – but it takes years of such ridiculousness for a committed officer to finally see the light.

Anyway, it was Friday night, about 2.00am, and I was on the 'hooli-van' patrol – a minibus staffed with a number of officers ready to attend to and deal with any untoward hooligan element in the city (we really only ran this during this shift pattern as we couldn't staff it during the others).

These vans are only as effective as the officers who staff them, and you always hoped for a good crew when you climbed aboard. Fortunately, this van was staffed with my PSU colleagues on the shift – all handy and confident officers. We not only worked together as a close team on shift, but had worked together on PSU training days, getting petrol-bombed together and putting one another's flames out, and, as we had given up patrol duties to the oncoming shift, we were relaxed yet geared-up for the night's disturbances.

A report of a fight at a notorious pub in the centre of the council estate in the north of the city proved to be a false alarm. The fast, blue-light drive across the city meant that our adrenalin levels were sky-high by the time we arrived ready to confront mass violence. Disappointed at the lack of action, and fully pumped-up, we began to head back down town to be central for the next such incident.

Whilst driving along one of the roads in the middle of the estate, a young man saw us and flagged us down. Obviously drunk, he explained to the acting sergeant up front how he had been stabbed in the hand and thrown out of his flat by his flat-mate. He did have a hand injury so, as one officer attended to his bleeding and an ambulance was called, we got out to investigate the stabbing incident.

Directly opposite from where we'd stopped was a small block of flats, two storeys high. The large upper left window as we faced the building had the lights on and no curtains. The two windows were open and music was blasting out as two very drunk men danced around inside, jeering and gesticulating at us out of the windows. You'd have thought they'd just won free booze for life and a 'get out of jail free card'.

The injured man explained that he actually lived in that flat with one of the two men, but his flatmate had come home that night with another friend. They were all extremely drunk, and for some inexplicable reason, they had stabbed him and thrown him out of the flat.

It was quite clear to us: the police needed to go into that flat and arrest those two men for a serious assault and bring to an end this disturbance and potential for more injury. Fortunately, nobody felt more able to do that than the crew of the van I was on.

Several of us went up the stairs and knocked on the door to the flat to talk to the occupants. It's the British way – despite the obvious violence, we always give talking a chance first. From the outside, our colleagues could see the men barricading the door with a sofa and other furniture. Fair enough, it wasn't going to be that simple.

As officers went to and fro below the windows, the men began throwing household objects down at them. We didn't have our PSU equipment with us, but we did have several shields on the van, just in case. These were brought out and used to protect our heads.

The acting sergeant with us agreed that we should try to gain entry into the flat to bring this incident to a close, so, with shields at the ready, we went up the stairs and began to look for a way to enter. Fortunately, big Steve the karate man was there and he just began to smash the locked door to pieces with his hands, pulling out pieces of sofa and armchairs as he did so. As the gap slowly increased in size, we could see the two idiotic fools prancing around inside. They were dancing and singing and drinking and jeering, seemingly excited at what was to come. Funnily enough, so were we.

As we ferried the furniture out onto the front lawn it became apparent that quite a large crowd of onlookers had gathered. I also noted that the requested dog van had arrived. The Exocet ...

Once the door and barricade were sufficiently removed, we were able to see into the flat. Still dancing and laughing, both men were beckoning us in. We wanted to go in, but we knew we would be entering their domain, and we had no information as to who they were or what the flat might contain. We did know they were willing to stab their flat-mate over some petty quarrel, so by entering unprotected we would be putting ourselves at unnecessary risk, and our kit-bags were all back at the station.

It was at this point that one of the occupants was seen to have a large knife in his hand, which he was concealing behind his back as he faced the door. This was clearly visible to the officers and crowd standing below and looking up. His mate had also armed himself with something. They were both preparing for the inevitable: the police entry and arrests.

The order was given to hold back – we just weren't suitably equipped to enter such a situation. And then I saw The Exocet dragging his handler up the garden path.

"Out!" I yelled at my colleagues on the stairs. "Dog coming, everybody out!"

We cleared the stairwell just in time, as the dog dragged the handler up the stairs. We followed them at a reasonably safe distance – we didn't want to miss the action but neither did we want to get bitten.

Once at the 'missing' doorway, the dog-handler screamed at the two men to put their weapons down. They just laughed and danced and jeered at him, so he warned them that he would come in with the dog.

And he did.

As The Exocet and his handler entered, the man nearest the door raised his right arm above his head, holding a knife: a direct threat to the officer. He was instantly neutralised with a baton across his face. I'd never seen a man turn into instant jelly until that day. That threat was eliminated efficiently and left no room for re-emergence.

The dog was simultaneously released and given free rein to deal with the second threat. The fool had stepped back as the dog-handler dealt with his mate, and had hidden his hand behind his back.

"He's got a knife!" wafted in repeatedly through the window. The dog seemed to know this already. Or just didn't care either way. The Exocet sank his teeth into the man somewhere mid-torso, causing him to crash heavily to the floor with the attached dog thrashing its head from side to side, growling horrendously. It was at this point that the man came to his senses and gave up, showing his hands were free of the knife. Within seconds, both men were in handcuffs and the flat secured. They both needed medical treatment.

I heard a spontaneous round of applause break out from the crowd outside. They'd had ringside seats to the drama and were unusually pro-police – or just anti 'those-idiot-neighbours'.

"That was excellent, fucking excellent!" exclaimed one resident as we brought the two men downstairs to the ambulance. "About time you lot did something!" and "Better than the TV, that!" It felt good to be appreciated for once.

The following day I came back to work and was immediately tasked with going to the local hospital to fetch the Jelly Man back, as he'd been there receiving treatment all night and morning. I'd had dealings with him several times before, so he recognised me when I saw him, although I couldn't say the same about him. He had a huge bruise to his forehead and cheek, big fat lips, and a huge gap where several teeth had once been.

"You look a bit of a mess. What happened to you?" I asked, feigning ignorance.

"Yeah, me own fault. Apparently I pulled a knife on one of your lot last night and got this for me troubles." He smiled, lopsidedly. I laughed with him and took him back to the station to be dealt with. Both men were eventually charged with wounding their friend and myriad other offences, and sent to prison.

The officers involved in the incident all received letters of commendation from the city boss for quickly dealing with a dangerous and unpredictable incident. Our supervisor at the time, the acting sergeant, wasn't so fortunate. She was investigated for neglect of duty for allowing officers to go into the building without the appropriate protective equipment, and for not calling for a negotiator. To be fair, I don't think she could have stopped us from going in there if she'd tried.

That incident was something that I might describe as fun – frightening yet enjoyable. Obviously not so for those injured in it, but that's the life they'd chosen. For a police officer, this kind of unexpected and exciting event – that you just stumble across – can be very memorable for many reasons.

We hadn't worn any protective gear to deal with it, as we didn't have any with us; otherwise we would have. Yes, we should have sent somebody back to the station to collect our kit, got kitted up, and entered the place safely, but then the sergeant should have ordered us to!

It's probably fair to say that most of the time I actually spent wearing PSU gear was during training. The only real incident of note, when I wore the kit and was pleased that I was wearing it, was on Saturday 14th September 1996 – a date that should be etched into the history of Cambridge.

Three months earlier, a new protest group called *Reclaim The Streets*

(RTS) had brought the M41 motorway in London to a standstill. Eight thousand protesters-cum-revellers had turned up, and, in the ensuing party, dug up the road and planted trees in the holes.

In September, RTS decided to come to Cambridge. As their protest seemed to be against cars, most of them turned up by train. The local cycling group met them, and, together, they marched around Cambridge causing severe traffic disruption to a city that already suffered daily from traffic problems.

In light of previous RTS protests, all police leave had been cancelled, and Cambridge PSU units, supported by other forces' PSUs, were on standby at a nearby school, ready to be brought in once the expected trouble started. Meanwhile, other officers were escorting the various groups around town, attempting to mitigate the chaos and keep everyone in good humour.

By mid-afternoon, the thousands of hippies, cyclists, new-age travellers, anarchists, and just about everybody else had caused chaos all over the city, leaving the police guessing as to where they would finally set up shop. They settled on Mill Road, the trunk road leading out from the city centre where I had caught my quality jewellery-shop burglar.

The police allowed them to stay in Mill Road for several hours, which caused severe gridlock in the surrounding streets. The local pubs and supermarkets did a roaring trade in alcohol, and sofas and chairs appeared out of nowhere as the road became one great play area. Sound systems were set up, some acrobatic individuals were raised up on huge poles above the seething crowds, whilst others climbed up onto shop roofs and danced – to the delight of the crowds below. Some even stripped naked.

Whilst the police sat back and tolerated this behaviour, the crowd continued to empty the local stores of alcohol, and the behaviour of some became more and more outrageous. It was inevitable: we would be ordered in to reclaim the streets from *Reclaim the Streets* before long. We had total confidence that we were up to the task, and, rather looked forward to it, we just didn't know if they would behave themselves and go home quietly or cause a riot.

As we sat around the school playground waiting for the order to move, we decided a pre-mission photo of our serial was in order. Our serial's radio call sign was *Victor Bravo Four Alpha*, which was too similar sounding to Andy McNab's book *Bravo Two Zero* to be ignored. So, having taken the photo, Keith Fallopian Tubes subsequently used his computer skills to black out our eyes SAS-style, and gave each of us a codename. I was to be known as 'Bookman Burden.' I have no idea why, maybe I was reading a book at the time or it was some kind of future prediction?

By early evening the boredom was causing a few of the guys to doze off in the van. Everybody was instantly awake, however, when word came across the radio that we were finally going in to clear the road of protesters. We kitted up and boarded the vans, and, before long, we arrived at the end of Mill Road, near to the police station.

In order not to seem too aggressive, several serials had been deployed in a line across the road between the street party and us, wearing the good old standard police helmets. We remained on our vehicles and awaited instructions from our sergeant.

We were a PSU *serial*, which consists of one sergeant in command, six PSU officers, and a driver who usually stayed with the van. Three serials made up a PSU *unit*, commanded by an inspector. Our unit, consisting of eighteen officers and three sergeants, was in the first line of vans. Behind us were numerous other PSU units.

Our unit was in the perfect spot to watch the goings-on at the front. We could see the PSU unit spread out across Mill Road, their backs to us, with the humming crowds of extremely drunk protesters to their front. They were told to try and reason with the protesters and encourage them to move on.

As much as we had been waiting for this moment, no doubt the protesters had too. Despite being given pretty much free rein all afternoon by the police, it was obvious that they weren't going to pack up and go home that easily. For some of them, the day wouldn't be complete without a fight.

It started with plastic cups of beer. The officers stood their ground and got wet. As the cups were exhausted, in came the half empty beer cans. Even when half empty, beer cans hurt. Finally, the full, unopened cans and the odd bottle were thrown. These objects were lobbed from deep within the crowd and travelled some distance. As a result, they weren't very accurate, but the danger was that one of those full cans was going to hit an officer and cause serious injury.

Without any order to the contrary, the officers stood there and took it. As the barrage of incoming missiles intensified, we were cursing the senior officer for letting this situation continue. We were kitted up, we were ready, and we should have replaced those guys in that line as soon as the first missile had been thrown. The line of officers was being pelted with increasingly heavy and more dangerous objects: they were unprotected and they shouldn't have been there.

As soon as the order came, we were off the van and racing forward, in full protection, carrying a long shield each. We pushed past the unprotected officers and stretched out across Mill Road with our respective sergeants behind us, ready to give us orders, and the inspector behind them, telling them what to do. It was possibly the quickest and slickest de-bus we'd ever done.

We were now the front shield unit, and, on seeing us, the crowd went into a frenzy.

Some ran at our line and launched their full weight against the shields. Numerous missiles were being picked up off the floor and re-thrown at us. They approached us and spat at us, flashed their arses at us, and swore at us. We held firm because we could take it. We were well protected, our shields were fully interlocked, giving added strength to our line, and we were young and fit. It was actually quite fun to finally put the training into practice.

Our shield wall became the focus of attention of every angry young man and woman in that crowd of thousands. The sensible people moved away from us, and the anarchists moved towards us. The quantity of full beer cans raining down on our heads wasn't a problem: we had faith in our kit and we held fast.

Unfortunately, as we stood there taking the full, first wave of anger from the crowd, what we didn't know was that our softly-softly initial approach had left us woefully unprepared to deal with this sudden surge in uncontrolled violence. There was no way we could even turn our heads around to see what was going on behind us, we had to focus solely on the seething mass of anger writhing before us.

When the protesters realised that beer cans had zero impact on our padded shoulders and helmets, mostly bouncing harmlessly off our shields (not to mention the awful waste of beer), they decided to focus on the shields themselves. That solid, impenetrable wall of protection must have caused them so much frustration.

Again, we weren't particularly worried. We knew from training how difficult it was to penetrate a shield wall like ours – we'd all managed to keep our eighteen-stone instructor on the other side of it, and he'd been armed with a baseball bat.

The Romans had invented the system, and the reason it was still being used two thousand years later was that it damn well worked.

A fully grown, overweight man of about fifteen stone was being used as a missile, being catapulted by the crowd at our wall. This was an interesting experience for us. Clearly out of his head on booze, the human canon-ball was causing some damage to himself each time, but he kept getting up off the floor and allowing himself to be re-launched at us.

Each time he slammed into our shields, we would bang him away with as much force as we could muster. The impact on our shoulders and arms was tremendous, but we held those shields up in front of us and took the crap, hoping that his pain would eventually get to him, and he'd give up and go home.

This continued for about fifteen minutes, and it was at this point that I realised I had stopped enjoying it, and wondered what was going on behind us. We had no idea what was happening because we were unable to take our eyes off the wild animals a few feet away trying to kill us. My shield was beginning to feel like it was made of lead and I was worried: how much longer might we be expected to hold off this avalanche of unwashed rioters?

Standing on my right was Simon, a colleague I had worked with for a while. A rioter had managed to grab the top of Simon's shield and was pulling it down and forward. Others joined in and were attempting to reach up and pull on it. Simon was obviously weakening too, and there was a danger they might manage to yank his shield out of his hands. If they did, it would cause a problem for several reasons. First, they would be in possession of a shield and be able to use it to strike at us. Second, it would give the rioters a huge moral boost. Third, it also meant that Simon and the two guys either side of him would be vulnerable to attack or missile strike until we closed the gap and interlocked shields again. There was also the possibility of Simon not letting go of the shield and getting pulled to the floor with it, putting himself in serious danger.

As the battle of the shield seemed to be going in the crowd's favour,

our shields became unlocked. That meant Simon lost the added strength of being locked in with mine and was about to be lost to the rioters. I did the only thing I could have done to protect both Simon and the shield. I raised my shield up high and slammed the bottom edge down into the nearest aggressor's thigh as hard as I could. I knew it would hurt him – it was supposed to – although I hadn't expected to hit him in the bollocks.

The power and weight punched into his flesh through a very thin but solid shield corner; it must have caused him damage. He immediately let go of the shield and fell down, swallowed up by the crowd, who backed off slightly from my strike. Simon quickly interlocked his shield with mine again, and the crowd, having seen what had happened to one of their number, wisely decided to stay a few paces away from us for a few minutes.

They obviously weren't too impressed with my action and eventually built up the courage to begin attacking the shields again. Before long, we were back to bouncing overly fat blokes off our shields and hoping for reinforcements, until the line really did break.

It must have been another fifteen minutes of this torture and my arms were close to collapse. How we managed to maintain the shield wall for so long was anybody's guess.

The crowd began to pull away from us, some showing fear and some a challenge. It took me a second to understand what was going on when the sergeant barked into my ear to 'Break the wall!' In that instant, I understood.

With uniform precision, our shields were instantly unlocked and turned sideways, allowing three-man snatch squads behind us to punch through the gaps in our shield wall and sprint at the protesters.

These teams consisted of two officers with short or circular shields, with a third officer tucked in close behind them for protection, carrying no shield but with baton out, ready to strike at anybody nearby.

I knew from our training days what they were about to do: they would run forward ten yards in-line, pushing the cowering crowds back, striking out at any that resisted them and arresting any ringleaders they had previously identified. They would then hold a new line as our shield wall advanced beyond them, stopping ten yards further on, offering them protection as they restrained any prisoners. If a snatch squad arrested anybody, they would go back with the prisoner, and another three-man snatch squad would quickly form up to replace them.

214

The teams quickly identified more targets and, in unison, ran through our shields again and repeated the process. In this method, the PSUs were able to advance along the street in a swift and dominant manner, clearing the streets of rioters and arresting identified targets, whilst sowing fear and chaos in the crowds.

We'd done it in training, but here we were, about to do it for real.

The PSU serial of Victor Bravo Four Alpha, just prior to the Mill Road riot. I'm top centre. Others of note: top right is Simon (seated), bottom right is Mark, and Keith Fallopian Tubes is centre left.

THIEF TAKER Chapter Nine

EXHAUSTION CHANGED INSTANTLY TO ELATION. It was like watching the bulls being released in Pamplona – the previously brave and foolish crowd, soaked in alcohol and sweat, instantly in a panic, scrambling over anyone and everyone in order not to be the one that got caught.

I anticipated fresh shield units following them through our wall to replace us, but I was gob-smacked when our sergeant screamed at us to leapfrog the arrest teams. *Us?*

We heaved our shields up with dead arms and sprinted the ten yards to the arrest teams, and then another ten yards beyond them, before forming a line across the road as before. This time we didn't link shields because this action was too fluid and fast; the arrest teams would be coming through again, and very quickly.

They did, and they punched through once more, and yet again we were ordered to sprint beyond them. As we passed side streets, serials following us were detailed off to form lines across them to prevent any offenders from looping back and coming in behind us. I envied them: they'd had a cushy start and were now able to lean on their shields and watch the action.

Meanwhile, we were still receiving a constant barrage of missiles on our heads from the lob-and-scarpers who were intent on having the last word.

I still hoped that somebody somewhere might realise that we

216

seriously needed relieving, and would peel us off to collapse on the next side street. But no – on we went. We maintained that solid police wall across Mill Road and did our duty, the adrenalin pushing us onwards. We passed numerous brick walls that had been knocked down, leaving broken bricks scattered across the pavement and gutters. So that's where the missiles were coming from? It was like running through a war zone; I couldn't believe that all of this was happening in the beautiful city of Cambridge.

After dozens of sprints and holds, sprints and holds, we ran out of protesters. Facing us were a few startled reporters and a line of cars: members of the public waiting to drive down Mill Road. I don't think they had expected to come face-to-face with a running police shield wall; the look on the faces of the occupants was quite comical.

With nobody to charge at we rested and looked around us. Mill Road was now clear of any rioters. They had either been arrested, or had split up and legged it down the side streets, or melted off into the night when the situation had got serious. The place was like a bombsite, but we'd done it. Not only had we cleared the road but we had also done it as the front shield unit from start to finish, the whole length of Mill Road, and – it appeared – none of us were injured.

We were exhausted and soaked in our own sweat, but we were unharmed. The relief was obvious as we leaned on our shields, catching our breath. We smiled and laughed, and began recounting incidents from memory, such as the thigh-chop to Simon's protester. It was the first time we'd been able to speak to each other in hours, and we had so much to share.

Our sergeant made a quick radio call and, before long, our van arrived. We gratefully clambered aboard and fell onto the seats. We were kept in the area for a while just in case things kicked off again, but, before long, we were taken back to the station. The drive back along Mill Road gave us time to really see the devastation caused by the rioters to that quiet, cosmopolitan street. I felt sorry for the residents for having to put up with those people and the damage and danger that followed. It must have been absolutely terrifying for the elderly.

Once back at the station, we had more work to do: the writing up of our notes of the whole event, which had to be done whilst still fresh in our memory and before we went off duty. This took several hours and involved officers talking about and sharing their recollections. Contrary to what you might have heard in the papers, by sharing experiences officers' memories are prompted and incidents recalled much more easily. If each officer were to write their notes up in complete isolation, the results would be completely different. It's human nature to talk about what happened immediately after the event, not least to get the chronology correct. To say it is suspicious is to say cops shouldn't be human.

Once my notes were written up and kit stored away, and there was no sign of any renewed protests, I was released from duty. I grabbed my bike and cycled through the city centre, feeling naked now without my protective gear on. On arrival home, I immediately showered, then sank into the sofa with a refreshing beer, and soon fell asleep.

I was back at work the next day, back on shift as if nothing had happened, although I did feel as though I had finally been baptised as a PSU officer. I was extremely stiff, but the real pains wouldn't hit me until the following day.

Naturally, an unofficial post-mortem had already begun. Two things came to light as the day progressed. The first was the decision that had caused us to stay forever on that front line, resulting in Simon nearly getting dragged down by the mob. We had been made to stand for thirty minutes as the front shield unit, taking the initial, fresh violence for so long, because the other PSU's had been told not to put on protective equipment so as not to seem too overtly aggressive. I always found that an unusual phrase – we were riot police! We were trained and equipped to deal with all manner of violence, and looking aggressive often has a subduing effect on those that want to play rough.

This decision meant that, when it all kicked off – as we'd expected it to – those officers had to run back to their vehicles from their positions, kit up and finally come to the party. Whilst they were doing this, the front shield unit was taking a right pasting. That decision to play softball wasn't unexpected in the absurdly open society that we live in in the UK. We play soft until it gets rough, then we play rough too. We just have to try and please the unpleasable first.

As for why we never got relieved as the front shield unit after that? Nobody seemed to think of doing so as the incident progressed and developed. Perhaps the decision makers had never been in such a situation and had no idea of just how close we'd come to crumbling under that onslaught.

Possibly the worst aspect of the whole Mill Road riot for those officers on the receiving end was the reaction of the local MP, Anne Campbell. Ms Campbell actually lived in one of the side streets off Mill Road, and must have been able to hear the riot from her front garden. Far from being grateful for the police restoring law and order to her backyard, the day after the riot she spoke to the local newspaper, stating that she 'would be asking the Chief Constable why the policing commitment *had been so heavy*'. Thanks, Ms Campbell.

It's a pity she hadn't popped down the road to see what was going on in the real world – she could have chatted to the shield unit closing her road off. We thought she should have been more concerned as to who was going to pay for the rebuilding of her constituents' walls, and be thankful that the officers who bought normality back to her neighbourhood managed to do so without any serious injuries.

But then, she's just a politician.

It was a completely different politician who phoned up to question the police regarding another event, but this one was a real gent.

Easter 1998 was a dreadful time for residents of the Midlands and East Anglia – a predominantly flat part of the UK with much of the land below sea level. The worst floods to hit Britain since 1947 (as they were described at the time) put much of Huntingdonshire and Cambridgeshire under water.

As numerous people were ringing the police for help and advice, the calls were routed through to a specially set up incident room where the response could be co-ordinated, in line with the other organisations involved.

The incident room was located at Huntingdon Police HQ and, for one day, I worked there, on overtime, as a call-taker.

Most of the calls were simply asking for advice or notifying us of various incidents, such as roads being flooded, etc.

One call I took was different. The caller identified himself as John Major MP, the man who had been Prime Minister until the year before, and the then MP for Huntingdon. Many of his constituents had been hit by the floods.

He said he just wanted to get an update on the current situation, as he was down in London. I glanced around the room for a senior officer, only to see all eight of them sitting around the table in the meeting room.

"Er, sorry, Mr Major – they all appear to be in a meeting right now. I can go and get one for you, or get them to call you straight back afterwards, or I can tell you what I know?"

"No, no, don't interrupt the meeting, I'm sure what they are discussing is important. OK, if you could brief me a little I'd really appreciate it."

And so it was that John Major and I chatted about what was happening for the next thirty minutes. He was so easy to speak to and very down-to-earth.

Afterwards, he thanked me for advising him, and I asked him if he wanted to speak to a senior officer before he went.

"Oh, well, yes I suppose I'd better. Protocol and all that," he said.

I put him on hold and knocked on the briefing room door. As I put my head in all eight heads turned and looked at me.

"Sorry to intrude, but I've got John Major on the phone. He'd like to speak to one of you."

There was a moment of silence followed by a round of looking at each other, as they couldn't decide who should be the one to speak to him.

"He's all right," I smiled. "We've been chatting for half an hour and he knows what's happening – it's just a courtesy chat he wants, that's all."

I may have over-stepped the mark a little there, but then I had just been chatting with the ex-PM!

And what a nice chap he was, too.

THIEF TAKER Chapter Ten

THE PERIOD FROM MY CONFIRMATION (at two years' service) to the time I really became a full-fledged, experienced officer suitable for crewing the van, took approximately four or five years. Whilst much of what happened during this time has long been forgotten, these pages are full of those incidents and moments that will stay with me for the rest of my life. Some of them have only been remembered after prompting by many of my ex-colleagues from that time.

One of the things I do clearly recall from that period was *change*.

At the beginning of this series, I stated how the police service hadn't changed much in centuries, and that officers were reluctant to, and suspicious of, change. Well, we made up for that during the 1990s. In fact, we embraced change so much that nobody knew how to stop it. The result was that change eventually spiralled out of control.

There were positive changes and negatives changes. A positive change came with our issued police equipment. It was gradually updated, improving the uniform to make it more practical, and providing officers with better tools to do the job, including side-handled batons, rigid handcuffs, and CS spray. Protective vests were still a long way off, but they could be found because American officers often donated their cast-offs to us. Yes, I know – a terrible state of affairs.

Cars were much improved: diesel engines were changed for diesel engines with turbochargers or even petrol engines. Sirens and strobe lights were commonplace. It became acceptable to expect city officers to respond to emergency calls on 'blues and twos', as they were now receiving annual driver training. We no longer had to pretend it didn't happen.

Such long-overdue changes were seriously welcomed by the guys at the sharp end, and improved morale significantly.

There were also less welcome changes: computers began appearing in offices, with all staff eventually having their own email account, the end result being that the first hour of every duty was spent going through the numerous emails received from various departments, sent just to cover their arses.

The word *cascade* entered police jargon, meaning that each email you received you sent to everybody below you, just in case. It wasn't unusual to have five or six copies of the same email sent from various bosses, all tagged *Urgent*. In fact, nobody knew how to change the tagging system, so all emails were routinely marked as *Urgent*.

New Command and Control systems, the Crime Computer System, and incredible mapping programmes were greatly welcomed, as they all contributed to a better way of working.

Another great change was in the station accommodation. The shifts were elevated from the grubby basement where they had been since no one can remember, to the first floor – a place that actually had windows.

Other departments were moved around too, and, just as staff got into the routine of going to the correct, new office, senior management changed it all around again. It was great fun. I spent many hours going to the wrong department looking for certain staff only to be told that they'd recently moved to another floor, office, station. Even the traffic department was primed to move out of the city to one of the smaller, rural stations, meaning we'd all have to move again just to be sure of filling in their soon-to-be-vacant office space.

Shift patterns also went through *numerous* changes, just to make up for working the same one for the last century. I must admit, I was so happy to dump the seven days on-duty, two days off-duty pattern. I did like doing seven *nights* (11.00pm–7.00am) in a row, although the two days off afterwards were crippling. You usually slept on your first day off, re-adjusted slightly on your second day off, and then went back to work like a zombie. The work/life balance was all one-sided, and that was without the cancelled rest days due to some big event happening in Cambridge.

I even enjoyed the seven *lates* (3.00pm–11.00pm) but who the hell wanted to do seven successive *earlies* (7.00am–3.00pm)? You had to be there by 6.45am for briefing, every morning, for seven days in a row. Who thought that one up?

I usually made it on time for the first two, sometimes even the third morning, but those last four were cruel to me. How many times was I called into the sergeant's office for a bollocking for being late? Every set of earlies? Eventually the sergeants were so fed up with me arriving mid-briefing that they called me into their office and made an entry in my pocket book to the effect that I was late again.

"Consider it a formal, written warning," they said. I asked them what would happen next time, when I was late again.

"To be honest Dave, we have no idea," they said.

Nothing ever did happen, and eventually that vicious shift pattern was dumped into the history bin of foolish shifts, never to return again. We moved into a new, all-singing, all-dancing pattern that created shift overlaps at peak times, meaning we had enough officers to do the job at peak times, but were dangerously low at 'quiet' times.

The officers who worked it loved it. The first night it came into operation (a busy Friday) was amazing – there were so many officers on duty, even the public commented on it. We had two fully staffed hooli-vans and about eight officers out walking, and all the cars were double-crewed. Every cop's dream. Also, we only worked four days in a row (lates) with two days off, followed by three days in a row (earlies) and two days off – only three earlies! I didn't have to be late for duty ever again! We then did seven nights in a row followed by six days off! This meant that officers could re-adjust their biological clock back to sleeping at night and working during the daytime before coming back to work. We worked longer shifts – ten hours minimum and often more – but we loved it, the public loved it, and the crooks hated it: the *filth* were everywhere. And so the powers that be changed it to something less successful.

I don't recall what came next but it would never be as good as before. There was nothing the officer on the ground could do about it – we just got on with the same old job, even though it was clear that life on the streets was getting much more aggressive and dangerous.

Just to keep us on our toes, somebody somewhere invented Political

Correctness (PC), and the police jumped on it enthusiastically and took it to new heights. No longer could we ask for a 'white coffee' in the staff canteen – it had to be 'coffee with milk'. A 'black coffee' became absolutely taboo, unless you happened to be black: then it was OK.

Briefings became a minefield, as the 'C' word of PC was 'nitty-gritty', which was something we could no longer get down to anymore due to its apparent origin. Everyday English, something with totally harmless connotations today, became dirty words, language that could easily get you fired. That's probably why police officers these days never speak. *Ever.*

Despite all of these changes, one thing that took ages to change was the personal radio. No matter what we did, by listening into our wavelength with a cheap scanner stolen from *Maplins*, half of the city knew we were doing it. It was a hobby for many, a must for criminals. I was amazed we caught anybody at all, but then, crooks really are very stupid. Perhaps we only caught the idiots; maybe those with half a brain fled the scene when they heard a car being allocated over their scanner.

Eavesdropping was an occupational pain. There was nothing we could do about it: the crooks knew our call signs, and even which officers were on duty and where. Most officers, when booking off watch at the station, refused to do it over the radio and did so in person in the control room, especially if they were the last one in. Those listening in could tell when the city was un-policed, as it often was. Management repeatedly told us that a huge programme at national level was underway, and that the equipment would be upgraded – eventually.

It was, but long after I'd left the police.

It was one thing having people listening in to us, but it was hell if they had the means to *transmit* on our wavelength. This was only possible if they managed to get hold of a police radio, and, as they weren't personal issue, a 'lost' radio wouldn't necessarily be traced back to the offending officer. It rarely happened, but as the radio attachment clips were often broken and holsters defective, many officers carried their radio either in their hands or pockets. Obviously, you can see where this is going.

Let's just say that those idiots who over-transmitted officers who were either dealing with jobs or trying to receive important information on their way to jobs put other people at risk. It rarely happened but caused immense problems when it did. Fortunately, not all 'lost' radios ended up in the hands of idiots.

"Hello, is anybody there?" said the unknown voice over the radio channel. I was talking to the radio operator at the time, in the control room. He frowned.

"Hello, yes? Unknown call sign go ahead," he replied, professionally.

The transmit button was pressed again and a woman could be heard in the background.

"Go on, go on! Say something," she said, prodding the reluctant speaker into action.

"Yes, yes! Be quiet … er, hello? This is a private person speaking …" said the man, once more.

"Go ahead, private person," said Ian, the fat controller, a hint of mirth in his reply.

"Yes, er, well … a police man just drove away, and he left this walkie-talkie on the roof of his car and it fell off into the road. Shall I bring it to the station?"

I looked at Ian and said an officer's name. He nodded.

"No, stand b– … Er, wait a minute, please. Where are you exactly?"

The gentleman named the road he was in. Ian nodded sagely at me. The officer I had just mentioned was in that area doing a job. We somehow had guessed it was him, but there was no way we could call him up to go back and get his radio off this Good Samaritan.

"I'll go," I said, and quickly left the station. A few minutes later I was with the elderly couple, and thanked them profusely. I then waited.

PC No Name had no radio, and sooner or later he'd realise it, and when he did, he'd come back to his last job where he'd had his radio. And he did.

He was daft to have left his radio on his car roof, but then, the constabulary was stupid for not providing us with suitable supports and clips. 'They're obsolete, we can't get them anymore' was the standard response.

The personal radio was a cop's lifeline to the station and his colleagues. Without it, he put himself in danger.

So you can understand how I took umbrage at the following Cambridge University student who was 'Head of Security' for his college's May Ball.

College May Balls were, and probably still are, enormously lavish and formal events held by each of the thirty-one colleges that made up

Cambridge University. Bizarrely, May Balls were held in June, and on different nights, so that you could go to more than one.

These all-night events often had famous comedians or singers performing, as well as free champagne and sumptuous food. With prices as high as £500 a ticket, they were *the* places to be.

Naturally, they had gatecrashers. In fact, they had professional gatecrashers who annually tried a variety of methods to get in for free. So security was high, with anti-climb fences surrounding the venues, private security firms brought in, a student security team running the show, and, at the big events, a couple of cops. They had to pay a huge amount of money for the privilege of our presence, of course, and for us it was a great source of overtime, so every officer wanted to do it.

And one year I drew the lucky straw.

Trinity College, like a few others in the centre, had a flaw in its security that nothing could be done about: the River Cam. The backs of these colleges are known as 'The Backs', and it was here where the river cuts through the college grounds, and it was here where they held their balls, surrounded by security fencing and teams.

I spent twelve hours generally wandering around, eating great food, and marvelling at the outfits of the ball-goers, and got paid sixteen hours salary for this (time and a third). It was great to see how the other half lived. Then I remembered how much these students (or their parents) had paid for their tickets. The bump in my monthly salary would be nothing next to the price of entry for this event, and there were hundreds of young people there. Not forgetting that many of the students went to *numerous* Balls during this busy two-week period – if not all of them.

I arrived as the queue to enter stretched all the way down Trinity Street, a target for the tourists who were busily snapping away at the men in their tuxedos and women in their ball gowns. I marvelled at the opulence of the occasion, and looked forward to the new experience that awaited me.

The porter, who was ex-police, pointed me in the direction of the security office for the night. There I met a man of about twenty years of age, who was bounding in self-importance and perfect syntax. He, he beamed, was Head of Security, which meant that, for that night, he was 'my boss'.

I took an instant dislike to the guy for no other reason than he was living on a different planet to me, but I played along. It was good money. For me.

"Oh," he said. "You'd better have this. It's a walkie-talkie."

I looked at him. *Do people really say 'walkie-talkie'?*

"Be careful – they're really expensive and we've rented them. I seriously need to have it back in the morning, yah?"

Be careful? Be bloody careful?! I'm a cop, for Christ's sake, I live with professional personal police radios, and this is just a cheap playground walkie-bloodie-talkie.

I nodded. "Yah, don't worry. I know how to look after these kinds of things."

I got up and walked off, professionally doing a reconnoitre of the college. It was impressive, really impressive: no expense had been spared. There were various marquees with different events inside – bands I'd heard on the radio, comedians who were household names, and so on. Every so often I bumped into a champagne station or pig roast. The staff manning these stations were outside caterers, and were very glad to see a bobby on the beat. Perhaps I was a glimpse of normality in an ocean of decadence? Needless to say, I didn't have to pay for anything either.

As the night wore on, I was able to ignore the ridiculous goings-on on the amateur radio as no concern of the police, and instead I observed another universe. The majority of these students were, in my expert opinion after watching them at play, complete jokes. Worryingly, they'd be running the country in a few years' time. I couldn't wait for the night to finish so that I could go back home, to real people doing real things.

Unfortunately, at about 4.00am, *Trinity Plum One* came over the radio rather excitedly. A gatecrasher had been spotted trying to get in. It was battle stations!

Now, under normal circumstances I would have left it to *TP1* and his team as I'd just been given a rather nice bap of spit-roast pig with apple sauce – my fourth of the night.

However, the excitement in the voices over the radio forced me, reluctantly, to listen in. As the information slowly revealed itself amongst the amateur 'over and out' team, I decided that I had to go and see it for myself. The gatecrasher was currently under the bridge, mid-stream, and heading directly towards the ice carvings tent.

This guy was in the river? He was. The guy was not only swimming directly up the centre of the river so as to avoid the eager security patrols on either side, but also the idiot was swimming against the current. I leaned against the bridge and watched as the poor, exhausted fool finally made landfall followed by a desperate dash to vanish inside the marquee, which was full of ice carvings, champagne, and drunken 'hoorays'.

The pack of security students were on him in an instant, although he managed to slip free due to the fact that he was slippery-wet, and ran off at a pace across the bridge. As he passed me I noticed he was wearing a – now soaking wet – tuxedo.

As I finished off my bap, I watched as he was finally cornered down by the anchored balloon flights and was unceremoniously frog-marched through the revelry, occasionally applauded, and chucked out through the front door.

"That'll teach him," said TP1 over the radio. "Well done, team. Jolly good work. Jolly good."

It was the only time that night that I used my walkie-talkie.

"This is Cambridge Police. For your information, he'll be back. Be ready, be vigilant, and stand by your river banks!"

Silence. I then wandered off to look for something to wash down the last of that perfect pork.

Sure enough, an hour later came a report of 'swimmers' at the back of the college, but this time not in the river. Now, I knew from experience that there were numerous brooks and channels in this area feeding into the Cam, and that the area was in darkness. It was where I'd lost one of three burglars many years ago.

Huge amounts of alcohol and swimming were a dangerous mix, so I ambled down to where it was happening, ensuring I passed the spit-roast on the way.

An excited student-guard let me through a gateway and pointed me in the right direction. A few minutes later, I found myself standing in the shadows in my black uniform, at the side of a stinking, black water channel. I remained motionless as somebody paddled what looked like a child's toy of a canoe along the fetid channel, towards the venue and me.

As he pulled level with me I stepped out of the darkness and said calmly, "Can I see your ticket, please?"

I think he over-reacted a bit as he crashed into the opposite bank and capsized the canoe. Startled, he fell into the evil water and began sinking. I realised that I had to do something as the situation was now becoming a tad dangerous – a drunk in the devil's urine at 5.00am in a dark field.

"OK, OK, listen carefully to me," I said. "I'm actually a cop and I'm going to give you two choices. If you climb out onto that *other* bank, I'm going to arrest you for being drunk in charge of a river craft." Truth was if he did climb out on the far side I'd have lost him, as I didn't fancy trying to jump the ditch, which was about two yards wide.

"But, if you climb out onto *this* side, I'm just going to take your details down, check you out and send you off home. Deal?"

Despite his obvious drunkenness, he agreed to my offer and began wading towards me. Then he stumbled and had difficulties climbing the bank, so, reluctantly, I bent over, reached down to him and took his hand, and pulled with all of my might. I heard a dull plonk as something landed in the water at the very moment that I propelled him out of the channel and onto dry land.

I stared at the disgusting blackness as I wiped my hand on my thigh, pleased that I'd only made second hand contact with it, especially as the smell from the intruder was now overpowering me.

"Did you lose something?" I asked him.

"What, like my ticket?" he replied, laughing.

"No, something small and heavy, like a–" *Ah*. And then I realised. I had put the walkie-talkie in my coat breast pocket and left the Velcro flap open so that I could hear it. As I'd bent down to pull the guy up, the radio had slid out of my pocket and vanished beneath the hell water. As I tapped my breast pocket to confirm its absence, I noticed that the Man from Atlantis was still wearing a tuxedo.

The stinking, black channel was only half a yard deep, and I managed to get the walkie-talkie out without falling in, but my right arm was stinking up to my bicep. The intruder was quickly sent packing, with a warning that if he returned I would arrest him, if only for his own safety. He admitted he was a student and didn't need an arrest on his record. I warned him that if I saw another guy – any guy – swimming up the Cam in a tuxedo that night, I would give *his* details to his college which would result in discipline proceedings against *him*.

A few hours later, I watched as dawn broke. The students that were still standing congregated on the main lawn for a champagne breakfast and the mandatory survivors' photo.

I headed back to the security office to find *Trinity Plum One* to explain how, when pulling the gatecrasher out of the black water, I'd almost fallen in but, alas, his beloved, rented walkie-talkie actually had. I couldn't find TP1 anywhere, or indeed any of his staff. I guessed they were joining in with the champagne breakfast.

As I had been awake all night and wasn't getting paid to be there past 8.00am, I left the walkie-talkie on his temporary desk. It didn't look too bad now it had been rinsed off, and looked and functioned exactly as it had when he had given it to me. The only noticeable difference was the smell if it got too close to your nose – which it did if you put it to your mouth to speak into it – but I guessed he wouldn't need to do that, as he had his own.

I never heard anything from Trinity College in the weeks that followed, and have hated walkie-talkies ever since.

THIEF TAKER Chapter Eleven

IT WASN'T ALL FUN, GAMES AND RODNEYS. Guns and knives were always our biggest fear. We had no protection from either. Towards the end of my time in the job, a patrol car was routinely equipped with two firearms officers, but, once again, the politics made them all but useless.

I recall the first incident I attended that involved firearms, which was a routine call to a newsagents late at night in my first year as a cop. Expecting nothing more than a false intruder alarm or maybe even a smash and grab, I recall the excitement as I approached the front door and discovered that its glass had indeed been smashed to gain entrance. Then there was a moment of elation as I saw a person moving around inside, followed by numb shock as a gun was pointed out of the broken window directly at me, no more than two yards away.

A colleague pulled me roughly to one side as a young man followed the gun, clambering out through the shattered glass of the door, only to be struck down by several officers armed with nothing more than wooden truncheons. Wooden clubs do hurt, but in truth there should have been guns pointing at him, not desperate and foolishly brave officers making do with what they had.

A qualified firearms officer (unarmed) was called in to inspect the weapon, only to declare that it was a fake, something homemade. A search of the suspect's home also revealed homemade bombs and guns. The guy was a raving lunatic and was eventually put away, thankfully.

Apart from personal attack alarms at banks, most calls we went to were unlikely to involve firearms, but, when they did, it usually came as a complete surprise to us.

It was another busy Friday night and I was driving the hooli-van with Simon as passenger. We knew it had been a busy and successful night because, apart from us, the van was totally empty. All of our officers were in the cell-block dealing with the numerous prisoners they had arrested. It had been a brilliant, action-filled night, and Simon and I were in great spirits.

The call to the flat sounded overly dramatic, which usually meant a waste of time. As we were just around the corner, we parked up and went for a walk into the small court of flats just off Station Road. Despite the caller saying she had just been threatened/robbed in her home by a man in a balaclava armed with a gun, it just didn't make sense. Surely it was just high jinks or some mad informant seeing things at the bottom of a bottle.

We patrolled all around the ground floor of the flats and reported in that the place was in total silence. We were pretty relaxed as the dog-handler asked for the flat number.

We watched from the car park below as he was dragged along the open, first-floor balcony by The Exocet. He stopped at the door to a flat and rang the bell. Simon and I continued chatting until the door was opened by a man wearing a balaclava and holding what looked like a pistol. The officer screamed at him, The Exocet went mad at him, and the robber took his cue and fled along the balcony.

He knew what came next and he didn't want any part of it – perhaps he'd already met The Exocet. After a ten-yard sprint and perfectly timed jump, he launched himself off the balcony to avoid the salivating creature on his heels. Alas, in his effort and panic to evade the dog's famous teeth, he didn't quite clear the balcony. His feet caught the wooden railing, sending him head first over the edge.

Simon and I had a perfect viewpoint as we watched him, in slow motion, fall over the balcony upside-down. It was like a scene from a film: a balaclava-clad robber falling headfirst towards the camera. Only this time, Simon and I were the camera.

He managed to miss the two parked cars, slamming into the tarmac floor between them, just a few feet in front of the wide-eyed van crew.

"Fuck me!!" I screamed. "Grab his hands! Grab his hands!" I can hear the pitch in my voice getting higher as I recollect shouting that.

Simon and I jumped onto the crumpled and groaning figure, me clamped onto one wrist and Simon the other. Thankfully, he had dropped the gun; we didn't know where it was, but we just had to secure his hands urgently to prevent any possible shooting of the gun. The guy was too dazed to resist and was soon handcuffed. With the excitement of The Joker finally unmasking Batman, we pulled off the balaclava only to be disappointed not to recognise the guy. The gun was discovered under one of the cars nearby, and was found to be no more than a very realistic imitation.

Simon and I became much more attentive and less casual after that night. It was around this time that my reputation began to grow: a reputation for things happening around me, and its rarely being a quiet duty if I was present. To be fair, it did have a ring of truth to it.

Simon and I often worked together on the van at that time, and I really liked his sense of humour. Plus, he was one of the nicest guys I knew.

I remember one afternoon driving back from the north of the city with a well-known drunken tramp in the back of the van. Despite the guy being handcuffed, he was screaming and kicking at the sides of the van. He was in a security cage with a door that could only be opened from the outside, so I knew he couldn't get out, but it was difficult to drive with such a one-man riot going on just behind my head.

Without speaking, I pulled over onto double yellow lines, activated the blue lights, and looked at Simon. He nodded at me. He knew we were going to have to put the guy into a restraint and that he would draw the short straw and have to ride the rest of the way, holding the disgusting fellow down.

We put our gloves on in a silent, business-like manner as we marched to the rear of the van. I opened the outer door only for the tramp to start spitting at us and cursing our mothers through the grill.

"Ready?" I asked Simon. He nodded. We were fully synchronised, two officers who understood each other and worked seamlessly together. I swung open the security door, and we simultaneously launched ourselves at the spitting, cursing, stinking drunk, and flattened him. We moved so quickly that, before he knew what was happening, we had him face down on the floor so that he could neither spit at us nor kick us. He would have to remain in that uncomfortable position until we got back to the nick –

a short ten-minute ride – but it had been his choice. Simon knew he was to sit on him for the rest of the journey, but that was the deal. If you were a passenger in the van, that's the sort of thing you routinely did, and Simon had no problem with that.

However, Simon and I both saw the problem at the same instant.

"Oh, bugger," we said.

It was a serious problem and a highly embarrassing one: the security door had slammed shut behind us as we had entered the back. There was no way I would be able to open it from the inside!

We had two choices: radio a colleague to come and let us out, or ask a passing member of the public to do so. We knew that we'd never live it down if word got out, so the first person passing by was very surprised by my call.

"Hello? Excuse me! Sorry, could you do me a favour please? I'm a police officer and I seem to have locked myself in the van. Would you mind letting me out, please?"

Thankfully, the bemused gent did just that and walked off, shaking his head. We managed to get back to the station without any further drama, and nobody ever did discover what happened to us on that drive back.

As mentioned earlier, the van was usually crewed by two experienced, capable officers, and often left to its own devices, offering back-up and support where needed. It was the job all officers angled for, and I was only too delighted when I became that man.

As patrol cars got bogged down with enquiries, domestics, sudden deaths, and RTAs, the experienced van crew were generally left alone and expected to do the 'right thing'. That meant being in the right place at the right time. It involved backing up at violent domestic disputes, and attending all incidents where violence was likely to occur, or where people were likely to get nicked. We even backed up at RTAs when necessary, but we were always the first to be released to continue our supportive role. When we weren't supporting, we were proactive – something most cars seldom had a chance to be, as they were generally reacting to the immense workload as it came in.

Driving a Ford Transit van at high speed takes great skill and courage. They hate going round roundabouts at anything more than a crawl, so, to use it as a response vehicle shows that we do have a sense of humour.

Earlier on in my career, it was the only vehicle fitted with a siren, which made it something special, but, by this time, all vehicles had one. The van's only virtue was its imposing presence, as it barrelled through the traffic-choked streets of Cambridge with numerous strobes flashing, and its immense, intimidating size.

I think it was this, more than its handling, that allowed us to catch thieves in high-powered cars in a standard Transit, made heavier by its steel cage and additional equipment. Perhaps they all think the police drive super-charged vehicles, whereas the reality is one of bog-standard or sub-standard engines.

Mark was my partner that day, as the stolen car passed us in the opposite direction. Spotted by Mark, pursued by me, the vehicle made off at speed and should have out-run us easily. Mark gave his usual calm-tinged-with-excitement commentary as we gave chase. Within minutes the driver had made a mistake and driven down a dead-end. (Yeah I know: there's a pattern emerging here.)

I have no idea why he did this, because he could easily have vanished had he driven off at speed through the traffic instead of continuing his futile twisting and turning. Maybe it was just the panic at having this large vehicle behind him with all the lights and noise? I'll never know, but I do know crooks do stupid things, and this guy had just done one. Furthermore, he had Mark and I on his case.

He knew he was trapped, so he tried to give himself some distance from us before decamping. He drove down the grassed side of a tennis court, the gap between that and the brick wall being barely wide enough for the car to fit through. At the end was an old brick wall, so he'd have to stop and leg it across sports field.

I guess he'd expected us not to follow, but we did. With the wing mirrors grazing the brick wall, we piled down that small gap and came to a stop right behind his car, boxing it in completely. The single occupant had only just climbed over the eight-foot brick wall in front of us as we exited our vehicle.

Now Mark was a super-fit cop and very agile. I knew this car thief didn't stand a chance against the two of us. We were both over the wall in a ridiculously short time and sprinting across the sports field after him. I think he was very surprised when he glanced back and saw how close we were. In fact, I think it was at this point that his belief in a successful escape left him.

Within another hundred yards, Mark rugby-tackled him to the floor, and had him restrained even before I could ready my quick-cuffs. He was in the back of the van before he knew it.

Mark was one of those cops like me: capable, fit, and adaptable. He rarely gave up, and usually got his man. He was a superbly fit kick-boxer and often attended an evening aerobics class at one of the local schools in the city. His wife was the instructor and I even went along with him one night.

Mark had heard a rumour that a pervert would sit in the dark gardens outside the windows and peer in at the predominantly female participants as they bent and twisted and danced their calories away. Mark was incensed.

The following event found Mark sitting up a tree outside of the window. After about half an hour of sitting absolutely still in that uncomfortable position, Mark was rewarded with the appearance of the pervert.

After watching him sufficiently to gather enough evidence of his purpose, Mark jumped out of the tree, landing on top of the guy. It was a superb arrest and one the man won't forget in a hurry. Mark's wife later said she'd known he'd got the guy because, during class, she saw a flash of something falling from a tree, followed by a manly scream of surprise. She just carried on with the class, with a permanent smile.

As mentioned, the van generally stayed central in order to be able to respond to any part of the city, and spent much of its free time proactively. Because of its central location and the policy of double-crewing, it made an excellent intruder-alarm response vehicle, especially considering the density of alarmed premises within the central area.

As most alarms were false alarms, the van would be released quite quickly. If it was a genuine alarm, having two officers attend – one at the front and one at the rear – improved our chances of catching anybody.

At about 4.00am we were cruising the deserted streets on the edges of the centre. The radio was silent and nothing was moving. It was at times like that that crooks often hit. And so they did, and not just our petty local crews either.

"Intruder Alarm, Fitzwilliam Museum – units to attend, please?"

The Fitz is the art and antiquities museum of the University of Cambridge: a large building with a neo-classic facade and imposing columns. The alarm rarely activated, but, when it did, every officer wanted to attend, as it was usually an unknown cause. And the unknown could only be known by walking around the museum, checking if everything was OK. At night. With the lights off.

Few people ever get to enjoy an experience like that, yet I did it twice.

By luck or by chance I was seconds away from the museum, and soon turned into the street where it was located. All was quiet, except for one car driving away from the scene towards me.

Nick had been walking the centre that night and was also near, as was another walker. They both booked at the scene within a few seconds of each other, which told me they weren't actually together. It was an impressive response time.

I slowed down as the car approached me, crossing the centre line and driving slightly head-on to it, forcing it to slow down to a crawl. It contained two worried-looking, young, white males staring intently at our vehicle. I needed to check them out.

"Car leaving the scene," I transmitted, and read out the vehicle index as they passed us. I hit the brakes and went to turn the wheel into a U-turn, just as Nick transmitted.

"Runner at the scene!" he said, in his usual over-excited voice. I made a split-second decision and chose Nick. If he was at the scene and had a burglar there, he needed our support. Most probably, the two men in the car were just on their way home after a night out, and were frightened by my driving across the white line.

I slammed the throttle down and raced towards Nick, who was no more than two hundred yards away, whilst checking to see which way the car turned in my wing mirrors. Just in case.

"No. Cancel, cancel," said Nick, laughing. "The runner's C311."

Nick had seen the other foot patrol officer in the shadows and mistook him for a thief, yet they had both booked at the scene within seconds of each other.

I swore and did a U-turn in the wide road in the hope of maybe catching up with the suspicious vehicle, calculating that it was probably a good three hundred yards away by then.

And then Nick transmitted again. "Yeah, confirmed break here," he said, telling us that there had indeed been a burglary at the Fitz, which told me that the most likely culprits were the two guys in the departing car.

I swore many times and accelerated as fast as I could after the vehicle, taking the last turn I had seen it take. *It had to be them!*

The registered keeper came back as an address in London, and it hadn't (yet) been reported stolen. A traffic car called up saying they were in the vicinity, covering the nearby junction which led to the M11 southbound and London, but it hadn't come their way yet.

All the pieces were in place for a successful outcome if we could just re-locate that vehicle and the two worried-looking young men.

I asked the control room to phone the registered keeper as I searched the side roads nearby. Did they know the vehicle was in Cambridge, and was everything OK with it?

I knew that if the vehicle hadn't immediately left the city it must be around somewhere, hiding up, and waiting for things to calm down.

Within minutes, the control room came back and said that the vehicle was indeed stolen. *It was them …*

I never saw the vehicle or the occupants again.

The following night, I was told the vehicle had been found abandoned in a side street near to where I had been looking, and that – obviously – a second vehicle must have been used to leave the scene.

I was also told that the thieves had escaped with over £300,000 worth of antique watches from the Fitz.

I was also told that the two men I had seen had hit numerous museums all over the country, stealing similar articles.

Clearly, they were a prolific, professional team from London and, had I turned after them when I had initially wanted to, and with the perfect proximity of the traffic car, the outcome might have been significantly different.

It took me ages to forgive Nick for that.

THIEF TAKER Chapter Twelve

IN AN IDEAL WORLD, ALL POLICE OFFICERS WOULD BE highly trained in two things: first aid and martial arts. I'd done a lot of first aid training in the army, but in the police it was more or less non-existent. It is something I feel really should be taught to officers. In fact, it should be taught at school to children; imagine the lives that could be saved?

The same goes for martial arts – I used to do judo for a while as a child. Then I won a medal – the only time ever in my life I won a medal – whilst at police college. I was so proud when I came second out of my whole course for fighting, second out of well over 150 officers.

Having officers trained up to a high level in some type of martial art would not only make their lives easier and safer, but would also give them a lot of confidence in violent situations.

However, training officers has immense cost and time implications, so basically it's just not done.

Fortunately, at Cambridge, our physical training and self-defence instructor – he who taught baton and quick-cuff techniques to every officer once a year – was a third dan in a martial art, and he wanted to start a club at Cambridge. I jumped at the chance.

The art was Taiho-Jutsu, a system created and developed by the Japanese police. It was designed to disarm and restrain an assailant, and was introduced to the UK police in 1973. At national level, police self-defence was subsequently based on it, using arrest techniques from Taiho-Jutsu that are still used today. It was a Home Office approved system.

We had been taught the basics at police college, and were graded at the end of our time there. According to our ability, we were then awarded either the first belt (yellow) or the second belt (orange), so, in effect, all officers *do* have a martial art grading. The idea was that it would give officers a taster, and hopefully some officers would continue to develop their abilities in self-defence.

The sad truth is, though, that once officers got back on division, the only follow-up training they received was just for a few hours, once a year.

So we started the club at Cambridge, me with my orange belt, and a few police officers and civilians. The club was free, open to all, and located at the police station gymnasium. I quickly progressed through the ranks to brown belt and became the club secretary. I even created an early website for our club, long before websites were commonplace.

Eventually, it was time for me and another officer to attempt our black belt grading, something which our own instructor wasn't prepared to do out of fairness.

We attended a national meeting at Leicester Police Headquarters only to be told on arrival that we would be doing the 'new syllabus'.

Sorry? What new f***ing syllabus?

Apparently, the syllabus had been updated, and nobody had told our club about it. About eight people in the country were trying for their First Dan that night, including the two of us from Cambridge. Naturally, not knowing the new syllabus that we were expected to do knocked us for six: we were demotivated and out of sorts.

Rightly, we weren't awarded our Black Belts and, shortly afterwards, I became very bitter towards the organisation for messing up my opportunity. I should have persevered and tried for it again but I didn't, and achievement of one of my lifetime ambitions was lost forever. Shortly afterwards, I dropped out of the club, never to return.

I highly recommend martial arts to everybody, young and old. It gives you much greater belief in yourself, and, as I rose through the ranks, my self-belief rose with it.

Possibly the clearest example of the benefit of this was when I was in the middle of the street in the centre of the huge estate in the north of the city at about 3.00am. I can't recall what I was doing there, but I and one other officer were standing in the middle of the road talking when a well-known trouble maker saw us as he was walking home drunk from the city centre. He was the younger of two brothers, both of who were known for two things: their hatred of the police and unwarranted violence.

He was a good head taller than me and had been drinking heavily. As soon as he saw us, he came over to me and started being aggressive. I was very dismissive of him, acting as if he wasn't really there.

He didn't like this and came up closer to me, standing face to face, although I had to look up at him. I didn't flinch and waited for a slight movement to indicate that he was about to cross the line. I was ready for him.

"Why aren't you afraid of me?" he asked, genuinely concerned, his face telling me he was fighting his inner demons. He knew that I knew who he was as I had addressed him by his first name, and he couldn't comprehend my lack of concern.

There we were, standing face to face, him standing over me and known for his violence to police, and he just couldn't accept that this little copper was so dismissive of him.

I expected him to do something stupid. He didn't. Possibly for the first time in his life, he backed off, lost face, and sulked his way home.

That's what martial arts do for a person. Far from creating violence, it often negates the need for any at all.

The other thing that began to boost the confidence of this experienced thief-taker was knowledge of the law. We'd had to study it in a lot of detail at police college but, after that, it was often just a working knowledge that officers had. I decided, after about six years of service, that I wanted to prepare for the sergeants' exam.

To get promoted, constables have to pass a law exam to qualify them to the level of sergeant. To go further, another exam exists for inspector rank. After that, it's done on merit or the old tie network. Never, ever, is promotion achieved through arrests, as the TV would have you believe.

Why take the exam at that time? I think I felt ready and fully prepared for it. I certainly hadn't wanted to be one of those young-in-service sergeants who ended up less experienced than the constables they commanded. Also, financially, it made sense.

Up until the eight-year point, constables received an annual increment, but, once you hit eight years' service, that dropped to every two years, until you reached twelve years of service, when you were paid the same as a newly promoted sergeant. From that moment, constables received no more annual increases, apart from the index-linked raise that all officers received, regardless of rank or time served.

I liked my annual raises and didn't want to lose them. On promotion to sergeant, I would jump to the twelve-year pay band of a constable and begin annual increments again for five years. At five years, a sergeant would be on the same salary as a newly promoted inspector, and annual increments would cease. I guessed I'd go for inspector rank at that time and continue receiving increments.

It was time to start preparing for the sergeants' law exam, and I knew how tough it was going to be.

And so I began to study criminal law in detail, and with that newfound knowledge came newfound confidence.

My sergeant recommended I become a tutor-constable. A tutor is an officer trained to take out new officers and teach them how to do the job. I liked the idea, so I trained as a tutor-constable as well.

Shortly afterwards, the city was to go through another working change, one that was completely different to anything we had done before and one that I didn't think made sense. It took ages to set up and prepare for the radical new system, and, during that time, I decided that I would leave my beloved shift (which I'd joined as a wide-eyed, naive civilian being chased by a mad axe man on his first day out), and join a newly created unit – one that I thought would help me to develop towards my objectives.

THIEF TAKER Chapter Thirteen
Edinburgh, Scotland

EVEN THOUGH THE NEW WORKING SHIFT PATTERN was many months away, I continued to enjoy myself at the sharp end of city policing, especially as, by then, I was one of the more experienced officers on shift. This often meant getting the best jobs, so when I attended briefing one morning and was asked if I'd like to go to Edinburgh that day and stay overnight, I jumped at the chance.

A man had been arrested in Scotland the night before, having been circulated as wanted on a warrant at Cambridge. That meant he had to be transferred from Edinburgh to Cambridge to be dealt with. As the issuing force, it was our responsibility to go and get him. There was just one problem: he had warning signs for violence and had been violent on arrest, therefore flying him back was out of the question: we'd have to drive up there and get him.

Because of the distance involved and his being a violent prisoner, three of us were selected to go and get him. A mere six-hour drive should have been easy, except for a few things.

The first thing was that we had to take one of our minibuses, which had a secure prisoner cell at the rear. Nothing wrong with that, except that it was absurdly slow.

During the journey, the other two officers kept saying it was bad luck to take me, as things would surely happen. I laughed with them, but none of us could have known exactly how many incidents we were in for.

After three hours we stopped at my parents' house – which was en route – for a coffee. We only stayed for half an hour, and on getting back to our vehicle we discovered a local police parking ticket on the windscreen! The offence was parking facing the wrong way, even though the van was covered in highly reflective police markings. I went back into the house, called my inspector and explained to him why this had happened.

Several months earlier, I had been home and was leaving a local pub late one night with my brothers, when a local police sergeant had walked along the road and started physically pushing people along the road, telling them to 'get off home', despite the fact that we were all doing that – presumably too slowly for him.

When he pushed me, I resisted, identified myself as a police officer, and told him he was abusing his powers. I really hated to see that. What was wrong with being professional? I later made a complaint against him for physical assault, which was promptly ignored by his inspector. Again – a total lack of professionalism.

So, when the idiot spotted a Cambridgeshire Police van parked outside my parents' address, he knew who had left it there, and he pounced and put a ticket on it. Clearly my fault …

My inspector said not to worry and that he would deal with it, and he did, and that was the end of the matter. What he thought of the local police of Uttoxeter was anybody's guess.

So, as we approached the Scottish border with one officer map reading, we debated whether it would be faster to go by the coast road or take the direct route, driving centrally through a National Park and over the mountains. Looking at the map, we foolishly chose the direct route.

As the van was a flat diesel, driving uphill was slow work, and, as the snow started falling lightly against the windscreen, we laughed – snow at this time of year! And it got heavier. And heavier. We were eventually reduced to a first gear crawl, unable to see the small road in front of us. We had to stop at one point because the snow had compacted behind the plastic headlight protectors, reducing their beam to zero.

We eventually reached the highest point and then began descending into Edinburgh. The blizzard slowly subsided. Obviously, we should have taken the coastal route, but none of us knew how bad the mountain route would be and just laughed it off as one of those things that happen when I'm with them. Clearly my fault …

Running very late, we arrived at our hotel on the outskirts of Edinburgh at about 11.00pm. I was driving and, as I pulled up at the entrance to the hotel, a young man came running up to our police vehicle. He was very excited and spoke in a thick Scottish accent, which we found hard to understand.

"Come quick!" he bellowed. "My house is being burgled!" My colleagues looked at me.

"What house?" I asked. He pointed at a housing estate behind the hotel; he was probably speaking the truth, but as Scotland has a separate legal system to the English/Welsh one, it meant that we had absolutely no police powers whatsoever there, despite driving a marked police van. We were just civilians and had no idea if we had even common-law powers of arrest as fellow citizens did in England.

"Sorry mate," I said. "We're from England and have no powers here. Go to reception and call the local police."

He cursed and ran off back to the houses. Clearly my fault …

We booked in. The whole time, my colleagues were blaming the 'Dave Factor' for what had just happened. Having spent the whole day driving over mountains and through blizzards, we were starving and decided to catch the local bus into Edinburgh for some food.

We managed to find the best Indian restaurant in all of Scotland and sat down to a well-deserved meal, knowing that our allowances would be paying for it.

Afterwards, we walked along the main street looking for a taxi to take us back to the hotel, burning off our gluttony and laughing in high spirits.

And then the Dave Factor came into play again.

The road was very wide and few people were about. In fact, there were only three people visible to us – one man was lying on his back, apparently unconscious, and two large men were repeatedly stomping on his face and kicking his head. They were on the other side of the road, a good twenty yards away.

"Fuck me, come on!" I said to my two colleagues.

"No, no, no, no – we don't have police powers here, remember!" they said.

Yes, I knew that, and it was an uncomfortable feeling, but we had to act: they might end up killing the guy.

"It doesn't matter – we clearly have the power to intervene in a situation like this – come on!" I said. As they hesitated, we watched another man try to remonstrate with the two aggressors. He was instantly grabbed by the lapels, by the larger of the two men. The guy was then manhandled across the road directly towards us, whereupon he was slammed into the shop window next to us, smashing the glass, then pulled out and thrown across the bonnet of a parked car. The big guy set about punching him whilst holding him down on the bonnet, oblivious to the three of us standing next to them.

During this incident I clocked that the type of premises the guy had been thrown at was probably alarmed, and that this meant the police would be here very soon.

My colleagues still hesitated, unsure of their powers, when I said to them, "OK, if you're not going to intervene, I am," and stepped towards the huge and violent guy, knowing that they would back me up if needed.

And then a police car came racing towards us, blue lights flashing. I pulled the big guy back and held onto him so that he couldn't run. An officer came over to us and I yelled at him.

"We're English police officers, this guy has just smashed this little guy through that window and has been stomping on that guy's head," I said, pointing to the motionless man still lying on his back. "He needs serious medical help – now. And another offender has run off in that direction."

For all I knew, the initial victim could have been dead, but I stayed with the officer as the big, aggressive guy was with him and needed handcuffing. Another officer ran across the road, calling for an ambulance as other cars arrived.

My colleagues and I were picked up and taken on a search of the area for the second offender, but he had disappeared.

I was impressed with the response and the way they handled the incident. Unfortunately, we had to go to the police station for several hours and write out witness statements.

We were given a lift back to the hotel, finally getting to bed about 3.00am. Again, I was blamed for the incident. In a light-hearted way.

The following morning, we returned to the police station, this time in uniform, to be told that the outstanding offender had been named by the arrestee and would be arrested in due course.

The violent criminal we'd gone to collect was eventually brought out of his cell. He was tiny and as good as gold. He apologised for 'kicking off' when arrested, claiming he had been drunk and didn't know what was happening. He was curious as to why he had to go to Cambridge, but seemed totally OK with it.

He was not going to be a problem in the slightest: we could have taken him on the plane after all. Thankfully, the journey back to Cambridge was totally uneventful, *and* we took the coast road.

Six months later, the three of us were called back to Edinburgh as witnesses for the assault trial. This time we flew up, went straight to court, and flew straight back. Nobody wanted any Dave Factor this time.

The unconscious victim in the case had suffered a seriously broken jaw and had to receive plastic surgery. The two offenders were convicted of an unprovoked and pointless assault on the victim and the Good Samaritan, and were sent to prison.

THIEF TAKER Chapter Fourteen

Cambridge

ONE OF THE JOBS I REALLY HATED DOING was being the Gaoler. This job was usually done by an officer on the shift, and it was a job that needed a capable officer and a calm head. The more you did it, the better you became at it.

It was one of the many jobs that was eventually civilianised, and was probably staffed by ex-police officers who didn't know how to enjoy retirement.

As Gaoler, you worked in the custody office under the custody sergeant, and did all the tasks required in there. You fed the prisoners, helped restrain violent ones, checked on vulnerable detainees, and entered details on the respective custody records. It was a place that was highly controlled, where everything had to be done by the book, and which had far too many rules and regulations to follow if you were only doing it part-time. It needed to be a full-time, professional job, and I hated having to cover in there.

It was a dangerous and hectic place where anything could go wrong, either through a deliberate act or by accident or omission – and when it did, heads rolled.

It also kept me away from the streets and the job I loved so much.

I wasn't Gaoler that day – Steve was, and he was really good at the job. I was in the custody office on another matter.

I was standing at the desk, waiting in line for the custody sergeant's attention. He was but one man, and the cell-block was very busy that day.

I casually watched as Steve microwaved all of the ready-meals and went to each individual cell, giving the prisoners something to eat and a hot drink. He had a firm but pleasant manner, and few would challenge Steve. As he closed the heavy iron door of the last one, he quietly spoke as he passed me.

"Ah, I forgot to get her some cutlery."

I knew who he meant – it was a young girl who'd been detained under the Mental Health Act. Brought in for her own safety, she was subject to fifteen-minute welfare checks until the doctor arrived to see if she needed committing to hospital. A police custody office was not a place for the mentally ill, but, as there were no facilities elsewhere, it was the only option, and was fraught with dangers.

I casually registered that Steve returned seconds later, carrying a plastic spoon for the girl – one that she couldn't use to harm herself – and, juggling with his huge bunch of keys, he opened the heavy cell door.

"Oh no," I heard him curse in his gentle way, as all hell broke loose.

Steve had hit the panic alarm, one of which was outside each of the cells, instantly setting off a unique, piercing alarm that could be heard in the cell-block, the control room, and all over the station. It basically meant *I need help down here and I need it now*!

Officers were programmed to respond to this alarm, and, within seconds, every officer in the station would be in the cell-block. A call would also be put out over the radio, telling patrol officers to attend as well, if able.

I was the closest to Steve, and I ran into the cell behind him. Sitting on the bench was the ready-meal Steve had given to the young lady, steam still rising from it, whilst the girl was curled up in a foetal position on the floor. Her face was a horrible blue, her hands clutching at her neck. And, just visible, deep in a fold in her neck, was some type of cord. She was strangling herself and, from the colour of her face, she would have achieved her aim in the next few minutes.

Steve dropped to the floor and tried to undo the cord with his fingers, but couldn't. I helped him and it was clear that it had been wrapped so tightly around her neck and tied off that we would not be able to undo it in time. She was dying and needed help quickly.

"Scissors!" I yelled. "Get some scissors or a knife!"

He ran out of the cell and, as I looked up, I saw numerous officers looking in – those who had responded to the alarm. I tried to undo the cord and noticed that the girl was now completely unconscious.

"Ambulance!" I yelled, knowing that the custody sergeant would have been able to hear me and would get hold of one, if he hadn't done so already.

Within seconds, but what seemed like an eternity, Steve returned with some toy-like scissors he'd got from the pathetic first aid kit.

He passed them to me and I wriggled them under the cord around the girl's neck until I had enough length to attempt to cut it without cutting her. It was hard work but I managed to cut through the cord, breathing out in relief as it fell away.

It had been so tight that the compressed skin around her neck gave the appearance that the cord was still there. I thought she was dead and put my ear to her mouth. There was a very faint rasp of air coming from her, so faint that it was difficult to detect.

I looked up at the ashen-faced sergeant standing in the doorway.

"She's alive. Just."

I knew there would be an inquiry – especially if she died – and that heads would roll, and that the custody sergeant had ultimate responsibility for those in custody. The first question asked would be 'Where did she get the cord from?'

I didn't know the girl, but I did know that she was filthy and smelly and seriously unwell, and that I didn't want to have to give her mouth-to-mouth if at all possible, but nobody deserved to die like that. I would have, if required, but I knew she was taking in oxygen now, and, as I waited with her for the ambulance to arrive, I cursed the fact that there was no oxygen mask available in the building.

She had known that she was on fifteen-minute checks, and she knew that once Steve had given her her dinner, he wouldn't be back for another fifteen minutes, by which time she would have been well and truly dead. It hadn't been a cry for help – it was a genuine attempt at suicide.

Where did she get the cord? It was the waistband cord concealed in her baggy sports trousers. Such items are routinely taken off all prisoners, and especially those suspected of being mentally ill. How it was missed I don't know, but I'm sure the reason was eventually discovered.

Thank Christ Steve had forgotten her spoon and was conscientious enough to go and get one for her. She survived – the poor tortured soul.

I felt sorry for what was to come, and that's one of the many reasons why I hated working in the cell-block.

Sure, things could go wrong out on the streets, but you were less supervised, less scrutinised, and had the authority to make decisions based on the facts before you. Hindsight occasionally proved your decisions to be incorrect, but that was a part of being a constable: you had to make life and death decisions based on the circumstances, and hope they were the right ones at the time, often in the face of conflicting information.

When the call came in, I knew it was going to be a bad one. It was 3.00am and the rain was sheeting horizontally across the hospital car park. Officers love the rain – there is no greater crime preventer than the weather. But cars would still get stolen from the hospital, and that's why I was there, quietly crawling around with my lights off, looking out for any sign of movement. There was nothing else happening – the weather had seen to that.

"C514, injury RTA on the A1307 just outside Trumpington – start making your way, please."

I was covering the southern part of the city and, typically, I was single-crewed. I knew the road mentioned: it ran from the southern edge of the city down to the M11 interchange. It extended beyond the city limit – the 30mph zone – to the 60mph zone down to the motorway. It was single carriageway and unlit.

It's gonna be a bad one …

"Apparently it's between a cyclist and a lorry."

Shit, it's gonna be a bad one …

"Ambulance has been called."

I realised that the ambulance would be attending from the hospital, and that if it had already left for the accident, I would have just seen it, and I hadn't. As I activated my lights and accelerated out of the car park, mentally drawing the fastest route to the scene in my head, I knew that I would be there well before the ambulance. In fact, I knew I would be the first of anybody there.

It's definitely gonna be a bad one. Where the hell were traffic?

Under normal circumstances, a traffic unit would be attending this type of accident due to the probable seriousness of it, as well as its location. It wasn't even in the city so, technically, it wasn't my responsibility.

However, I was professional enough to know that I was the closest officer to the scene and that somebody was in need of help. None of these thoughts entered my head at the time, except for hoping for the practical traffic support.

As I left the illuminated streetlights of the city and plunged into the darkness of the countryside, I had to slow right down. The rain was incredibly heavy and blowing directly across the road. It was seriously difficult to see anything, and the last thing a police officer wants to do is to drive into an accident and add to the carnage.

After what seemed like an age, I saw hazard warning lights ahead. There was a car on the opposite side of the road, facing me, parked up. There was nobody with it. *Close now …* I crawled past it and noticed a larger dark mass slightly further on, on my side of the road. It too had its hazard lights flashing. As I got closer I saw that it was a lorry.

"C514 at the scene," I said, as I reached for my fluorescent jacket and confirmed that my emergency lights were on and that my vehicle was protecting the scene. Under such terrible conditions, other cars do drive into accidents.

In my headlights I saw two people standing behind the lorry on the grass verge. As I approached them I saw that they were a middle-aged man and woman. The look of relief on their faces was clear to see, even in the darkness.

"What's happened?" I asked, as I still couldn't see any casualty.

They pointed down at the grass verge next to them, and then I saw him in the darkness: the man was lying face down in the mud and the grass, motionless. The rain was running down the bank and his face was buried in it. If he weren't already dead, he'd be drowning.

I dropped to my knees and put my ear to him. He was breathing; a rasping sound could be heard coming from his chest through his back. He was alive.

"Shit, come on, I need you to help me turn him over," I said, looking up at them.

Civilians are often reluctant to get involved in incidents, but generally can be encouraged to if an officer forces the issue. Technically, it is an offence to refuse to assist a constable when requested, although in all my time I never saw anybody prosecuted for this. People have their reasons for hesitation, but the response of these two was totally unexpected and caught me off guard.

"No, you can't move him – he might be injured and you're gonna make it worse."

"*Worse*? There's nothing worse than *dead* and that's what *he* is gonna be if he can't breathe! He needs to breathe and we need to move him, and move him now, so help me!"

I assumed that he had been like this since the accident, when these two had stopped, and that they were the only people here. I instantly calculated how long it must have taken for the call to get through to the police and for me to get the message and then to drive to the scene.

I was not happy at all and yet they still said moving him was the wrong thing to do. I knew *they* were wrong; all of my training and experience told me they were wrong, but I could not sit there and argue with them. The seconds were ticking by and I needed to tilt his whole body so that his mouth was out of the mud.

Without their help to support and immobilise his body, I knew that I could have caused serious problems if he had a broken spine, but he still needed to breathe.

I had begun groping down the side of his face to stick my fingers in his mouth to let air in when, through the noise of the rain, I heard another siren, and soon a vehicle pulled up behind my car. It was the ambulance.

A lady paramedic approached me and I yelled at her that he couldn't breathe. She reacted immediately and seemed angry that nothing had been done to alleviate that. She jumped in and took over.

I was grateful and relieved, as I always was when these guys turned up.

The two people were standing there watching the ambulance crew. I was angry with them but it wasn't really their fault. They had obviously never had any first aid training in their lives. If they had, they might have recalled the priorities known as the four 'B's: breathing, bleeding, breaks, and burns, in that order. Breathing is *the* priority, and for a very good reason.

Sadly, a lot of people panic or freeze when faced with such life or death situations. They can't think straight or fear doing the wrong thing. Yes, a lot of it is common sense – like breathing is essential to surviving – but this happens often. This is where training all school kids in first aid would make a difference – some of it might stick.

Within seconds, a spinal support was put on the guy and he was rotated out of the mud. The paramedics were in full flow and I didn't want any of us to get in the way.

"Are you the lorry driver?" I asked the man.

"What? No, I was just passing with my wife," he replied.

"So, *where* is the lorry driver? Have you seen him?"

"Yes, he's in his cab, I think. He looks like he's in shock or something."

"Is that your car?" I asked, pointing up the road. It was, so I told them to go and sit in it, out of the rain, and wait for me.

I spoke to the radio room and gave them the important message: 'This is likely to prove'. What that meant was that the accident was likely to prove fatal. I was no medical expert, but under the circumstances I could see that it was unlikely that this casualty would survive. A fatal accident required traffic officers to attend because the accident needed to be fully investigated by specialists who had the appropriate expertise in that area. General patrol cops don't, and the sooner the experts get there the better it is. It is for this reason that we pass this message.

I opened the lorry cab passenger door and climbed in out of the rain. The driver was sitting there and clearly in shock.

"I didn't see him, I didn't see him," was all he said.

I looked through the windscreen at the rain and the darkness. I couldn't see anything either.

It did prove to be a fatal accident. The elderly cyclist had been cycling home in that awful weather when the lorry, travelling at speed, had hit him from behind. Every bone in his body was broken. He didn't stand a chance.

The driver was prosecuted for careless driving, but maintained that he never saw the cyclist at all. It was just another tragic incident that officers have to attend on a daily basis.

The decisions officers make at such incidents are scrutinised at the coroner's inquests. Sometimes a decision might save a life, or it can take a life, and sometimes there is nothing you can do to help at all, no matter what.

I was driving into work with my wife when the traffic ahead slowed down because an oncoming bus was stopped at an angle across our lane. Straight away I knew something was wrong.

I pushed my way through the traffic and saw that an RTA had just occurred. Somebody was trapped under the front of the bus and it was serious.

I had my police shirt on under my civilian jacket so I left my jacket in the car and told my wife to take the car back home as the main road was completely blocked.

As I approached the bus I saw a young girl beneath the wheels, a bicycle mangled up with her. Another officer whom I instantly recognised was cradling her. I could tell that the girl was dead, and the look on the officer's face told me that too. There was clearly nothing to be done for her.

I knew I should have tried, and I should have been with the officer at that time. If for nobody else, then for him, as he was clearly in terrible shock.

Maybe it was my unpreparedness for such horror, my being on my way into work, or my awareness of the training that says 'do the next thing that needs doing', but I found myself directing traffic around the bus whilst waiting for the emergency services to arrive, whilst my colleague cradled the dead girl.

Within minutes, a volunteer *Magpas* doctor arrived and began working on the girl, and, as other services arrived, I found myself continuing to control traffic but with a reflective Magpas doctor's jacket on. I've no idea of how I came to be wearing it.

The first officer on the scene was Nick, and I told him to tell my boss that I was going to be late for work.

Eventually, as the doctor travelled in the ambulance with the casualty, I was left with his car keys, and ended up driving his BMW to the hospital for him.

The girl was an eighteen-year-old foreign student studying in Cambridge. She had just left her house and crossed the road, pushing her cycle with her. She'd stopped in the middle of the road as the bus came towards her, standing between two traffic bollards. Unfortunately, her cycle had been sticking out into the traffic lane and, as the bus passed, it caught the bike.

By chance, she was standing on the wrong side of the bike. It scooped her up and dragged her under the wheels of the bus. Had she been standing on the other side of the bike, it would have just been ripped harmlessly out of her hands.

The impact at the base of her skull killed her instantly. What made this particularly pointless death even more difficult was that, as the bus skidded diagonally across the road to a halt, with the cyclist trapped beneath the wheels, it came to rest outside the front door to her house. Her fellow students were standing on the doorstep, a few feet away from her body, ashen-faced.

Sometimes, trained and untrained people are confronted with situations that are unexpected and horrific, and are suddenly expected to make a decision – to act or not? What should they do?

Most make the right decision and heroes are born. Many make the wrong decision, which often has tragic consequences. But, should anybody be blamed for getting it wrong, especially when they actually did *something*, and what they did was done in good faith?

What about you? Would you know what to do in such circumstances? Maybe you've already been there and been tested? If not, would you act or not?

And more importantly, would you know how to save somebody's life?

Book Five in THE ROZZERS Series

COP
OUT

A TRUE STORY by

DIEM BURDEN

This book is dedicated to all of the young police officers across the world, as the commitment of such untarnished and idealistic young men and women never ceases to amaze me. It is their resilience, unending motivation and relentless drive to do the job and to do it well that keeps the police service afloat. They carry the burden for all the officers above them, despite the constant crap dumped on them on a daily basis by those very same supervisors. Lions, each and every one of you, led by donkeys. Thank you for your unswerving devotion to duty. I salute you all!

COP OUT Chapter One

Cambridge, circa 1996–2000

IT'S NEVER WISE TO FEEL INVINCIBLE, but I did, and I was loving every minute of it. I had recently been awarded a brown belt in martial arts and was ambitiously working towards my black. I was a tutor-constable training new staff, and I had become one of the most experienced officers on my shift. This was the most satisfying and enjoyable time for me as a cop. It was a period when I felt there were no limits to what I could do, that I could be who I wanted to be, and achieve whatever I wanted to achieve.

Despite absolutely loving going to work each day, I was sensible enough to also be planning ahead. I began to study criminal law in my spare time so that, if and when I decided I needed a new challenge, I could sit the sergeants' exam and put myself up for promotion. I'd always considered it an option, but only when the time was right. I didn't agree with young, inexperienced officers becoming sergeants, so I wanted to have the relevant experience to bring to the new position.

I was being routinely allocated the shift transit van to drive at briefing – a position only allotted to the most experienced and capable officers available, and for good reason. The van was intentionally left out of any prolonged enquiries such as sudden deaths, and generally kept central, so that it was ready to assist with whatever was needed. Its principal role was prisoner transport, but crews were also available to give advice at scenes to less experienced officers, and, reassuringly, as the van was routinely double-crewed, to back up at violent incidents. Officers always prayed that the van was nearby when going to such incidents.

One day, when I went down to briefing, I was introduced to a new face – a guy called Neil, who was a transferee from another force. I was asked to show him around Cambridge and to get him accustomed to the different procedures used by our force, so the van was an ideal starting point for him due to its flexible roles.

We hit it off straight away. Neil was as experienced as I was, was preparing for the sergeants' exam, and had a great sense of humour. Over the next few months, we were constantly crewed together and, with our combined experience and knowledge of law from our studies, along with my local knowledge, we made the perfect van crew, and I loved going out on patrol with him.

Supporting less experienced officers was one of our tasks, and our deeper understanding of the law, which we had gained through our studies, was invaluable. Whilst out and about, we often bounced legal or procedural questions off each other, which helped us both prepare for the impending exam. In many ways, we were able to take work off the shift sergeant, as we often attended an incident in support, and advised the newer officers.

One afternoon briefing, our shift were asked to look out for Jamie, an escaped prisoner. He was a lad of about nineteen years old and already a prolific criminal in the city, so much so that most officers knew his face, full name, and date of birth by rote. Information had been received that, whilst absconding, he had been seen at his girlfriend's house in the city, and intelligence suggested he was staying there.

I volunteered to do a knock-and-see, so, after briefing, I headed across town to the house in question, to introduce Neil to Wendy, Jamie's girlfriend. I parked up short and walked in, so as to arrive unannounced. It was a nice-sized, semi-detached house in a quiet cul-de-sac in the middle of a council estate. I knocked on the front door to silence.

I smiled at Neil, rolled my eyes, and banged again, shouting, "Wendy, it's the police!"

Still no response, but this time, with my good ear pressed against the door, I could hear a couple of voices murmuring on the other side.

I stepped to the side and looked through the net-curtained window into the lounge. Pressed up against the wall was a young woman I assumed to be Wendy, and next to her was the unmistakable face of

Jamie, the escapee. They were whispering urgently in hushed tones, trying not to be seen from the front door.

Got you.

I slowly stepped back out of sight. "Neil," I hissed, "he's in there! Cover the back!" I didn't need to add *quickly*. Neil knew his job and instantly flew down the side passage into the back garden to cut off any escape.

As I turned back to the window, I came face to face with Wendy. She was drawing the curtains, but pretended not to notice the cop standing just outside of her window, looking in. This action prevented me from seeing inside the house further, but, just before the curtains were fully closed, I was able to see the absconder, still in the lounge behind her.

OK, time to let them know that we know. I banged on the front door more forcibly.

"Wendy!" I shouted. "I know Jamie's in there. I've just seen him through the window. Now, I need you to open the door for me. Understand?"

Silence.

I was fully aware that, having confirmed that Jamie was on the premises, we had a power to enter and search the property to locate the escaped prisoner, using as much force as was necessary under the circumstances. This meant that I knew I was going to break that front door down if Wendy continued to refuse to open. We had the kit in the van for such an eventuality.

I called for further units to assist, as it seemed that we were going to have to do just that, and drag Jamie out screaming. As we waited, I continuously tried to engage Wendy in conversation. After a while, she came to the closed door and spoke to me through it.

"What do you want?" she asked, in an innocent voice.

"Jamie, obviously," I said. "He's got to go back to prison, and I know he's in your house, so if you don't open the door to me, you know what's gonna happen, don't you?"

Silence.

"Wendy, if you don't open the door right now, I'm going to have to break it open, and that'll get awfully messy, won't it?"

Silence.

"It'd be much better if you just opened the door, wouldn't it?"

There was a moment more of silence, followed by a hushed voice and muffled movement, before I heard the door locks slowly being undone. She was unbolting the door.

"What do you want?" she whined, as she opened the door an inch and peered through.

"You know what I want. I want *him*!"

"He's not here. He's in prison – you should know that," she said. I was fully aware that I could have just barged her aside and stormed in, but that wasn't my style.

I let out a long, slow breath, and patiently explained that I had seen Jamie through the window, that I knew he was in there with her, and that he couldn't possibly have legged it out of the back door, as I'd had the back covered from the start. I informed her of my power of entry and, glancing back at the several officers now waiting in line along the front path behind me, I encouragingly pressed the door open and felt her resistance fade. I was in the house, along with the guys behind me.

She sat down on her sofa in a huff as I stood and watched her.

"Where is he?" I asked, having confirmed that he was no longer in the lounge.

"I told you. He ain't here – he's in prison. How many times have I gotta say it?"

"You'll be in a lot of trouble for lying to me about him – you know that, don't you?"

"Yeah, whatever …"

I gave the nod, and my colleagues began searching the kitchen just beyond, the three upstairs bedrooms, and the bathroom. I stared at her with my best know-it-all look for the five or so minutes it took my colleagues to search the house, waiting for the shouting and the inevitable thud as Jamie was manhandled to the floor and handcuffed.

They came back looking sheepish.

"Well?" I asked, aware that all was not well.

"Nothing," they responded.

Nothing? What do you mean nothing?

"He's definitely here somewhere," I said. "Search again, but this time check inside small spaces as well – cupboards, boxes, anywhere and everywhere you might not expect a man to fit. Check everywhere, please."

Off they went again, and this time they took a while longer before coming back to me.

"Still nothing," they said, shrugging their shoulders. I was reminded of the scene from my favourite film of all time, *The Life of Brian*, when the Romans couldn't find the rebels hiding in the flat despite searching twice.

Tell me this isn't happening ...

Neil joined me in the lounge, having been replaced at the rear of the house by a new arrival. I updated him as to what had happened so far, which obviously didn't take long.

"Have we checked the loft?" he asked. I looked at my colleagues and they looked at each other before trotting off to find a chair and a torch.

Following more bumping and scraping sounds, one of them plodded back down the wooden stairs. Nope, not there either.

I shook my head disbelievingly. A man can't just disappear in a house that easily.

"Did you actually go *into* the loft?" I asked him, my irritation and frustration beginning to show.

"Well, not *exactly*," he said. "I just put my head up and shone my torch around."

I looked at Neil and he at me.

He's in the loft. It's the only place he can be.

Neil took control and went upstairs, climbed onto the chair, and shone the torch around. He wasn't totally convinced that the loft was clear, so he asked for a volunteer and proceeded to shoulder the guy up into the loft before handing him the torch.

"Look everywhere," Neil called up to him.

After five minutes of shuffling and cursing, the officer's face appeared at the opening, his head shaking in the negative.

Neil came back downstairs and confirmed that the guy was not hiding in the loft. Together, we looked around the house to see if officers had missed anything, any small place that he might be.

Nothing.

Time was passing, and most of the shift was in attendance – meaning the city had very little police coverage at that moment. Pressure was beginning to mount. The control room staff were getting agitated, asking if we could release officers for other work that was beginning to pile up. They even asked me directly if I was sure it was him I'd seen through the window. Doubt was beginning to creep into the eyes of a few of my younger colleagues too, although they did their best to hide it.

I didn't like being doubted. I still don't.

An impatient sergeant duly arrived, and Neil and I went out into the front garden to speak to him. As we were the two senior officers present, it would have been unkind for him to have just overruled us on the radio, so I was thankful that the sergeant came and spoke to us in person. Whilst clearly aware of the urgency of putting this one-man crime wave back behind bars, he explained that he seriously needed to release some of the officers for the growing backlog of work. He knew me – we had worked together for several years – and he lowered his voice when he questioned if I might have actually been mistaken.

I was quite firm with him. *He is here.*

"OK, but five minutes, Dave," he said. "Then we need to leave. *All* of us. *Five* minutes. OK?"

After the sergeant left, Neil and I stared at the front of the house.

"Are you sure it was him?" Neil asked, quietly.

"Absolutely," I said. "And if it wasn't *him*, I did see *two* people in that lounge: a man and Wendy. Could the man, whoever he was, have just vanished like that?" I turned and looked at him.

"No, of course not."

"And, is it possible that he got out of the back door before you got there?"

"No chance," said Neil. "I was there in a flash."

"Then he must still be inside, whoever he is, and we're missing something." I looked at him. "Are *you* doubting me, too?" I asked.

"Davey-boy!" He laughed. "If you say he's in the house, he is *in* the house!" He put his arm around my shoulder, and together we went back into the lounge. Neil never did doubt me, always called me 'Davey-Boy', and often put his arm around my – and other officers' – shoulders. That was the kind of man he was, and it was easy to warm to him.

Back inside, Wendy was still sitting on the sofa, and I knew that it was she who held the key to Jamie's whereabouts, so if I wanted to get this guy *and* save face, I had to work on her, and quickly. I had to get a clue from her, one way or another, as the clock was now ticking down.

Five minutes …

I sat down in an armchair opposite her and, leaning forward, looked into her eyes. *Pressure time.*

"Wendy, you are committing an offence by assisting an offender or absconder, and you will be arrested for this," I said. "It's a serious offence, and you could go to prison. You do understand this, don't you?"

She nodded her head, and we both knew that, without Jamie, she was not going to be charged with diddly.

"I saw you with him," I said. "Through the window, just before you shut the curtains on me. We had the back of the house covered, so I know he's still in this house somewhere."

She shrugged her shoulders, avoiding my stare.

Four minutes ...

"Why did you close the curtains, Wendy, if he isn't here?"

She shrugged her shoulders again. "Well he ain't here, obviously, is he?"

Why did *you close the curtains, Wendy? There was no real need to do that.*

They obviously knew I'd seen him – my fat head had been at the window, hand up to cut the glare, staring through the nets. It didn't make any sense to me – all they had to do was go into another room where he could hide in his hiding place, quickly, before we smashed the door open.

Unless ... Unless she closed the curtains because wherever she had hidden him was visible from the window I was looking through.

I glanced around the room, frowning. She had had to close the damned curtains to hide from *me* where she was going to hide *him*! She must have hidden him in *this* room somewhere, but where?

Three minutes ...

I walked around the room and checked every tiny piece of furniture. I stood Wendy up and turned over the sofa she had chosen to sit on, and tapped all the lounge walls for any hidden cupboards. I could sense her discomfort at my sudden interest in the lounge, her eyes watching me as I searched. I also felt Neil's eyes appraising me. He knew I was onto something.

Still nothing.

She sat down in my armchair now, facing her upturned sofa.

Two minutes ...

"You hid him in *this* room, didn't you, Wendy?" I said matter-of-factly, but watching her intently, looking for any sign from her.

I liked to think that I'd become a bit of an expert on what the police called NVCs, or Non-Verbal Communications, more commonly known as body language. I loved the science of NVCs. I'd volunteered to do courses on it, applied it to the work I'd been doing over the years, and often used it in self-defence and martial arts. People lie all the time, but NVCs never do.

I stared at her, ready to pounce. *Pile on the pressure.*

"*Where*, Wendy? *Where* did you hide Jamie?" As I spoke, her eyes gave the tiniest of flicks to the far corner of the room – almost too quick to see, but not for me. I'd been ready for the giveaway NVC, and, predictably, she'd just given it to me.

I stared at the corner of the room she'd indicated without knowing she had. It was just behind the upended sofa and wasn't really a corner, just a dogleg in the room with no furniture in it. The sofa had initially been nestling tidily into it. Now, with the sofa turned over, it was just an empty corner with a tatty bit of carpet turned up at the corner.

Her NVCs told me further that she was uncomfortable with my sudden interest in that area.

One minute …

I walked over to the corner to see if I was missing something, and stood there, staring foolishly down at the floor. There was nowhere else to look.

I glanced back at Wendy, and could see the barely concealed terror in her eyes.

There was nothing in the corner except for the tatty, turned up carpet with wooden floorboards peeking out from beneath. I bent down and pulled back the carpet. I tapped the floorboards with my knuckles, and the hollow sound told me there was air beneath them. They also rattled a bit, indicating they were loose. I stuck my fingernail into the edge of one, and pulled it upwards. About half a yard of board lifted out. I shone my torch down and saw a space beneath the floorboards about three feet deep, down to the bare earth beneath the house. I couldn't avoid a smile.

I pulled up several more half-yard long floorboards until I could fit my over-sized head down there. I ducked down, shining my torch into the darkness. The three-foot gap extended beneath the whole ground floor. It was a great storage space, and an even better hiding place.

Zero minutes. Time's up!

My torch wasn't particularly powerful, but I could see a dark, human-like shape huddled in the far corner.

"Hello, Jamie," I purred, my voice thick with oh-I-told-you-frigging-so. "What you doing down *here*? You coming out then, or should I come in and get you?"

I think he was amazed to have been found, and didn't really fancy going head to head with me after being crouched over for so long.

"Yeah, yeah, yeah," he said, resignation in his voice. "I'm coming out."

Sure enough, he shuffled towards me and the gap, put his arms up so that I could handcuff him, and let me help him out of his hiding place.

"Nice try," I said. "But not good enough, I'm afraid."

I then transmitted over the radio, "Yeah, control, one in custody here."

The cheers from the control room told me all I needed to know, and the look in the eyes of the officers still at the scene filled me with job satisfaction.

"Oh, and you're nicked too, Wendy," I said, as I led Jamie out of the house, into our van, and back to prison.

I loved being a cop, especially at times like that.

COP OUT Chapter Two

BEING AT THE SHARP END OF POLICING wasn't always so dramatic and joy-filled. Being a response cop certainly had its downsides. For example, when most 'normal' people finished work and got together and partied, it was usually at the weekends. For cops like me, because of the shift pattern, weekends only came around once every five weeks, and even then it was impossible to plan anything because weekends off were often cancelled at short notice. *Princess Diana's coming. The President of China's coming. There's a protest. Another special operation.*

It was never-ending, and, to rub salt into the wounds, people would often moan about the police having 'all these extra cops' available for special events but not enough to police the streets. They'd say it to our faces, write letters of complaint to the newspapers, and generally bitch about the police at every opportunity, without having a clue what they were talking about. I guess if you are reading this, you're not one of them, but I bet you've met them!

These professional whiners really think the police produce extra officers from a box hidden in the basement, not realising that if we did have such a magical box, then we'd use the officers to double-crew with our single-crewed officers apprehending knife-wielding maniacs, so that our colleagues and friends would be less likely to get killed or seriously injured.

Losers aside, such work wreaked havoc on social and family life. I so envied the family-friendly shift pattern of CID.

Another downside was some of the incidents I'd rather not have seen. How would I ever forget the image of the alcoholic, drug-addict woman who had bled to death in her own flat whilst out of her head on drink and drugs? She'd had a vaginal haemorrhage, and had been incapable of stemming the flow herself or simply dialling 999. She had obviously wandered all over the flat whilst bleeding profusely, but had eventually bled out on her own sofa, smoking a spliff. I'd initially thought she'd been stabbed to death due to the large amount of blood soaked into the sofa beneath her, and had to investigate further, which meant taking a closer look, of course. It was an awful death and a tragic waste of life, without a shred of dignity. The sight and smell of that woman's sad and pointless demise will remain with me forever.

Then there was the unpredictability of suddenly being confronted with danger of the worst kind. The feeling of dread doesn't always creep up on you; it often jumps up and pokes its finger in your eye with full force.

Kevin had been sent to a violent domestic in the north of the city, and had just booked at the scene. As usual, he was single-crewed because the 'box with the extra cops' was locked, and nobody knew where the key was. As the van crew, we should have been on our way to back him up, but we had a detainee in the back of the van, and were committed to heading to the cells with him. Consequently, another unit had been dispatched to support him, but they were still some way off when Kevin keyed his radio and transmitted to anyone listening:

"Look, mate, just put the knife down, will you? Calm down, I'm a police officer, and what you're doing is a very serious matter."

There was a lot of screaming and shouting in the background, and it was clear Kevin was in trouble. He was obviously being threatened by a man with a knife, and was unable even to transmit a distress call in case it inflamed the situation. He'd done the next best thing and surreptitiously transmitted the conversation over the radio. The control room immediately put out a 10/16 urgent assistance call on his behalf, and everybody dropped what they were doing and raced towards him.

It was acceptable for the van crew to race to such a scene with a prisoner on board, but there was always a danger that he might get thrown around too much in the back of the van and get injured, or that the van might be involved in an accident. 'Officer in need of urgent assistance' was the one call you went hell-for-leather to get to, and a judgement call had to be made: Kevin's welfare or the prisoner's.

As we were almost at the station, I knew that we'd get to Kevin long after several other officers, who would then need the van to bring the offender back to the station, so I opted to drop our prisoner off first, arranging for somebody to meet us on arrival and take the guy off us, so we could immediately attend the incident. I just hoped Kev could keep it under control until somebody got to him.

Kevin faced a danger all police officers have faced at some time, often numerous times, in their careers. Usually out of the blue, and with very little support, the only thing preventing a dangerous situation from becoming a lethal one is the officer's brains and mouth in managing to keep things calm until back-up arrives. Such dangers are ever-present and routinely accepted, and, sadly, no matter how qualified the officer is in these two skills, it often isn't enough. The Thin Blue Line only ever gets thinner, both from death and injury, and to save some money somewhere.

Unfortunately, there comes a point when the (too few) officers out there should be armed for their own safety. I'm not in favour of routinely arming British cops as that would fundamentally change the way we operate, as well as the type of cop we'd need to recruit, but if we have to choose between risking single-crewed officers attending such incidents or giving them an advantage over a knife-wielding lunatic, then arming wins the argument, surely?

For all of these issues and more, my reasons *not* to do the job I loved were steadily mounting up. Nevertheless, once a call came in, we'd race to the scene and get on with it as professionals, often revelling in our abilities to deal with such incidents. There was often little time to think, very little point in complaining, and, thankfully, most incidents were safely resolved. Just as Kevin's was that night.

Having been at the ceaseless sharp end for around six years, I felt like I needed a break. Maybe a different job for a while. Any job that took me away from such constant action was like a holiday. A chance to breathe, and relax, and take stock.

So when I was sent to Force HQ to do a follow-up HOLMES (Home Office Large Major Enquiry System) computer course, I welcomed the opportunity. Although I was already trained on the major incident computer, a refresher course was needed for anybody who hadn't been used on an operation in a while.

It was a nine to five job for a couple of weeks – a small group of officers from Cambridge taking a company car up the motorway to Huntingdon. We joined other colleagues from around the force, drank lots of coffee, and generally unwound. Oh, and we also got to have three weekends off in a row with our families!

After the second week, we were informed we were actually going to help out on a national investigation that was growing in complexity and whose workload was backing up. Cambridgeshire Police was involved in a nationwide investigation centred on care homes dotted across the country, which were being implicated in systemic abuse of resident children. As the number of suspects increased, so did the lines of inquiry. There was a huge backlog, so, as we were trained HOLMES operators, we were tasked with indexing a large quantity of statements for that inquiry. This required reading each inputted statement thoroughly for references to people, places or events. If, for example, the witness mentioned a particular person in his or her statement – say a doctor they had been examined by, or a friend they had mentioned something to – we had to link that name in the statement to the record of the person mentioned. If the person didn't exist on our system, we had to create a nominal record for them and add all the information we could: names, descriptions, links to places and people, etc. In this way, the computerised version of the investigation grew like a giant web, with links between all statements, people and records.

Initially, we were excited to be going live with an operation of such magnitude, but, before long, it soon became apparent that most of the statements were from victims of sexual abuse when they had been children in the homes. My stomach churned at the calm, detailed description given by a then adult in respect to abuse they had had to endure, often repeatedly, whilst still a child, at the hands of monsters charged with their care. Those people did dreadful things to the children for their perverted lust, nothing of which I'm going to mention here, despite the damage they were causing to the kids.

After a week or so of this work, we were able to return to our teams as much wiser and chastened officers. I often wondered what such an inquiry did to officers who had to do that type of work, day after day, month after month, sometimes for years on end.

Back on shift meant no weekends off again. Many of my days off were also being cancelled simply because I was a PSU officer. Public order trained officers were in great demand, and were often needed in Cambridge, due perhaps to some contentious speaker at the Cambridge Union Society, or illegal raves which were all the rave (!) back then. There were numerous large public events that also had the potential for disorder, and I was often called up to be on standby in case disorder did indeed occur. And this wasn't just in Cambridge – we could be sent anywhere we were needed in the *county*, and Mutual Aid meant we could be sent anywhere in the *country*.

Many a time, I, like others, had considered hanging up my riot helmet just to free up my rare, rostered weekend. However, the tasks of a PSU officer were far too enjoyable to let others do them, and I just couldn't resign from it, despite my desire for a weekend off.

The Cambridge Midsummer Fair was just one of the many reasons for cancelled rest days. Held every June on the city common ground for the last 800 years, this previously quaint family event was now regularly hijacked by tens of thousands of young people intent on getting stoned and drunk en masse. This often led to incidents of a nasty, violent nature, which were extremely unwelcome to the local residents. Hence the need for standby riot trained officers such as myself, in case it all kicked off.

Over the years as a foot-patrol officer, I had often skirted the border between the fair and city centre beats. The gardens of the houses alongside the venue were often used by the fair folk as toilets or places to shoot up out of sight. The mere sight of a lone uniformed officer walking along those back paths often resulted in a starburst from those perfectly manicured gardens. I knew that once I had left, they'd be back, but I felt I owed it to the long-suffering residents.

This particular June was a hot one. In fact, it was the hottest day of the year so far, and I was in full PSU gear. The sweat was rolling off me. So, you can imagine how delighted I was to leave the busy hubbub of the rear yard, which was bustling with cops and police vehicles, and go back to the cool darkness of the basement to retrieve some kit from the store room for our van. As it was too heavy to carry back upstairs in that heat, I pinged the lift.

It took a while for the lift to arrive, but, when it did, it was occupied by four officers whom I recognised instantly. They were disguised as fairgoers and known in the job as 'test-purchasers'. It was their job to get in amongst the festival folk and look for the drug dealers, then to purchase drugs from them, which would be 'tested' and confirmed as drugs, resulting in a nod being given to standby teams who would go in, arrest the dealer and seize the drugs. This often happened in the midst of large crowds, and the potential for disorder and danger to officers was huge.

The officers in the lift were surprised that it hadn't stopped at the ground floor to let them off, but had continued on to the basement instead. They stepped back inside almost immediately and made room for me. One of the guys in the lift was a rather wayward ex-Caribbean Police officer now working with us. Another was a rather good-looking female officer from one of the other shifts, called Emma, who, I noticed, was wearing a very low cut top, which did little to hide her feminine form. They were all full of the joys of the fair, and they all certainly looked the part.

The lift was a tiny affair with an ambitiously stated five-person capacity. I was the fifth in, and, as I dragged my heavy bag in behind me, I pushed the button for the ground floor where we all wanted to be. I can't say that I was in a particularly good mood, given that I was having to work on my day off, and on such a gorgeous day too. Sweat was dripping down my back. My own sourness contrasted markedly with the good-natured banter and behaviour of the test-purchasers, who were clearly getting in the mood for the festival. So much so that, as the lift ascended, the Caribbean guy began bouncing up and down in a kind of excited dance. I was just about to ask him not to do that when the unthinkable happened.

The lift jolted to a sudden halt midway between the basement and the first floor.

Silence.

Then giggles.

The bouncing culprit pushed the 'In Case of Emergency' button.

More silence.

Followed by more giggles.

Had they just spent the last hour at the frigging pub or what? I was now

273

ultra-irritated. It was hot, I'd be late, we'd be laughed at, and for what?

Dancing boy took the initiative and spoke into his covert radio, asking for 'Talk-through off' before explaining our predicament to the control room. 'Talk-through off' meant that no other officer would – thankfully – be able to hear what he said, in this case to save our blushes. However, everybody *could* hear the radio operator's response, and it soon became clear to all the extra officers on duty that day what the problem was and where. Especially when the operator said she'd call for the fire brigade to attend to help release us.

The fire station was right next door to the police station. Firefighters were advised of the situation and asked to quietly 'pop round' to help us out. Meanwhile, as the interior temperature rocketed, we stood uncomfortably in the confined space. With so many people in the lift on the hottest day of the year, it was clearly going to get very hot very soon. We'd need to be released before long.

A moment of panic rose in my throat like vomit, and, as I turned away to hide my discomfort, I came face to face with Emma, just as a bead of sweat broke free from her throat and rolled teasingly down, vanishing into her low cut top.

I looked away. Slowly.

And then we heard it. The siren got louder and louder as the fire engine arrived in our police car park. It must have taken them twenty-five seconds to drive from their garage into our car park, no more than one hundred yards away, and they did so with full lights and sirens. The bastards had now got the attention of the hundreds of police officers milling around the grounds and within the station.

Despite their overly dramatic arrival, they were good at what they did. Before long, they had the doors open, and we had to clamber out of the lift between floors, all dignity forgotten, to applause and cheers from the multitude now gathered there. I was so irritated with the whole thing that I stomped off to my PSU van, where my colleagues burst out laughing once they realised I'd been involved in the drama.

I wasn't sure who I was most angry with: the dancing police officer who created this incident in the first place, or with the fire brigade, for getting us out of there so publicly. Or, just the job.

Whatever it was, it was just another nail in my sharp-end policing coffin.

274

COP OUT Chapter Three

THE MORE THE ORGANISATION MESSED ME AROUND by cancelling my rest days, the more I yearned for a change of job, just to have some kind of personal life. I knew that promotion to sergeant would not help me with time off, but it was a completely different type of job to the one I'd been doing for the past six or seven years, and one that I was beginning to relish having a go at. A change is as good as a rest, after all.

My law knowledge had already been pretty high as a constable. I can still recall today (twenty-seven years after studying them!) most of the legal definitions I'd learnt verbatim at police college. I studied when I was able to, and also took advantage of numerous opportunities during my career to discuss points of law with other officers, thus silently comparing my knowledge with theirs.

I believed in myself, and I knew I could qualify for promotion, if I just tried. I was reaching a point in my career where all of my experience and knowledge would stand me in good stead as a sergeant, if I could just pass the exam.

Promotion to sergeant was no easy task, though. The service had relied solely on a knowledge based exam since policing had been invented, until, in 1991, during my career, it chose to update the promotion exam system and give it a fancy new name: OSPRE (Objective Structured Performance Related Examination). Once I looked into what was now required, I realised that I should really have taken the old exam pre-1991.

The first part was the old multiple choice theory exam. This was a test of legal and procedural law consisting of one hundred and fifty questions to be completed in three hours. It was held locally, once a year in March, usually in the station gym. If you failed it, you had to wait another twelve months to try again, thus adding a one-year delay to your career as a sergeant. I knew of some constables who sat the exam year after year after year.

Once you'd passed part one, you then had to pass part two. This new concept was a practical exam taken in August at a national centre somewhere in England, which was a ninety-minute exam consisting of various role-plays. The idea was that knowing the law wasn't enough to make a good sergeant, so a practical element was incorporated to test performance. Faced with a relatively new process, few had any idea of how to pass this weird second part. Part two was also only held annually, and if you failed it you had to wait another year for the subsequent exam, thus adding another year to the process. If you failed it twice in a row, you had to retake and pass part one again before having another go at part two. It was a long process if you *were* successful first time at each exam, but if you failed *any* stage, it was seriously long.

Once you managed to pass both parts of the exam, you were then qualified as a sergeant, although that didn't automatically mean you would become one, just that you *could* be one if the boss saw fit, or if there was really no alternative available but you.

Needless to say, this absurdly complicated annual process could add years to your life as a PC because an initial failure at part one followed by a failure at part two, twice, meant having to resit part one. That added a mind-boggling four years before you would be available to start the whole process over again. No wonder Cambridgeshire had a shortage of sergeants.

Seeing as I was then approaching eight years as a PC, which is when my annual salary increase would become just biennial, and, as front-end policing was seriously wearing me down, I knew I'd have to consider starting the process before long. On promotion to sergeant, not only would I get a new job, new challenge, and renewed motivation, but my salary would jump to the highest rate for a PC, followed by annual increments again, raising my salary step-by-step, within five years, to that of a newly qualified inspector. Financially, it was a no-brainer.

However, I had no idea of exactly how much more law I'd need to study to pass the sergeants' exam. I knew that what I'd studied to be a constable would be insufficient, as sergeants had to study laws that constables had no need to study, and the laws we did know had to be studied at a much greater depth as a sergeant.

Because I was curious as to the level of the exam, and of how much study time I'd need to set aside to pass it, I made a choice. As the exam was free, and I wasn't quite prepared to be a sergeant, I decided to sit the theory exam without any study beforehand with the clear understanding that I'd fail it. The idea was that I'd get first hand experience of how difficult the exam actually was, and thus target my studies accordingly.

So, it was at seven years of service that I, along with a dozen other constables, sat the exam in the gymnasium at the police station. A few had been trying to pass it for years and years, whilst others were sitting it for the first time. We were a right old mix of potential sergeants, and one couldn't help but look around the exam room and contemplate what sort of sergeant each candidate would make.

As expected, I failed, but – surprising even my overly confident self – by just six percent. I had come so close to passing the exam without any extra study! However, I then knew that I'd have to pass the exam at my next attempt to avoid being counted amongst those old sweats trying to do so year after year.

After that initial failure, I had one year to fully prepare myself for the following year's exam. The studying increased week on week, even though shift work left me constantly tired, and what little social life I had between the unsocial hours took a serious hit.

Between the studies and my wife's complaints, life as a bobby still went on.

It was around this time that Neil joined me on the shift, and, due to our common interest in law, my own knowledge of higher law grew exponentially.

However, being a senior on shift still allowed me to have the occasional 'jolly', as special jobs were named.

A 'Category A' prisoner had been brought to the station for interview one morning, and would need to be returned to Bedford Prison in the evening. Category A meant that 'his escape would be highly dangerous to the public or national security', so special security measures were taken when moving such prisoners.

"Dave, would you take three lads with you and pop him back to HMP Bedford?" the sergeant said, nonchalantly, towards the end of our shift. "John'll go with you. He knows the way."

Sounded like a good jolly. It wasn't too far, and we might even incur a bit of overtime. We all liked a bit of extra pay at the end of the month.

Now, if you've read all the books in this series, you can see where this is going. The sergeant had completely failed to take into account the 'Dave Factor'.

Bedford wasn't that far away, and we knew we could probably be there and back before the end of the shift at 11.00pm. *If nothing went wrong.*

So, I supervised the prisoner, who was still handcuffed, as he was put into the small cage at the back of my minibus. Two officers had to sit in the rear to keep him under constant observation, whilst John-who-knew-the-way sat up front with me as navigator. None of us had any inkling as to what he was doing time for, and little did we care. This was going to be a quick transport job across the county border to Bedford Prison. Our instructions were simple: don't stop for anything.

As we left Cambridgeshire and entered Bedfordshire, we followed procedure and changed radio channel to Bedfordshire Police. We called in, feeling rather grand with ourselves by telling them we were a 'Cat A' en route to HMP Bedford, and were feeling relaxed as we approached the outskirts of Bedford.

And then it started.

Just retching at first. Then, actual, stinking vomiting. Then, gagging – awful gagging followed by a heavy fall to the floor as he began convulsing and making horrendous noises. We knew this wasn't normal and he was either seriously ill – maybe dying – or a very good actor. And if he was acting, what was his purpose? There was no way I was going to stop the police van on the side of the road and check on the Cat A prisoner, nor ask the two in the back to open the inner door to check on him, in case he was armed with something sharp. If he escaped, we'd *probably* all be out of a job, but if he died, we'd *definitely* all be out of a job.

As the senior, this was all on me now. We were entering unknown territory in unfamiliar surroundings. John contacted Beds Police via the radio and told them to advise HMP Bedford we were inbound with one of theirs who appeared to be ill or was play-acting.

I stepped on the gas and followed John's directions towards the prison.

Five minutes later, Beds Police called us back and said that the prison would *not* accept their prisoner if he was ill.

WTF?

"Take the prisoner directly to Bedford Hospital. We'll notify them of your imminent arrival, and have local officers meet you there."

OK, OK, that sounds like a good solution.

"OK, John, the fastest route to the hospital please?" I said, my worry clear for all to hear, as I activated the sirens to help clear a way through a line of traffic as we approached the outskirts of Bedford Town.

"How the fuck would I know where the *hospital* is?" replied John, who was also becoming stressed. "I don't know Bedford at all, just the way to the *prison!*"

It suddenly made sense. John had been a gaoler for a time for the Cambridge Courts, and had spent many days ferrying prisoners back and forth between the courts and Bedford Prison. That's why he'd been picked to come along – he knew the way to the prison. But, *only* the prison.

Bugger!

Driving an unwieldy police van on blue lights at speed, with a Cat A prisoner dying in the back or planning his escape, whilst not knowing where the hell you are or where you're going, and with all other officers looking to you for a solution, might sound like your worst kind of nightmare, but for most police officers it might be considered just another day at the office.

Then I saw it: 'A&E 3 miles'.

Thank God for signposts! I managed to follow the signs all the way to the Accident and Emergency wing of the hospital, whilst driving at speed on blue lights in an unknown city, and quite possibly being pursued by unknown conspirators! On arrival, I was soon parked in a reserved bay. I told the guys to lock the doors as I ran into the hospital and up to the desk.

Panting for breath, I managed to get it out: "We've got that Cat A prisoner for you!"

The nurse looked at me and frowned.

"Cat A? *What* Cat A? Nobody told us about *any* Cat A prisoner ..."

I looked around for the promised Bedfordshire Officers or Prison Officers but there were none.

To cut a long story short, I managed to get the prisoner into the department, in a room of his own, with our officers posted at the door. After about thirty minutes, a couple of local officers ambled along the corridor and spoke to me.

"Are you the guys with the Cat A?" one of them asked, disinterestedly.

"Nope," I said, as I called my lads out of the room. "*You* are. Have fun!"

We were back in Cambridge before the end of the shift with another tale to tell.

Such testing incidents helped make me the man I am today, and I'm not complaining or apologising. If you can cope with those sorts of incidents, you can cope with anything, and, for that, I'll be eternally grateful to the police. But I'll never accept that they should have buggered up my personal life so much by routinely cancelling my rest days when they fell on a weekend.

This was partly the reason I began to desire change so much. And change came out of the blue, with a typical police reorganisation that required somebody of my experience and skills to volunteer for.

And so I did.

COP OUT Chapter Four

THE CITY CENTRE OF CAMBRIDGE HAD ALWAYS BEEN the responsibility of the on-shift team of officers, who had responsibility for the whole of the city as well as the centre. Under the reorganisation, the city centre was to be policed by its own team of officers, named – with typical police logic – the City Centre Unit. This new team of officers would also have sole responsibility for tutoring new police recruits.

Although I feared I might miss the action on response work, I loved the idea.

First, the city centre was so small it could be policed on foot. That meant no more racing around from emergency call to emergency call – and that was attractive in itself. I could get back to the grass roots of policing, stopping and talking and being nice to complete strangers. In a panda, you usually raced up, arrested somebody and spent the rest of your shift in the station. The city centre had no real need for vehicles. Any emergency calls could always be dealt with by one of the response cars covering the newly formed Northern Sector or Southern Sector.

Second, to really train new recruits properly meant being away from response work. Racing from job to job was no way to gently introduce somebody to the procedures necessary to progress to confirmation. I recalled my violent first day out on patrol and realised that that kind of incident would be much less frequent now. Being on foot-patrol meant we could generally be left to our own devices. That allowed us to focus on quality training that would ensure recruits got all their boxes ticked to move onto the next phase of their training. During research for this book, I see that some of my wards are now at the top tier of police management: chief constables and deputies, and such like.

There was one other aspect that interested me, too. The unit wasn't allocated sufficient officers for twenty-four hour coverage, so a rather strange arrangement was decided on – the new unit wouldn't have to work nights. From 1.00am, the city centre would revert to the responsibility of the other two shifts that were responsible for the northern and southern halves. As much as I loved working nights for the action it usually offered up, I seriously hated sleeping days, so I was totally sold on the idea.

The new job was so different. We arrived at work and casually self-briefed, knowing that if an alarm activated on our patch, a car would be sent to it, and not one of us on foot. We had time to do all the necessary paperwork, and time for a coffee too. I smiled as I remembered the amount of enquiries I use to have to handle at any given time, and dropping the files as I raced off to yet another urgent call.

We were able to fully brief each probationer, make a plan for the day – generally going out on foot-patrol – and enjoy the job. It was just what I needed after years on response work. And, not working night shift meant I was less tired than before, and was able to focus on my sergeants' exam studies.

Don't get me wrong – I hadn't retired. Policing the city centre was obviously a great change in pace for me, but, like all city centres, something interesting could be just around the corner, and usually when you least expected it to be.

That day, I'd been on my own in the centre, chasing down errant cyclists, stopping car drivers who had taken a chance at cutting through the pedestrian zones, taking statements from shoplifting victims, and generally feeling good about my decision to move. It was mid-afternoon, the sun was shining, and I was getting hungry. I decided to head back to the station for a late lunch, knowing full well that I wouldn't have to stop mid-lunch and race off to another intrusive emergency. I could continue eating *my* lunch even if others abandoned theirs.

As I walked along Regent Street, a long straight road full of shops and offices, my attention was drawn to a man walking in the same direction about a hundred yards ahead of me. There was something about his gait and purpose that caught my experienced eye.

He was in his mid- to late twenties, stockily built, and of medium height. He smashed his way between a young couple walking towards him, who looked back at him in surprise and disgust.

I quickened my pace to try and catch the man, but he was walking very quickly. As I passed the couple, I indicated that I would deal with him.

It was obvious that I wouldn't be able to catch him unless I broke into a run. *Cops Don't Run* made sense at that moment – it wouldn't have been correct for a uniformed officer to run down the High Street in broad daylight.

I asked over the radio if any vehicle was in the vicinity to help me intercept him, but none was available. As he seemed intent on shoulder-barging his way into any person or couple walking towards him, I decided I had to catch him up before he hurt somebody.

Have you ever seen a cop running whilst trying to look like he isn't? Well, that's what I was doing, so as not to draw too much attention to the situation, but at the same time managing to gain ground on the angry young man.

After a few hundred yards, he turned off the street and cut across a large green in front of the police station, known as Parker's Piece. It was here that I was able to catch up, eventually reaching him mid-green.

He failed to acknowledge my calls for him to stop, and continued to storm forwards. I had no choice – I reached up and took hold of his shoulder, demanding he stop for a police officer.

I was surprised by the strength of the guy as he shrugged me off and continued onward. I updated the control room, and went in again for the stop. Once again, he violently shrugged me off.

I decided there and then that he had to be arrested, and warned him under the Public Order Act that, if he continued, he'd get nicked.

On he went.

As I took his arm to stop him, he once again became aggressive and silently threatening towards me, and I could detect from our brief contacts that he was a well-built and very strong young man.

I knew I had to arrest him, and I knew he would become very violent on arrest. I also knew that no other officer had responded to my call for help.

So, I gave him one last chance. I grabbed hold of him, and, as expected, he responded violently towards me. I took him straight down to the floor in an attempt to get an arm lock on him, but he was quick, angry, and very strong. We were soon facing each other in the dirt, before standing up and facing each other again, waiting to see who'd make the first move.

I released my CS Spray for only the second time in my career, spraying it directly into his face. It had no effect except to make him even angrier, and down we both went again, wrestling on the grass in a sunny park, surrounded by foreign students and afternoon sun-worshippers.

This was getting ridiculous. Clearly the gas went unnoticed by the offender, but he was covered in the stuff, and we were grappling around on the floor, so the spray began to get onto me. My eyes stung, and tears streamed down my face, and, as we both stood up facing each other yet again, ready for the next match, I realised that my lack of vision was putting me at a dangerous disadvantage. And there was no knowing what this guy was capable of.

I managed to put out a 10/16 emergency call before we began grappling again, then back down we went. I knew it wouldn't be long before help arrived, especially with the station no more than two hundred yards away.

I seemed to be getting the better of him, despite not really being able to see him, and glanced up to see if help was on its way. I recall seeing a blurred block of high visibility vests increasing in size as a flock of special constables descended on us from the station. I don't know if it was my arm lock, or the fact we were now surrounded by six or seven (special) constables, but the fight eventually went out of the guy.

I slammed on the quick-cuffs and shouted to my helpers: "Here, take him. I can't see shit."

I then tried to remove the CS gas from my clothes and skin by jumping around and waving my arms like a demented chicken, as per the training. I have no idea what the general public made of events on Parker's Piece that afternoon, but Mr Angry was eventually charged with a public order offence. It turned out he had been blind drunk in the middle of the afternoon and on his way home.

As for me, I swore that I'd never use CS spray ever again, and I never did.

COP OUT Chapter Five

CAMBRIDGE WAS, AND IS, A PICTURESQUE CITY and often attracted TV crews for this very reason. It also attracted numerous stars and actors, not to mention those who lived there.

Silent Witness, featuring Professor Sam Ryan, was a BBC TV series about a fictional forensic pathologist working in Cambridge. The series was filmed in and around Cambridge, and, occasionally, they needed real police help to deal with road closures, crowd control, and so on. The BBC paid for the officer's overtime, and it was all done on a voluntary basis (no extra cops were used from the box in the basement). It was a good series, and I loved to watch it. Amanda Burton played the lead role, and I must admit to an attraction to her, partly because she played a doctor. I've always been attracted to smart women.

As previously stated, I hated working on my days off, but the money on offer to a city centre officer was too good to turn down. Life was currently much easier and relaxed, I had plenty of rest days, and I'd also get to meet Amanda Burton.

I'd never been anywhere near a film set before, but I was soon standing on the beautiful riverside location known as Quayside in Cambridge, observing Amanda Burton sitting at a café table next to the river, filming a scene with her co-star. TV paraphernalia surrounded them, and the general public watched from a discreet distance. I stood nearby in case I was needed, but to be honest, I was a waste of money. There was no need for a police officer to be present at all, but I wasn't complaining.

Amanda chatted with her co-star for a few minutes before another actor approached their table and spoke to them. This was repeated numerous times with cameras recording the same scene over and over again from different angles. Having watched Amanda from various angles for over two hours, and with no police work to do whatsoever, I was beginning to get seriously bored.

Finally, they decided to 'wrap up', and Amanda stood up. She was tiny. It amazed me that this never came across on the TV!

After lunch we spent a few hours in a cobbled street doing more or less the same. I was thoroughly fed up, but I did appreciate the opportunity to see a familiar TV show being created, despite never – to this day – seeing that riverside scene on the screen. The additional money was also worth the boredom.

One day, I was selected to take a camera crew out on patrol with me for the morning, so that they could follow me around and film me. It was for a debate programme about some proposed changes to the police service (yet more changes). I recall walking about a hundred yards along the cobbled surface of Trinity Street followed by a camera positioned just inches away from my black-booted heels. For several hours, they filmed everything I did – dealing with vagrants, stopping errant cyclists, posing with tourists and answering questions.

They told me the timings of the programme, and, later that week, I eagerly settled into the sofa with my wife to see my moment of fame.

Four seconds. Of my heels. I should have realised after the *Silent Witness* experience that the three hours of filming would be edited down to about three minutes of the TV episode, if that. I stood no chance of becoming a celebrity that day.

Celebrities often came to speak to me in the centre …

Rod Hull (without Emu) was performing at the Cambridge Arts Theatre, and strolled up to me to ask for directions. It took me a second to register who he was.

Rory McGrath, TV personality, comedian and writer, was a resident of Cambridge. I liked his humour, and would often see him around Cambridge, going from pub to pub. I saw him so often that I would wave to him, and he'd wave back. Rory, if you're reading this, I was the copper who used to wave to you from across the road. Just so you know.

The late Professor Stephen Hawking needs no introduction. I often saw him around Cambridge, and even attended an intruder alarm at his house. He wasn't home, but I had to check his house fully to ensure nothing was amiss.

A colleague of mine was good friends with a local girl. Dina Carroll, the singer, lived in a flat in the centre, and my mate Rick (and whoever was with him) often called in for coffee. That way, lots of officers got to meet her. It was at around this time that her amazing voice propelled her to national stardom. I'd often seen her around in her Suzuki jeep – which was soon changed to a top of the range Land Rover following her success. Sadly, I never got to meet her through my mate, but, along with a load of officers, I went to see her in concert at her home gig at the Cambridge Corn Exchange. She won The Brit Award for British Female Solo Artist in 1994. After numerous hits, and two albums hitting number two in the UK, she slowly vanished from the music scene. Such a shame. I'm listening to her music now, and it brings back so many happy memories of my time at Cambridge. Wonderful voice.

Fame for me did eventually arrive, and it came from an unexpected source. One afternoon, I was asked to get a company minibus and head out to the M11 motorway as it passed by Cambridge. A traffic patrol had stopped an articulated lorry due to the fact that lots of faces were peering out of the back curtain. Coming from the docks on the east coast, the driver had driven inland, completely unaware of the stowaways hidden in his trailer, who'd concealed themselves whilst in France.

I pulled up behind the vehicle on the hard shoulder and approached the back. By this time, clearly tired people were disembarking awkwardly from the rear: men, women, kids and babies. Naturally, I went to help, and was handed numerous babies as mums clambered down. I directed them all to my minibus, and, once we were sure we had them all, I transferred them to a local charity where they were given showers and food, and documented.

I was completely unaware of the TV camera crew that had seen events unfolding before my arrival, and were now filming babies being handed to the copper at the back of the truck.

For months afterwards, friends and associates would often say 'I saw you on TV last night!' Whenever a news item involved illegal immigrants on trucks (which was almost every other day), they would use the library footage of me with the babies. I must admit fame got to be a bit routine for a while.

COP OUT Chapter Six

THE 1990S WAS A DECADE OF HUGE REFORMS within the police service across the country. Little by little the service was modernising like never before. Police drivers were being given the tools to get through traffic (sirens and lights), and clothing and equipment were being looked at to make them more fit-for-purpose. And pointless workloads were being tendered out to private companies, for example releasing two highly trained, traffic police officers from dawdling behind a wide convoy through the county. Not anymore, the companies would have to pay for private contractors to do that kind of mind-numbing work from then on.

Officer safety was still a concern to the rank and file – those facing the danger on a daily basis – but less so to the office-bound senior management. A number of frontline officers managed to receive donated protective equipment, such as heavy-duty cast-off stab vests, from their counterparts in the USA. That's right, British police officers were being given obsolete body protection kit from American cops because it wasn't being provided by our own government. This seriously rankled with the Thin Blue Line.

One night whilst off duty, I was in the Market Square, slightly the worse for wear, patiently standing in a queue for a kebab at the van that provided the best kebabs in Cambridge. Naturally, for such kebabs, the queue was always long, and there was the usual mix of locals and university folk, all very drunk. I knew from the statistics just how many fights happened there at that time of night, and was probably the one person in that queue who would be alert to the first hint of violence. I just wanted to get my kebab and go.

One lad just ahead of me caught my attention. He spoke with a very posh voice, and was wearing a very expensive, state of the art, ballistic and knife-proof, all-in-one vest over his glad rags. It must have cost a fortune. He looked like a complete knob, and would have been irritating without the vest, but, with it, he was drawing the wrong kind of attention to himself.

"Sorry, why are you wearing that?" I asked, curious and annoyed.

"What? This?" he replied, apparently pleased that somebody had noticed it. He then told me all about the ultra-protection it was offering him whilst he stood in the kebab queue in Cambridge Market Square waiting for his order.

"OK," I said. "What threat do you think you face here that others don't? Are you afraid that somebody might jump the queue ahead of you and shoot you if you protest?"

For some reason this stating of the obvious seemed to irk him.

"Look," he said, seriously. "My daddy is something high up in the Home Office and that puts me at grave risk, so, yeah, I'm like wearing this to protect me from unknown threats – something you wouldn't understand, chummy."

Fortunately, I wasn't so drunk that my mate couldn't reason with me, so this boy in his highly expensive vest lived to see another day.

That kind of confrontation could easily see a seasoned cop lose his job. I've often wondered where that vest ended up that night, and I'm certain he didn't donate it to his local police.

A few weeks after this encounter, I was on duty, earning good overtime, at a racecourse in Newmarket.

The twelve of us, all volunteers, were there 'for traffic control purposes' – essentially at the end of the racing when thousands of cars and buses would attempt to exit the racecourse simultaneously. We were expected to expedite departures at the various exits dotted around the course. That night, the reality turned out to be quite different.

Coachloads of people travelled to the races from all over the UK. Many had been drinking on their respective coaches from as early as 9.00am. They then spent the whole day at the races, drinking some more until the bars suddenly closed at 6.00pm.

Before the bar closures, the officers on duty had various tasks to deal with: theft from vehicles, drunk driving incidents, flare-ups in bars, people behaving badly, accidents, and so on – a typical Friday night in any UK city, but overlaid onto a nice racecourse during the daytime, with more expensive brands of car, and people wearing ties.

At 6.00pm, officers were required to make their way to their pre-assigned exit points to ease the flow of traffic, leaving behind a couple of bobbies to keep a watchful eye on the bar areas as they closed. Now, you can see what's about to happen here, right?

As is the norm when people know what time the bars close and want to cram one last drink in, vast crowds were now hanging around with two or three pints each to quaff before getting onto the transport to head home. Coaches usually contain about forty people. So, a typical scene might see forty drunk party-goers from Newcastle standing in one corner, and another forty from Brighton, with forty more from Liverpool milling between these two groups, all downing the last copious amount of alcohol available to them before climbing aboard for the long, sleepy journey home.

We were all seasoned cops that day, and we all knew what would happen next, and we always questioned the sense of the course management for putting ten officers at the car park exits, which were all over two hundred yards away from the bars. But, rich men in their Rolls Royces and Bentleys could not be left to queue in traffic. Heaven forbid.

However, as the course management were paying our overtime that day, they were effectively our bosses, so we all had to do as we were told. I found myself patrolling the bars on my own, smiling and encouraging the revellers to drink up, to move on, and get on their coaches. It was only when everybody was on their respective coaches that we would be able to relax.

I was in one outdoor bar area with about three thousand obliterated drunks, and my colleague was in another.

It was the sudden movement of the mass of people that caught my eye, just before the screams of the absurdly drunk ladies, and the sound of smashing glasses. I later learnt that one member of one coach had stumbled into a guy from another coach, knocking his three pints from his hands.

Within seconds, forty drunk people were fighting another forty drunk people. I put out a call to this effect, knowing that I would have one more officer with me within minutes, but it'd take a while longer for the other officers to trot in from their distant car park assignments. I decided to wait until the other officer found me, but, as usual, events took any form of control out of my hands.

The Geordies were clearly much better at this than the shandy-drinking southerners, and the battle suddenly became a rout as the crowd from Brighton began backing away before turning and running, followed by numerous airborne objects like pints of beer and plastic garden furniture.

I was watching carefully to see if I could identify any ringleaders – the ones causing the problem. If, once others arrived, we could arrest a few of them, then that might have a calming effect on the rest of the crowd. They had no idea we were just twelve officers, and would fear having to spend a night in a Cambridge cell while their coach headed north without them.

As the surging crowd passed me, the pursuers stopped, turned, and surrounded one of the enemy who had tripped over a *Coca-Cola*-branded plastic chair in his attempt to escape. As they ran into the curled up body, and began kicking any part of it they could reach, I reacted without thinking.

"10/16."

Putting out an emergency assistance call was always a wise thing to do before heading into such a crowd alone. I briefly pictured my colleagues suddenly having to break into a sprint across the car parks, and cursing me. I pushed my way through the aggressors towards the prone figure, and, not quite sure what to do once there, I instinctively stood over him like a protective bodyguard.

The miracle-like manner of my appearance surprised the drunken, baying mob, and they paused in surprise on seeing me, backing away slightly.

It took them about two seconds to realise that I was alone and therefore heavily outnumbered. They began moving in towards me and the apparently unconscious body beneath my legs. I drew my side-handled baton and held it up across my shoulder, acting confidently and confirming with my eyes that I would strike any man – or woman – who came near me. *Us*.

Up until that point, I had never drawn my new baton in anger and I didn't know then that I would have the baton out in the strike pose for the next hour or so. Neither did I know what a lot of people I would actually have to strike that night. It was like the best training course ever, and the two of us firmly bonded that night, forming a mutual respect for each other that would last for years.

One or two of the more foolish drunks came in and slung drunken kicks at the prone figure, and these became my first targets. I struck hefty blows across the sides of their knees for their troubles, just as I'd been trained to do. It worked! It clearly hurt like hell because they yelped in pain and fell back into the crowd holding their knees, and were never seen again.

In fact, my growing confidence with the baton seemed to be having a marvellous effect on the crowd, and, before long, the surrounding throng began to regroup on one side of the body. That, of course, just meant that the other group were growing braver, and they began encroaching again, behind me.

By now, somebody – I don't recall who, maybe a St John Ambulance staff member – was tending to the casualty at my feet as I continually feinted at the slow-moving group of men in front of me, and at the mob behind me.

As I waited for back-up to arrive, I reassessed the situation. First, the priority here was the casualty and his continued well-being. He was being attended to by qualified staff, but was still in danger from the mob on one side, whilst his own mob on the other side would have probably tried to retrieve him if they could have, possibly exacerbating any injury he may have had, and he did seem badly hurt.

Next, I had drawn my baton for the first time and actively used it on several people. All the training I'd received about using the baton on anybody had been about justification. If you hit somebody, you were certain to injure them, and would have to justify this later, maybe even in a court of law. The injury sustained had to be commensurate with the threat perceived. Forty raving drunks on one side, thirty-nine on the other? I quickly grasped that I could do more or less what I wanted with the baton and be vindicated in any court of law.

Finally, I thought about how we were going to go about ending this war – what was the solution? I knew we'd soon be twelve police officers against the eighty or so aggressors, and that at least one double-crewed traffic car was on its way, but we still had to get these clowns onto their respective coaches and heading off in opposite directions, and with the minimum of arrests.

Why no arrests? Simple maths. One detainee would take two officers away from the incident. We simply couldn't afford to arrest anybody who didn't totally need arresting that night, and I'd been unable to identify anybody in the confusing melee who justified such action.

It did mean, however, that to resolve the situation we'd have to be much more aggressive ourselves to get them to comply.

For each use of force an officer employs, he is required to make a pocket book entry to justify it. I briefly thought of the extra overtime I would earn that night completing entries for each baton strike made, once I got back to the safety of the station.

Just prior to the arrival of the first supporting officers, I briefly marvelled at the affect the baton was having on the mob. I was able to keep them all away from the casualty and one another just by acting as if I was about to strike somebody, or by actually striking them if they ignored my threat. I suspected this wouldn't have been possible had I been holding my original issue wooden truncheon.

Thwack! Another pocket book entry.

As troops arrived, I quickly briefed them as they drew their own batons to support me. The crowd soon began to realise that they would get hurt for sure if they continued to push their luck against an ever-increasing number of us – after all, they'd seen me doing pretty well alone.

By now, we were able to threaten them with arrest, even if we didn't mean it, and prod and push them towards their own coaches. Numerous skirmishes broke out in the coach park, and officers responded firmly and decisively to keep them moving. One drunk in front of me grasped a smaller guy's face in his huge palm, claiming that he'd spat at him. I shouted at him to release the man's face, but he continued squeezing hard, his fingertips digging into the sides of the man's skull. I had the baton extended along my outer arm, and I recalled a training strike like a downward punch, but with the baton hitting the subject and not the base of my fist. His wrist was within easy reach of a downward strike. I warned him once more and still he refused.

Thwack! Another pocket book entry.

He did curse at the pain, but the follow-up jab to the back of the ribs was the blow that encouraged him to get on his coach, and to do so quickly.

Before long, both coaches were heading towards separate exits, and the officers present were able to take a breather and take stock of events. And then the racecourse manager marched up and told us all to get on the car park exits and stop hanging around in the coach park.

At the end of the month, my salary was considerably boosted by that day's overtime, along with more overtime policing Cambridge United Football Club matches, and the handful of prisoners I'd had to deal with toward the ends of my shifts.

But, Newmarket Races? I never volunteered to go there again but I did have a newfound respect for our latest defensive equipment.

COP OUT Chapter Seven

I RECALL EXACTLY WHAT I WAS DOING on the afternoon of 19th November 1997, and not because Michael Hutchence killed himself that week. I was walking along the corridor from the City Centre Unit offices when the radio called me up and told me to call my brother at home. Now, I have four brothers, and 'at home' is a small town called Uttoxeter in the north Midlands. We rarely called each other, and when we did, it was usually just to pass a message. That's men for you.

I knew that, if somebody from my family had gone to the trouble of finding out the police station number, calling the control room, and asking the control room to get a message to me to call them at home, they weren't going to be asking how I was getting on.

I found an empty office, closed the door and sat down. I stared at the phone. All I could think of was 'Is it mum or dad?' My father had had a heart attack several years earlier, but he was on meds and controlling his diet, had given up smoking, etc., so he should have been healthier than ever.

I picked up the phone, took a deep breath, and called the only brother I had with a phone.

Peter answered.

"What's up?" I asked. Peter had to do something that I, as a cop, hated having to do.

"It's dad," he said. "He died."

It took a second to sink in. My father was gone, I'd never see him again.

Then, infuriatingly, the practicalities of being a cop took over to help me to deal with the discomfort of this new pain.

"What happened?" I asked.

"He had a nap, then came downstairs, spoke to mum, and just collapsed."

"Heart attack?"

Peter was obviously distressed at my police style of questioning.

"I don't really wanna talk about it," he said, his voice quavering. I realised how insensitive I was being, and stopped with the questions, reverting back to being a human again.

I later learnt that, when dad collapsed, mum knew he had died instantly and didn't know what to do, so she called my younger brother Peter. He asked her if she had called an ambulance and she said she hadn't. He told her to do so, and began to make his way to mum's house on his mobility scooter, and was the first person to arrive there, some fifteen minutes after beginning his slow, grim, solo journey.

I hung up the phone and made my way to my sergeant's office. I told him the news and he told me to go home, saying he would arrange for somebody to drive me. I declined the offer of a lift, but drove home and told my wife, and my daughter who was eight years old at the time. My dad had always wanted a daughter but ended up with five sons and three grandsons. My daughter was the first girl born to his family, and the two of them had a special connection.

A week later, I prepared to drive home for his funeral. I recall getting out of the car to fuel up at the garage at the end of my road, only to inadvertently drop kick my Nokia mobile phone that had been sitting on my lap. It flew across the garage forecourt and broke into half a dozen pieces. Miraculously, it all fitted back together again and worked as before.

I arrived at my mum's house to discover numerous relatives in attendance, some of whom I hadn't seen for years. Everybody was there. Everybody except for dad. I said my hellos, but there were so many people in the house that I ended up waiting outside the front door in a bit of a daze at the surreal situation I found myself in.

After a short while, the hearse pulled up with a coffin on the back, clearly visible. Reality hit me and I welled up: my father was in there, and I'd never see him again.

Uttoxeter has a large church – a place I only ever went into with the school on religious celebrations, none of which I took seriously. I recall it being a huge, cold and empty place. I only ever go into church for weddings, funerals and christenings, and even then reluctantly. That day I would be entering for my father's funeral.

My three brothers and I each took hold of a corner of the coffin whilst Peter walked ahead. As we entered the church, I was stunned to see the place was absolutely packed with people. There were hundreds in there. I'd known that our dad had been a sociable and popular character around town for a long time, but I hadn't expected that. I was very pleased to see so many people had come to say goodbye to Jimmy. The place was standing room only.

A week later, I was back at work and trying to focus on my career. I had four months to go before I resat the sergeants' written exam, and I had to pass it if I wasn't to delay my career for another year. I threw myself into my studies, taking less overtime than ever, just to ensure I wasn't tired at the end of a shift.

March soon came, and I entered the gymnasium along with Neil and the other candidates. I completed the exam and was full of confidence as I left the room. I was certain I'd done enough this time.

There was nothing more to do but wait for the results to be announced in due course. I continued to work the city centre, to tutor new recruits, and to work towards my black belt in martial arts. Life was heading in the right direction and I felt good about myself, despite having an aching heart.

The relationship with my father hadn't always been a rosy one. Of all his sons, I was the only one he had difficulties with, and, as a result, I'd always wanted to make him proud of me. In my heart I knew he had been, but I still had more to prove.

Don't talk to me of God's great slumber,
That man, my dad, exists no longer.

COP OUT Chapter Eight

INCREDIBLY, I HAVE NO RECOLLECTION OF receiving the all-important exam results, but I passed. I was ecstatic that I'd done it. In the 'good old days', pre-1990, that pass would have been sufficient to be promoted to sergeant, but those days were long gone. Now, I had to pass part two as well, and if I didn't pass it in August, I'd have to add another twelve months to my possible promotion and take part two again the year after. If I failed it twice, I'd be back in the gym once more.

Studying for a written exam is hard work, but you know what has to be done, and you get on with it. Anyone with the right kind of commitment can do that type of exam and eventually succeed. But this new practical exam was something else. How on earth would we be able to study to pass this one? Nobody knew, and there was very little information available about it, because it had only been run six times previously.

All the officers who were preparing for part two put our heads together to try and find out as much as possible about the exam, but with little success. Those who ran the exam were keeping their cards close to their chest, and those who had been through it and failed had no comprehension of why they'd failed, and those who had been successful were also unable to say what they had done to pass. It all seemed so random.

August came and we booked a minibus to take us up to Leicestershire. We arrived at the police headquarters and were told to wait in a large room. There were officers from all over the country. After what seemed like an eternity, we were called to order, given candidate numbers and, in turn, we were each placed outside a closed door in a long corridor.

Looking up and down the corridor, I could see there were fifteen other bewildered officers. We were instructed to read a small message on an A4 sheet on each of our respective doors. Mine said 'A Member of the public is waiting for you in the reception area. He wishes to make a complaint against one of your officers for assault'. And that was it.

Each of the rooms had completely different scenarios, from 'Your Inspector has asked to see you regarding the latest crime statistics from your beat area' to 'PC Jones has asked to speak to you in private regarding a comment made by a fellow officer after a few drinks in the bar last night'.

Behind each of these doors was the person or persons you were expected to talk to, along with two examination staff with clipboards. We were told that we would hear a beep, and, on doing so, we had to enter the room and deal with the people as we saw fit. After five minutes, the beep would sound again, which meant we had to leave the room and move to the next door, read the new scenario and, after thirty seconds, the beep would sound again, meaning we were to enter the room and deal with the next incident. This would continue until we had been through all sixteen stations non-stop.

Yes, it was exhausting. Yes, it was bewildering – the scenarios were so varied and often contained minimal detail.

And yes, I failed, along with most of the crew from my station, apart from Neil. That meant that we had twelve months to prepare for the next part two exam, and we absolutely *had* to pass it next year or we'd be back to square one again, in the gym!

During those twelve months, the candidates who had failed met frequently and shared ideas and knowledge we had gleaned re the exam. Still, I had to wonder if it was all worth it. So much of my free time was being spent on trying to qualify for promotion, and the force was doing very little to help. It was the police, after all, who were desperately short of qualified sergeants, and I could easily understand why. Few wanted to put themselves through this trauma, and not everyone was capable of passing such a stringent examination process. The worst part was that, after succeeding at this marathon, we still wouldn't be guaranteed promotion.

And I knew that if I ever made it to sergeant, there I would stay unless I wanted to go through it all again to get promotion to the next rank: inspector. Thereafter, it was based on merit/old tie network.

Twelve months later, we were back in the dingy corridors at Leicestershire Police HQ, awaiting instruction. I spent a large part of that time sat on the toilet, as did numerous others. A lot was riding on my performance over the next ninety minutes, and I seriously questioned my desire to go back to square one in the gymnasium if I should fail this exam again.

I didn't. I have no idea what we did any differently, but most of the crew I went with from Cambridge passed the exam this time, which meant we were fully qualified to be sergeants anywhere in England and Wales.

Needless to say, I was overjoyed – I'd never have to go through all that again just to be a sergeant. It was just a matter of time now.

COP OUT Chapter Nine

YOU MIGHT HAVE FIGURED OUT BY NOW that getting promotion in real life is not the same as getting promoted on the TV cop shows. You don't get promoted for arresting an evil murderer or for finding a huge haul of drugs – doing those kinds of things are just part of your job. No, to get promoted you have to show you have the legal and procedural knowledge to do the job, and prove it by passing a very difficult exam procedure.

Everybody had to do it if they desired promotion, regardless of who they were – even officers who had entered the police on a 'fast-track' scheme to get to the top more quickly.

The group of candidates who passed the exam with me all eventually received their three stripes. Some stayed their whole career as sergeants, some left the job and sought careers elsewhere, whilst others went on to greater things. Neil went on to become a Detective Chief Inspector in another force, and will quite possibly make Detective Superintendent before long.

Even so, passing the exam caused no immediate change to our lives, apart from the massive and justifiable hangover. We all went back to our old jobs just as before. I returned to the City Centre Unit with renewed confidence and status. I was, after all, qualified to do the job my sergeant supervisors were doing.

So what happened next? Well, wise officers put in for a transfer to another force on condition of instant promotion. Many forces were in dire need of suitably qualified sergeants, and were only too willing to pull you in and instantly promote you.

In Cambridgeshire, in order to save money, the force was often run with certain posts empty. For example, a city shift might have a requirement for three sergeants to be in post, but would often run with just two, thus saving the force a sergeant's salary over the course of a year. If this were repeated all over the force, then you can imagine the savings being made.

It meant extra work for the two present sergeants, but, obviously, if one of those two sergeants went on a course or sick leave, then a temporary replacement sergeant would be needed until they were back up to the strength of the original two. That's where we came in.

'Acting Sergeant' was a post given to a sergeant-qualified PC. It was a temporary situation, usually to help cover the absent sergeant. It meant that the PC selected for the post wore the badge of rank of a sergeant, and, provided it was for more than a few weeks, received a sergeant's salary.

It was the second step towards promotion, the first being to successfully pass the sergeants' exam. Acting sergeant posts served two functions. First, they provided the force with temporary and essential sergeant cover, in that a PC could be pulled in from elsewhere, given the badge of rank of sergeant and thrown in at the deep end. Second, acting sergeant positions gave the future sergeant a taster: some experience of what it actually meant to be a sergeant, to see if they could cope with the new job.

After about three months of walking the city centre, I was asked to speak to the boss. The city superintendent asked if I would be interested in an acting sergeant post in the city.

Would I?

"David," he told me from behind his desk. "There are those officers who are on the chief's train, and those who are left behind on the platform. You have to decide which one you are going to be."

With that, he gave me a set of metal sergeant stripes to put on my epaulets, and told me to report to the inspector that covered the northern half of the city, which I duly did.

Since the last great change to the shift pattern had occurred, Cambridge had an awkward setup at that time in respect to inspector supervision.

The city was effectively divided into two: the northern half and the southern half (ignoring the tiny City Centre Unit that only worked part of the day). An inspector was responsible for each of the geographical areas, but they only worked during the day. The policing of each area was the responsibility of the three shifts for the north, and the three shifts for the south, working eight hours each, thus providing twenty-four hour cover for both the Northern Sector and the Southern Sector (and the city centre over nights).

If I've lost you already, let's just focus on my new area of responsibility: the northern half of the city. Inspector Druff had sole responsibility for police coverage of this area. He attended local neighbourhood meetings, supervised the statistics for crime in the area, and ensured that the local foot-patrol officers were doing their jobs effectively. He had a number two, one Sergeant Lad, who worked in the same office, and both of them could come to work when they wished to, provided that the sun was still shining. It was these two who had to answer for the crime and disorder committed on their area, which was now my area too.

Aside from the local foot- and cycle-patrol officers, the actual response work was done by three different shifts, each working eight hours as mentioned, therefore covering the twenty-four hour period. Each shift consisted of approximately twelve officers, although, with leave, courses and other commitments, the true number was usually eight or nine. Each shift was supervised by three sergeants (although, for reasons previously mentioned, we only ever had two). I was to be assigned as the second sergeant to one of these teams.

To complicate matters further, we were to be supervised by a different inspector. As Inspector Druff worked hours to suit himself, the twenty-four-hour shifts were covered by 'Duty Inspectors' who worked eight-hour shifts alongside us. A duty inspector was responsible for the *whole* city, and had no allegiance to north, south, or centre, but to the city as a whole. As previously mentioned, the City Centre Unit ceased to exist from about 1.00am, and became the responsibility of the Northern and Southern Sectors, who often resented having to cover an area of responsibility that wasn't actually their own. However, rich pickings were to be had in the city centre at night.

I recall leaving the superintendent's office with my new sergeant stripes, which I immediately pinned onto my epaulets. As I passed the city centre offices, I popped in to say hello and show the stripes off a bit, naturally. I then headed along into the Northern Sector offices. I was very disappointed that the place was practically deserted, and that only one person noticed my newly placed stripes.

I was to be partnered with another acting sergeant, and he was a guy I had worked with many times before: Acting Sergeant Batty Biter! (I'll never forget his first arrest as a first-day probationer as he ran across the common to arrest the Yasume Club burglars in *Cops Don't Run*.)

Aside from Batty, I knew none of the team, and that was the way I liked it. Being a sergeant meant making difficult decisions, and having a team of friends would only have complicated matters.

Being an *Acting* Police Sergeant (APS) was worse than being a confirmed sergeant. It was temporary – everybody knew that, including those whom you currently had authority over. Being an APS meant that, sooner or later, you'd be back down to the same rank as those you'd been lording it over. It was a difficult position because we were being tested to see if we could cut it as sergeants, yet we were likely to be put back amongst those PCs before long, and they'd never forget or forgive us for what we did to them whilst in charge of them.

Some APSs managed it beautifully, simply because they had the kind of personality that everybody loved. The step from PC to APS ran seamlessly for such fortunate souls, but others found the balancing act far more difficult. I decided from the start that my promotion was more important to me than forming new friendships. Even so, I was mindful of the power and authority my temporary rank held, and was only too aware of the amount of crap that was being dumped on my new team of overstretched, uniformed officers.

I decided immediately that I would ensure I carried out my duties correctly, whilst doing everything in my power to shield my staff from the unnecessary bullshit and bureaucracy being dumped on them on a daily basis.

Part of my remit was to log onto the crime computer each morning shift and review all new crime reports. Crime reports for the Northern Sector needed allocating to the officers covering the north who were working the early shift. When we did earlies, they were my guys. It seemed relatively straightforward to do, but one had to check which officers had which crimes already, how many they had, the complexity of each one, and also their availability, taking into account their upcoming leave and/or course commitments. There was no point in allocating a crime if there was no chance of the officer ever getting around to looking at it.

There were enough new crimes awaiting allocation and investigation to give each patrol officer two or three new crimes per day, which would be on top of the already long list of crimes they were investigating. During a week of earlies it was easy to allocate each officer up to fifteen new crimes, which they would have responsibility for until they had exhausted all enquiries and requested they be filed. Having served at the sharp end for so many years, I was also painfully aware that these officers were, first and foremost, response officers, not CID. They had very little time for crime investigation.

I recall, as a probationer, being allocated a crime report requiring a visit to a multi-storey car park in the centre, where a car had had a window smashed over the weekend. All reported crimes back then required an officer to visit, regardless. I was required to do a 'scene visit', which meant that I was to see if there were any potential witnesses or other leads to follow up. Being the new probationer, I dutifully attended, located the parking space, which I identified due to the broken glass on the floor, and checked all around that there was nothing further that required investigating on the empty car park level. I wrote on the report 'Scene visited, no further action required'. Only then could it be passed back to a sergeant who, once happy that the visit had in fact taken place, and that I hadn't missed any potential lines of enquiry, would either file it or put it back in my pigeon-hole with a note for follow up actions.

We'd come a long way since that time, as victims were now permitted to report crimes over the phone. Paper crime reports were no longer handed out, and scenes were only ever visited if it was warranted – we just didn't have time for such stupidity anymore. However, old habits die hard.

I have big shoulders, and it didn't take me long to discover that, as an APS, if I wrote a crime report off as not worth investigating further, for whatever reason, it never came back to me. This was partly because few above sergeant were involved in crime reports apart from signing off hundreds a day, so, if a sergeant said 'bin it', it usually got binned, no questions asked.

I read every new report to see if it warranted further action. If it didn't, I binned it. If it was borderline, I paused before recommending it be binned, waiting with bated breath to see if it came back to me. They rarely did. I relished this newfound authority and attempted to divert as much crap away from my guys as possible. However, even by doing this, I had sufficient crimes to allocate each of my officers two or three per day, on top of their other on-going investigations.

Before allocating, I had to review the seven or eight crimes each officer had previously been given to see if they were being progressed or were ready to be written off and filed. If I could bin a few, great. If further work was needed, I had to chase each officer up or suggest alternative lines of enquiry that they perhaps weren't pursuing. If I failed to allocate any new crime reports to my shift whilst on earlies, I got a bollocking from Inspector Druff or, more importantly, from my fellow shift sergeants who then had more crimes to allocate to their own teams.

If I had to choose one part of being a police sergeant I really disliked, it was this. The officers being bombarded with these crime reports just did not have the time to have lunch, let alone investigate crimes. Whilst monitoring the radio, I would often hear an officer booking 'unavailable whilst on enquiries' meaning they were trying to action their own crime queue, only for the control room operator to say, "Sorry, could you just attend a report of a burglary for me? Informant's been waiting for six hours now." The majority of this kind of work should have been done by a non-uniformed – and therefore non-response – team, who would be able to turn off their radios and get on with the enquiries. Oh, wait, yeah, we already had a team like that: CID. If we valued our career, there was no point in saying anything negative about CID. CID were untouchable, and just did not work weekends (when most people were home and available to answer questions).

In the police, everybody had their work priority to attend to – traffic officers attended RTAs, CID officers dealt with serious crime, neighbourhood patrol officers dealt with local nuisances and built bridges, and so on. The exception to the rule was the patrol officers. They attended *all* RTAs in the city, attended and took reports of *all* crimes in the city, dealt with local nuisances and built bridges, and also responded to *all* emergency calls in the city. They had *everything* to attend to, and woe betide if any of them appeared to be slacking.

My working day would begin thirty minutes or so before the shift arrived. Along with APS Batty, I would speak to the control room staff re any incidents of note, and any incidents that needed attending were printed off and given to us. We also checked the crime computer for crimes and patterns of note. We also spoke to the custody sergeant to see if any prisoners needed dealing with, and to see if any prisoners of note had been arrested since our last duty. We also needed to speak to Inspector Druff as we were policing his area, as well as the duty inspector who was responsible for the entire city. Occasionally, we would have to provide officers for other duties such as returning a prisoner to prison, collecting a prisoner from another force area, baby-sitting a prisoner at the hospital, etc.

Once all that was done, we attended the briefing room to see how many officers we had for the day. We had a rough idea beforehand, but unexpected sickness or injury sometimes meant an officer was absent. We had a minimum safe number of officers, and, if we fell below that, we had to find a replacement from somewhere, usually by offering overtime to an officer from another shift or on a rest day.

We also had 'Special Constables' appear at the briefing. We were rarely told they were coming, and any that did, had to be allocated to a regular police partner. Specials didn't count towards the minimum staffing levels – they were additional.

Only once we were sure who we had available at the briefing could we decide which officers would drive which vehicles and with whom, although the van was usually crewed by at least one experienced officer and another regular. We often had to re-jig our plans during briefing.

We then allocated call signs, vehicles and beats to the officers (taking into consideration each individual's experience and needs), which they duly recorded in their pocket notebooks. They were then updated regarding intelligence: who was believed to be doing what, wanted persons, stolen vehicles, major crime patterns, who'd been arrested recently, incidents of note, and so on.

The briefing was primarily sergeants to PCs, but the flow of information ran both ways. The team sitting across from us were the guys out on the streets, and they knew the bad guys, and they often contributed with additional information.

A briefing often started with congratulating certain members on a previous day's arrest, and usually ended with the allocation of control room incidents to be attended.

Briefings started fifteen minutes before the hour, and staff weren't paid for this but had to be there. It usually took just fifteen minutes because, once the hour came, we were responsible for the northern half of the city, and officers had to be ready to respond to urgent calls.

For this reason, they usually went out to their vehicles to prepare them for a quick getaway, and then returned to the office. They had dozens of emails to check each day, all of which had to be read. No excuses. They then had to log onto the crime computer and update their on-going investigations, read additional comments from sergeants or other supervisors, and check for any newly allocated crimes. Good officers also dug deeper and checked for crime patterns on the respective areas. On-going paperwork also needed attending to – writing statements re any incidents from the previous day, processing books for traffic offences, accident reports, etc.

If they were lucky, they might get away with a second cup of coffee during this time, the first being at briefing. But, usually, an urgent incident would come in and they'd race off to their vehicles and blue-light it away from the station. And that was how it often went for the next eight hours of their shift. On a quiet day, they might get a meal break, but the paperwork and the crime enquiries just kept stacking up, day after day after day.

As for patrol sergeants, we generally didn't patrol. The idea was that a sergeant would pair up with a PC for a few hours and police with them. It was a great opportunity to get to know each other and for us to observe how they policed, and to give appropriate feedback as necessary. It was also a great time for the PCs to get anything off their chests. The patrolling sergeant could also promptly attend any incidents that needed a supervisory presence.

However, as we were one sergeant short, we just didn't have the time to do this, as we spent the whole shift in the station dealing with everything else. Crime allocation could take me several hours. Then all RTA files and traffic prosecution files came to us first to ensure they were ready to go through to the Crown Prosecution Service. Then there were the statistics to be recorded. *OMG the statistics …*

Staff supervision was generally done over the radio. Both sergeants monitored the radio, and intervened when required. We might have to ask the control room to allow one or more of our officers to get on with a crime investigation that was several weeks old, and not send them to a burglary that was six hours old. Only the sergeants had the fuller picture when it came to priorities.

Occasionally, sergeants were required to attend an incident either to support the PC with our better understanding of the law, or because of force standing orders. In such circumstances, Batty or I would find a car and go to the scene.

Despite the force requirements for a supervisor to attend *all* sudden deaths, often we didn't. If it was straightforward, and a seasoned officer was in attendance, we wouldn't go unless requested. It was just how policing was evolving. Sergeants drove desks now. IT, the great saviour of the office, shackled all supervisors to a desk.

I've already mentioned that PCs had to check their emails daily. As a patrol sergeant, I became sick of the word *cascade*, meaning to send an email down the chain of command to everybody under you. How did that work? Well, an email, often with *Urgent* emblazoned across its subject field – would be sent out by somebody higher up. That would *cascade* down to all the inspectors in the force. Inspector Druff would then *cascade* it down to all the sergeants in his list, i.e. all the Northern Sector sergeants, as would the duty inspector, but to all sergeants in the station. And there were four of them. The DI might also send it to all sergeants. As an APS, I was still technically on the strength of the City Centre Unit, so once the city centre inspector sent it to all of his sergeants, all of those sergeants would also send it to me (as one of their PCs).

It was not unusual to get the same email six or ten times, all marked as *Urgent*. And that's just one email. Imagine how many times the troops below us received it! And there were hundreds of emails each day doing the cascade route just to cover every supervisor's back.

Well, I know I sent him the email …

We also got emails marked as *Urgent* which, whilst clearly urgent when written yesterday, were no longer urgent and were just FYI. Nobody that I recall ever changed the subject field from *Urgent* to FYI. So, effectively, ninety percent of the emails I received both as a PC and a sergeant were marked as *Urgent*.

A few days off from this nonsense were so welcome, but a nightmare awaited you on return. I clearly recall, as an APS, after just three days off, logging on to see ninety-six emails all requiring my urgent attention. What did we, as sergeants, do with these emails? Well, if they were for our staff to be aware of, they got cascaded down to them. From *both* of us. Marked as *Urgent*. Yeah, we were part of the problem too but there just wasn't enough time to change the emails or to check who had sent what to whom. It was organised chaos on a massive scale. PS Lad also sent the same emails to our staff, because they were northern officers.

Poor buggers.

COP OUT Chapter Ten

MY TENURE AS AN APS REALLY OPENED MY EYES to how the police service really was run.

As previously mentioned, my team of officers were being pulled in all directions and expected to do everything given to them on time, despite having to attend all urgent calls on their sector. Any issues needing addressing by staff not on the immediate shift was normally done by email to shift sergeants. Marked *Urgent*.

The straw that broke this camel's back happened after working a manic week of nights (11.00pm–7.00am) when I came back to work on lates (3.00pm) and was approached by Inspector Druff, who was still at work because the sun was still shining. My career-driven, Northern Sector commander was concerned with the statistics I had provided him with for the previous week of nights we'd just worked (but he hadn't).

Each sector inspector had been provided with a list of statistics to record and report up the chain of command, which Druffy was intent on doing in glowing terms. His particular gripe was the lack of 'Section One' searches my staff had been doing on nights. A Section One search was a search of a person or vehicle when a police officer had reasonable grounds to do so, or when he had been given permission to conduct such a search by the person themselves. Afterwards, the searching officer had to complete a small form covering the details of the search, which they would duly pass to their sergeant at the end of the shift.

These would be checked for legality, etc., and passed on to Inspector Druff for collating and sending up the chain.

Now, that particular week of nights had been a nightmare for my team. They were on minimum staffing levels and the workload was relentless. Even so, they managed to make numerous quality arrests, which unfortunately took staff off the streets and added to the massive workload of the few remaining officers. For this, I was happy to praise them when they came back to work for lates after a few days off. The commitment of such young officers never ceased to amaze me, and it was their resilience, unending motivation, and relentless drive that kept the police service afloat and carried the burden for all officers above them, despite the crap being dumped on them on a daily basis. *Lions, led by numerous donkeys.*

But Druffy wasn't happy. He needed to submit his Section One search stats to his boss, showing that we (i.e. he) had at least hit the target for such searches. Apparently, we were about seventy percent off the Home Office target. I explained to him the problems we had been having with the massive workload, the amazing work the young lions had done all week, and the fact that they never stopped all night long, and that the figures he had were the figures of truth, the reality of the situation.

He wasn't listening. I reinforced my argument with the fact that if officers were too busy to be stopping suspects and searching them, then there clearly was a problem and we needed more staff!

Send the truth up the chain of command and let them see the reality!

He still wasn't listening.

"But your guys must have *spoken* to people?"

I stared at him open-mouthed. This was quite possibly the most stupid thing an inspector said to me during my whole police career.

"Yeah, obviously," I replied, not sure I was hiding my dislike of him, or indeed where this was going.

"Well, if they *spoke* to someone, you know, on the street, and got their details, then they could write up a retrospective Section One search form, couldn't they?"

I could hardly believe my ears. I'd just explained to my supervisor that my staff were swamped with work due to under-staffing, and now he wanted me to give them more work to fiddle the figures, so that *he* looked good?

I know I've just said that the forms only took a minute to write, but officers would have to look back through their notebooks for the whole week of nights to find anybody they'd spoken to, and write a search form out that didn't need writing but would help to perpetuate the fallacy to senior management and government that all was grand and tickety-boo, and that actually they didn't need extra staff after all.

I was furious but he was my boss and he didn't listen to those below, just those above.

"But, Sir, if we aren't hitting the figures, then surely it will say that there is a problem that needs addressing, that we need more staff or less work! By doing this, what we are saying is everything is fine, which is just plain wrong."

"Yeah, I know," he said. "But we ain't gonna get more staff, so it doesn't make a difference, does it?"

So, I make my staff work more, bend the rules, and help you look good in the eyes of the superintendent. Is that it? I couldn't say it, not as an APS, but I might do once I was fully promoted. However, I refused to give in completely to this idiot's massaging of the truth at the expense of the hardest workers I've ever met.

I sighed. "I'll *ask* them if they *want* to do it, but I won't *tell* them to do it." It was a small victory for me, and a big loss for him.

I did get a smattering of extra forms through, but thankfully not enough to hit the figures. Poor Druffy, I did feel for him.

From that day till this, I will never trust official police statistics for two reasons: first, inside such a hierarchical organisation, it is easy to force staff to fiddle the stats as they see fit, and, second, because the service is full of 'yes-men' at every level, who will always aim to please. Even chief constables want a knighthood, so they can't rock the boat either. Statistical lies and bullshit have destroyed a great job.

My action of standing up for what I believed to be right and in protection of my staff had actually meant I'd shot myself in the foot. If I'd ever passed my inspector's exam and been promoted, promotion thereafter would have been done on 'merit', which is ancient Greek for sucking up to your bosses. Every supervisor wanted the next rank up, and you knew that if you upset somebody along the way then it might come back to haunt you. Inspector Druff might have been the biggest **** in the police service, but he was guaranteed to be seen in a positive light by those above him, as he always gave them what they desired, and one day he might well have been my superintendent, and my chances of promotion beyond inspector would have been zero. Yes-men get on. Real men get off (the chief's train).

A word of advice for any potential or new police officers reading this book: don't upset the apple cart if you want to get on, but tip the damned thing over if you don't.

A year or so later, I was out with a group of off-duty officers from Northern Sector, celebrating something or other in a pub in Cambridge. It's fair to say we were drinking heavily. It's part of the job description.

Druffy, a rugby player, was there, as were a few other players. We were standing in a circle when Druffy said something stupid, and Ady, one of his rugby player colleagues, laughed at him disdainfully.

Now Ady was huge, not upwards-wise, but outwards-wise, and had a massive bald head. He looked terrifying, and few criminals argued with him. I knew Ady was a PC in the Northern Sector, and therefore Druffy was his line manager, but these rugby guys have blurred lines, and I didn't understand the relationship too well.

"You want to hit me, don't you?" Druffy said to Ady. "Go on then. You have my perm–"

Bang! The punch to the side of the inspector's face was so quick and unexpected that the only people who saw it were our small group. None of the revellers in the pub were aware that anything had just happened, thankfully, and Ady didn't spill a drop of his pint, so expert was he at smacking dickheads.

I don't know who was more surprised at the sudden wallop – the inspector himself, or us.

Ady laughed. "You don't hang around when you get a permission like that, do you?"

As big and ugly as Ady was, I wanted to kiss him that night.

COP OUT Chapter Eleven

ONE OF THE GREATEST LEARNING CURVES of your first APS job is dealing with awkward members of staff. I'd never met Henry before, but I could tell that the whole shift loved him. He was a real character, laid back and very likeable, but he just didn't like me.

I could feel his distrust of me every time he was in the room, and he often challenged me verbally. I couldn't fault his work out on the streets, although he wasn't particularly good with his follow-up admin. In many ways he was just like me: he preferred to be out cracking heads rather than waylaid dealing with monotonous paperwork when there was a job to be done.

After a few weeks, it came to a head. We'd had a few attacks in the city centre, on lone females walking home at night, by a suspect we had a good description of. Now, this is the kind of job we don't mind leaving our patch for, so we dropped our slightest WPC in the centre in plain clothes with a covert radio, and stationed several officers nearby, ready to respond should she have a problem.

In fact, because of this local operation, and the fact one of our staff was out there in danger, it was one of the rare nights that I actually took a car out and prowled around the centre. I'm well aware of how a team of officers gel, and that I was a newcomer – an outsider – but, to me, she was my responsibility.

In the early hours, she put a shout out for help, and we all responded. I was in Bridge Street, as was she, and I obviously got to her in seconds.

I could see everything was OK: it was a false alarm. Henry had also responded and had driven along Bridge Street towards us, but he was blocked from proceeding due to the automatic bollards in the road just twenty yards from me.

Now, each emergency vehicle was fitted with a small transponder at the front of the car, and we had been instructed to drive over the sensors in the road *slowly*, so that they might pick up the transponder and lower the bollards for us. As an ex-City Centre Unit officer, I was only too well aware of how these things worked, and of the dire consequences of getting it wrong.

Henry, in his justifiable urge to get to his colleague, drove over them too quickly and skidded to a stop, just inches from the dormant bollards. Realising his mistake, he slammed the car into reverse, wheels spinning, and sped over them again.

Nothing.

He repeated this wheel-squealing action several times before slowing down sufficiently to activate the bollards, eventually managing to drive through, and alighting a few seconds later.

I stood there, bemused and irritated by his actions – he was so focused on getting through the bollards that he wasn't able to see we were just yards in front of him and that everything was OK. He could have simply got out of the car and been of use had the WPC been in real need of help. It was also embarrassing to watch a police car wheel spinning backwards and forwards over the sensor in such an unprofessional way.

This was my chance to have a heart-to-heart with Henry.

That night, I called him into my office and had a chat with him. I decided there and then that I didn't have to justify myself to him. If anything, he should have been giving me a chance.

However, I trod carefully. I knew he was centric to the team and it'd be better if I could just make him calm down and see me for who I was.

It was instantly clear he didn't want to talk to me or listen. Henry had *already* decided who I was, despite not *knowing* who I was or what I was doing 'behind the scenes' for my team – *his* team. I was the outsider to him, and always would be.

I explained to him that, as APS, I was walking a tight line between doing what's right by my staff and looking after my career. I had to impress the higher authorities if I wanted to get promoted, but that I was prioritising my staff's welfare and workload as well. I wasn't one of the hated yes-men.

I wanted to tell him about all that I was doing for them, things that he wasn't even aware of, but that would have just sounded like pleading.

Tough, Henry. I'm the sergeant and this is how it is, and you are not going to derail me. Get over it.

The best way to deal with the likes of Henry, or anybody else in the team who considered you an outsider, or not suitable for the job, or just didn't like you for whatever reason, was to prove to them that you could do the job, and do it well. And *that*, I would do.

A few weeks later, a call came in from a frantic female saying her husband had gone mad and was threatening her with a knife. The initial officers on the scene confirmed that the husband was in the house and that the wife was terrified he might hurt somebody or even himself. They had also seen him with a large kitchen knife. I advised them to stay out of the house, along with the wife, and protect themselves as best they could.

I went immediately to the scene whilst Batty gathered all available PSU-trained officers, who kitted up and made their way over as soon as they could. This looked like a classic enter and search with full protection. The guy didn't stand a chance.

Having spoken to the officers outside and listened to the wife, I decided to enter the house with just her. This was a life and death kind of decision, one made on the balance of probabilities, with as much knowledge of events as possible.

I kept the two officers in attendance at the front door, holding it open for a quick escape, just in case. We three were wearing some heavyweight protective vest over our jumpers. I knew the PSU team was on its way and would arrive within half an hour.

I turned off my radio and spoke to the wife in the kitchen. We could hear movement from upstairs. She confirmed that he was the only other person in the house, and that it sounded like he was in the main bedroom. I asked her about the knife, and she pointed to a wooden knife block. The biggest knife was missing, and it was this, she said, that he had in his possession.

She explained to me that a few months previously her husband had reversed his bin lorry out of a driveway one morning in a nearby village, and had felt a bump. He'd immediately stopped, jumped down and walked to the rear to see what had caused the obstruction. The sight he was greeted with was enough to send anybody over the edge. A fourteen-year-old newspaper delivery girl, on her bicycle, lay crushed to death beneath his rear wheels.

Since then, she explained, he had never been the same.

I recalled the incident happening and realised how traumatic it must have been for the lone driver. I totally understood.

He'd been receiving therapy ever since, but had been acting strangely of late.

This guy was a victim of an awful incident, and I didn't want to see him slammed into the wall by a shield unit, roughly arrested, and frog-marched out of the house. He needed help, serious help, and that kind of police response just wasn't gonna help him at all.

I was fully aware that the wife had no protective vest on, and that the PSU serial had arrived and was unloading on this quiet cul-de-sac at 2.30 in the morning, primed for action.

I also remembered, as a PC, storming into a flat under similar circumstances whilst being supervised by an APS, who was later disciplined for letting unequipped officers go in the house up against an armed occupant. And I was about to do the same.

Batty duly arrived at the door in full protective equipment, with a complete serial, all holding shields, lined up behind him. I told him what I was going to do, and guided the wife out to the two responding officers at the door. She was taken into the street, visibly upset at the reinforcements and what was about to happen to her poor, ill husband.

Having learnt the man's name, I gingerly walked up the stairs to the closed bedroom door at the top, paused, and glanced behind me. Batty was like a dog straining on a leash. One word from me, and this guy would be a pancake. Behind Batty stood six heavily protected officers, all ready to do what they'd been trained to do. I had full confidence that they could and would do it.

I knocked on the door.

"Mike?" I said, gently. "It's the police."

Nothing.

318

"Mike, Jean has called us because she is concerned for you. Can I open the door, please, so that we can talk?"

Nothing.

"Mike," I continued, more forcefully. "I have to open this door, OK? Please stay away from the door as I open it."

I opened the door slowly, ready to jump back to let Batty and his storm troopers take over.

As the door opened, I saw Mike lying in bed, his head the only thing visible above the duvet. I could see he was lying unnaturally rigid beneath the bedclothes.

"Mike, I'm a cop. Now, I want you to listen to me. I *need* you to listen to me, OK? I know what happened to you. I understand what you have been through, believe me, and I'm here to help you, nothing more."

He nodded his head.

"But Jean says you have a kitchen knife?"

Again, he nodded. I suspected the knife was in his hand under the quilt.

"I need to see the kitchen knife, Mike. You understand that, don't you? I can't help you until I know the knife is out of harm's way? Where is it, Mike? Where's the knife?"

I spoke in what I thought was a quiet and relaxing, yet determined, way.

"It's under the bed," were the first words he said to me.

That was awkward, because the only way I could see under the bed was to enter the room and look from the side of the bed, due to the headboard and tailboard reaching floor level. I would have put myself at too much risk because, if he did have a knife in his hand, he would be but a few short feet away from my head.

I still had Batty and the Batterers behind me, but I seriously wanted to avoid using them if at all possible, but I also didn't want to get stabbed in the side of the head in doing so.

"OK, Mike. In that case, I just need to see under the quilt. You do understand, don't you? I need to see that the knife isn't under the quilt with you."

He remained silent and rigid. I feared he might have been lying to me.

"The spiders," he said. "The spiders are everywhere." He stared down at the bottom of the quilt in fear, as if spiders were crawling across it, towards his face.

"Listen, Mike," I said, as I glanced back down the stairs. "I'm gonna be up front with you, all right? I have a whole serial of riot-equipped cops behind me, all the way down the stairs, just waiting for me to give them the nod to pounce on you. Seriously, I've seen it happen before, and it's not very nice but it *is* very effective. But not tonight, eh? I don't think it's necessary, do you?"

He shook his head.

"So, show me what you have under the quilt, please?"

"I'm naked."

"Trust me, I've seen it all, Mike."

There was a pause before he threw the quilt off himself, exposing his naked body.

"OK, that's good. Now I just need to check underneath you, OK? Can you roll over?"

He was, by now, compliant with my requests, and, as he rolled onto one side, I quickly established that he posed no threat that I could see.

"Good man," I said, glancing back at Batty and making eye contact with him. We understood each other. "Now I'm going to look under the bed to see where the knife is, OK?"

I knew that if I saw the knife under the bed, then we would be able to safely take Mike into protective custody. If it wasn't there, however, then Mike just might have hidden it within easy reach of him, and I'd be in danger. The unspoken message I gave to Batty was 'Be ready, please'.

I bent down and breathed a sigh of relief – beneath the bed lay a huge carving knife. No others had been missing from the knife block, so I knew this was the one.

Mike was cooperating with me. I gave Batty a silent thumbs-up.

"OK, Mike, well done. Now, we need to get dressed, and go and see somebody to get you some help, OK?"

"Yes, Sir," he replied. He sat up in bed with his hands raised, got out of bed, all the time keeping his hands above his head. I felt so sorry for him.

Awkwardly, he dressed in front of me, his hands still in the air.

I'd silently given the signal for Batty and his crew to stand down and clear out.

"Mike, it's OK, it's over. Put your hands down, and let's go downstairs. Jean is worried about you."

He was briefly reunited with his wife, whom he hugged tightly and cried. They both cried, and it was difficult for me not to shed a tear.

He then came with me and was taken to a local mental health hospital for assessment and treatment.

I never knew what became of Mike and his wife, but I hope they got through that.

I'll never forget them.

COP OUT Chapter Twelve

THE DAY CAME WHEN MY TIME AS APS WAS UP and I returned to the City Centre Unit as a PC, albeit a greatly improved one. I now knew the pressures my sergeants were under, and I knew the importance of updating crime reports, and statistics recording, although my faith in police statistics had ended following the farce with Inspector Druff.

In truth, I was a much better officer for my experience as an acting sergeant, something that had lasted for several months and given me a great desire to get promoted. It was still a hectic life, but a different hectic – one with a real purpose, and I needed that more than ever.

Rumours were circulating that a large body of PCs were soon to be promoted in a single 'job lot'. The force had been running short of sergeants for a considerable time. In fact, they were actually losing sergeants because some would retire, others moved to pastures new, and, obviously, several got promoted to inspector. So, Cambridgeshire seriously needed a number of substantive sergeants.

I was advised, along with all the others who were waiting for promotion, to send my dress tunic to headquarters to have my sergeant stripes sewn on. A few weeks later, they were duly returned, bearing the new badge of rank. An appointment with the chief constable was confirmed for the following week. We booked a minibus for the twenty-minute ride to Police Headquarters in Huntingdon.

It was a day to remember, and yet, here I am, unable to recall it. I do recall having a group photo taken with the boss and all the new sergeants wearing their tunics with the shiny, new, silver stripes on the sleeves.

I have no idea if we celebrated that evening, although I'm sure we must have. It had, after all, been a long, long road.

I was immediately posted back to Northern Sector as a substantive sergeant, although on a different shift, but along with Batty as substantive too.

It meant that my pay scale jumped to the equivalent of the most senior PC, and that, for the next five years, I would receive a yearly increment on top of the national pay rise. After five years, I would be at the top of a sergeant's pay scale and only receive the national pay rises. It was then that I should consider repeating the traumatic promotion process once more, to reach inspector rank. The mere thought of going through it all again drained me.

I threw myself into my new role with my new charges, and I loved every minute of it. I still considered my role as not only supervising my team, but looking out for them too. Within months, I felt like an old hand at it.

One of my many roles was to monitor the development and progress of the shift probationers, which I had no difficulty doing due to my experience as a tutor-constable.

One young wisp of a probationer had yet to deal with any form of confrontation or aggression, and he needed a tick in that box before he could proceed. I was concerned that, after fifteen months in the job, he had still to prove that he could cope with violent situations. No matter what role he was given, he always seemed to be far away from physical involvement in arrests, and this happened on a daily basis. I have no idea how he had gone fifteen months without dealing with violence. It seemed to follow me around.

I considered putting him on the van, as it always went to the violent incidents, but I really needed it to be crewed by tried and tested officers, as the back-up it offered was too valuable to be played with.

We set him an action plan, and the control room was advised to assist where possible. He had to show me that he could be counted on in a confrontation.

One night, I was out on patrol in a panda, alone, when a report came in of screaming coming from the common in town. Despite all the possible exits from the huge common, I found myself in the exact spot that a young cyclist came out of the dark and rode towards me. I immediately stopped him.

The details were sketchy and we still had no victim, so I spoke to him as a potential witness, to buy me time until we knew what we had.

He was early twenties and average build. I explained to him what had been reported, and asked him if he was OK, whether he'd had any problems on the common.

He immediately puffed his chest up, and the corners of his mouth turned down, and he said, "Look at me – who do you think is stupid enough to have a go at *me*?"

Oh dear, he could obviously see somebody that I couldn't see.

His reaction told me that he'd had something to do with whatever had happened on the common, and I immediately had somebody in mind to deal with him, as he was clearly not going to accept being arrested if it came to that.

I let the control room know my location and that I had a probable suspect, and queried any update. Another officer then said he had two victims of an assault on the common in his car, and that he would do a drive-by to see if my guy was the one responsible.

Such offender identifications are not always good for a court of law, but I saw no other way to proceed, so I authorised it. The two witnesses then confirmed he was the one responsible for an unprovoked assault on them.

I asked for PC Wisp to join me for the arrest. I suspected the offender would kick off when arrested, as he still believed he was being treated as a witness, so an arrest would come as a complete surprise for him. Plus, he wanted to show me how tough he was.

Whilst I waited, I half hoped that he would play up on arrest, just so that PC Wisp could finally prove he could deal with such a man, and get the box ticked. The suspect was much heavier than my PC, and obviously prone to violence, but I guessed he'd be no match for me. If Wispy couldn't cope, I'd just step in and deal with it.

Wispy arrested him and he came like a lamb. *Damn …*

Maybe next time …

One scenario in which it was almost certain that officers would be confronted with violence was on a drugs raid on a well-known supplier's address. We knew of two adjoining first-floor flats where drugs were being sold, so our shift set up a raid on it. A couple of officers were tasked with setting it up, getting the warrant, and briefing the team.

We entered the communal front door silently, and went up the stairs. The two teams paused in line on the landing outside the two respective bedsit doors.

The plan was, as we were in an apparent 'happy hour' for dealing, to simultaneously knock on both doors as if we were potential buyers, and burst in as they opened up. I led team A, and I was second in line to go in. In front of me was a strategically placed officer called Wispy. I nodded to the other team leader to give the command to get on with it, and we simultaneously, and meekly, knocked on our respective doors.

I knew the dealer in my room very well. He had been a druggie for years, and a shoplifter to fund his habit, as many were. He was now moving into selling drugs to make enough money to give up the stealing, as he was dreadful at it. He was unlikely to be violent, but we had no idea who else would be cornered in that room and facing arrest.

After a few seconds the door opened up, and there he stood. I saw clearly that there were four young buyers behind him, sitting on his bed, with the product brazenly laid out on the table before them.

The dealer and Wispy were eyeball to eyeball, and nobody moved for a few seconds. They were all too stunned to appreciate the quantity of coppers peering into this illicit den.

Then the druggie-turned-dealer suddenly woke up, turned and ran to the table, and grabbed up all of the evidence. The whole time, Wispy stood motionless, watching it all happen in slow-mo. I steamed through Wispy as if he wasn't there, and jumped on the dealer. *Too late!*

He rammed the bag of white powder, about the size of a large egg, into his mouth.

I reacted instinctively. My hands immediately went up to his throat and applied pressure. There was no way I wanted to lose the evidence in this way. Also, there was enough drug in that bag for a serious overdose. A dead suspect on a raid always went down badly.

His eyes bulged and he gagged several times, but he kept on trying to swallow the stuff, despite my firm throat hold. I lifted him off his feet and swung him around by the neck, screaming at him the whole time to spit the stuff out. The table with all of its paraphernalia went flying. We both stumbled and fell against the bedsit windows, his head accidentally breaking one in the process. It might have looked like I'd rammed his head through the window whilst holding him in a throat lock, but appearances can be deceiving.

Despite having his head hanging out of the first-floor window, and with my hands around his throat, there was no way he was going to voluntarily give up the drugs and go willingly to jail. I knew that if I held his throat any longer, he might pass out. It was an option – I might have been able to retrieve the packet that way – but it was often not seen in the best light with tomorrow's hindsight.

I released him, accepting that he'd by now swallowed the bag of drugs completely. I let him fall to the floor, and turned to see what was happening with the rest of the offenders and my officers. Everybody was just staring at me. The buyers were motionless on the bed, eyes wide open, gazes locked on me, eyes occasionally glancing down to the seller on the floor, who was now holding his sore throat and gagging. Even my strike team were standing there motionless, not quite sure what to do.

"You lot," I ordered. "Empty your pockets onto the table, and no funny business, all right?"

"Yes, Sarge – no problem," they replied in unison, righting the coffee table, and emptying their pockets so quickly it was almost comical.

During the search of these suspects and the flat, I kept an eye on the seller. He was slowly but surely going on one hell of a trip. I knew he would not be allowed into the custody office like that, so I arranged for him to be admitted to hospital, just in case. That did, of course, take two police officers off the street to look after him for the rest of the night.

Numerous arrests were made in both flats that day, and a quantity of drugs taken off the streets, albeit in an unexpected fashion, yet one action plan still remained to be written off.

Boy, did Wispy get some feedback that night.

326

COP OUT Chapter Thirteen

ALL OFFICERS, BIG OR SMALL, COCKY OR PASSIVE, have to deal with violent situations – it is an essential and unavoidable part of the job. We were provided with various elements of kit to assist us with aggression, but the best bit of kit any officer had available came naturally.

The ability to talk was the first weapon in our armoury, as it could get you out of many uncomfortable situations, but there was always going to be a time when talking was a waste of time, either because the person was too drunk or high, too stupid, or just too nasty. Each incident had to be dealt with individually, and the threat of, and subsequent use of, force held in reserve.

A call came in of a violent domestic at a dwelling in the city. As local units responded, intelligence emerged that the complainant's house was that of the ex-wife of a big local thug. And I mean big.

As a result of what we knew of this guy, all available units went, and we considered it so serious that Batty and I both jumped into the sergeants' car and raced to the scene. We arrived shortly after other units had, and saw that they were speaking to Mr Big in the street. It was clear he was very dismissive of the officers. Other units were standing nearby in case he kicked off, but were looking a little unsure of themselves. Under such circumstances, the police need to show they are in absolute control – otherwise the suspect might spot their weakness and take advantage.

"Has *anybody* spoken to the complainant?" I asked, as I got out of the car.

"Er, no …" came back the reply. All thoughts seemed to be focused on the danger.

I tasked somebody with going to the house to speak to the ex-wife, to see if we had any offences for which we could arrest this guy.

Batty took charge of speaking to the suspect, and it was immediately clear that Mr Big was extremely drunk and provocative.

"You wanna arrest *me*? *You* lot? You don't have enough people here to arrest me. Go on then, arrest me, you wankers." He spun around and eyeballed the surrounding officers in a challenging and threatening way, possibly picking up on their hesitation.

"No," Batty said, firmly. "We don't want to arrest you if we have no reason to arrest you, but we've just got to see what's gone on first, mate, all right?"

"Why won't you arrest me?" he demanded. "Go on, I wanna see you pricks arrest me. I could do with a laugh."

"Look," I said. "We can't just arrest you for nothing. There has to be an offence committed first, followed by a complaint. That's what we're doing here – seeing if there's a complaint of an offence having been committed."

I looked towards the complainant's house to see if any update was forthcoming.

Mr Big followed my eyes. "She ain't gonna say diddly, she ain't."

There was a pause of a few seconds.

"What about …" said Mr Big, "… if I just twatted that c**t there in the face? Would that do?" He pointed menacingly at Batty as he made the threat.

Batty and I looked at each other and nodded, reading each other's minds. "Yeah, that'll do fine," Batty said, as we simultaneously pounced on him, knocking his considerable weight to the pavement.

He hit the floor hard, and was in two arm-locks, and then cuffed-and-stuffed before he knew what had hit him.

"Fucking 'ell," he struggled to say, as his face was pressed heavily against the gravel path, two heavy cops kneeling on his back. "There's no need for this now, is there? Can't a bloke make a joke these days, mate?"

"Well, if you're gonna make a joke, it needs to be funny, doesn't it, mate?" said Batty. "Threatening to punch a police sergeant in his face isn't funny, is it? What did you expect us to do?"

We got him to his feet, keeping him bent double in case he reacted aggressively again, and slowly frog-marched him to the open doors of the nearby van. As we closed the doors on him, I wiped the tarmac dust off my hands onto my trousers, whilst turning around to face the troops. They had been standing there the whole time, watching events as they unfolded. The look of shock on their faces was a sight to behold.

"Never take any shit from these people," Batty said in a matter-of-fact way. "Ever."

Once back at the station, Mr Big was taken out of the van and put into the custody waiting area. We released his handcuffs, and he was perfectly amiable, apart from complaining about the gravel rash to his face. He was, however, rather philosophical about his current predicament.

He held no grudges against us for his arrest or the manner of his arrest. He faced no charges from his ex-wife despite smashing her front door in, and he ended up being charged with a minor Public Order Offence for the threat against Batty.

From that night on, I detected that the new team wholeheartedly accepted Batty and me as their sergeants. These two untested and newly promoted sergeants had proven that night that they were formidable officers in their own right, and the kind of cops that you just didn't mess about with, whoever you were.

I was six months into my absorbing role as a recently promoted sergeant, when I was reluctantly sent away from my team for a number of weeks to Nottingham, to learn how to be a recently promoted sergeant. Batty was supported by a new APS in my absence.

The sergeants' course was made up of new sergeants from all over the region, and I was one of two sent from Cambridgeshire. We stayed in a beautiful old manor house just south of the city for a couple of weeks. Like most police courses, it turned into one huge piss-up.

I only recall learning two things on that course. The first was how to be interviewed on camera – by staring directly into the camera without looking away, just like a newsreader does. It was an interesting thing to learn, but I never used it for real.

The second thing I learnt was that Nottinghamshire police officers, of which there were many on our course, were some of the biggest and craziest drinkers I'd ever met.

After those essential two weeks were up, I returned to where I belonged and longed to be – the sharp end of supervising policing in Cambridge.

Even though the force had recently promoted more PCs to sergeant in one go than at any other time in the force's history, we were still short of that most essential of supervisory cover. This might have been partly due to the wave of promotions of suitably qualified sergeants to inspector rank that followed our promotions.

Whatever the reason, it is something that should never be allowed to happen, for anything. These lions needed to be supervised and supported, and that support only ever really came from the rank of sergeant, especially when the shift pattern left inspectors floating around with no real ownership or contact with any particular troops. Without sufficient sergeant cover, the troops suffer. And it wasn't just Cambridge that felt the pain.

The county of Cambridgeshire (and therefore the force area) is split into two policing divisions: north and south. The southern division where I worked had one major city: Cambridge. Cambridge City had its own station and its own officers, who policed Cambridge and only Cambridge, unless they were called out of the city to support the rural officers, which rarely happened.

The southern county area was covered by a number of sub-stations, including one at Ely – a small city of fifteen thousand inhabitants half an hour's drive to the north of Cambridge. It wasn't uncommon for one or two double-crewed cars to be covering the whole of the rural area in the southern division, which, geographically, was huge. Driving from one side to the other, even in an emergency, could take officers thirty to forty minutes.

The force control room operator asked me to speak to them over the phone. This only ever happened if they wished to complain or challenge something we were doing, or to give some sensitive information that couldn't be broadcast over the radio system. I didn't care much for their complaints, and would happily stand up to them if what they said was detrimental to my lions.

However, this was of a sensitive nature. The wife of a serving police officer had called the police to report a domestic dispute with her husband. As officers know, any incident involving a police officer has to be dealt with by an officer of at least one rank above, for obvious reasons.

The officer in question was a PC, so a sergeant or above was required to attend. The only problem was, not only did he live in a village just outside of Ely – a thirty-minute drive from Cambridge – but also there were no sergeants on duty in Ely that night, and the nearest inspector who could go was with me in Cambridge. That meant that a Cambridge supervisor had to attend.

As Batty was temporarily covering for the custody sergeant, and the duty inspector was otherwise engaged, it fell to me to deal. It also meant that I was the only sergeant available for the whole half of the southern county of Cambridgeshire, which had a surface area of 642 square miles, and a population of a staggering 530,000 people – that's over half a million. Me, a sergeant still in his first year!

It also meant that Cambridge City, the busiest place in the southern half of the county, would have no physical outside supervisory cover whilst I was away. The return trip was going to take me at least an hour, bearing in mind that I had no idea where I was going and had to navigate by a paper map, at night. Plus, the time at the scene to deal with the matter. And 'domestics' can take a long time to sort out. The inspector, though, in my absence, could 'make himself available if supervision was needed urgently'.

It took me about forty minutes to drive from Cambridge to Ely and then to the hamlet where the officer lived, navigating by map and torchlight. Once there, I called at the house and spoke to the officer. I then spoke privately to his wife. She was very apologetic and stated that she had made the call simply as a threat to get him into trouble with his job. She admitted that no offences had been committed, and no police action was warranted. She was very embarrassed, as was her husband when I told him that I would have to submit a non-crime report on the incident for the attention of his supervisors at Ely.

After another long drive, I arrived back in Cambridge in the early hours. I could hardly believe the ridiculous staffing levels in the southern division of Cambridgeshire Constabulary.

But to be 'on the chief's train' meant keeping quiet, accepting the situation without complaint, and just carrying on.

COP OUT Chapter Fourteen

THE FACT THAT SERGEANT BATTY HAD BEEN covering the custody office was nothing new. Being a custody sergeant was a full-time job, and was only given to seasoned sergeants, but even they needed a meal break. It was during those breaks that the new sergeants got a short taster of what that all-too-important job had to offer. So, one of the two-sergeants-that-should-have-been-three had to absent themselves from supervisory duties each shift.

Basically, as 'Custody Sergeant', you were the officer responsible for accepting all newly arrested or detained persons, ensuring their welfare whilst in your care, and ensuring all legal requirements were being kept in relation to every single person in custody.

I hated this particular job, yet knew that one day I would be required to take it on full-time too – once I became a seasoned sergeant. So, why did I hate it so much? I had a lot of experience of the cell-block from when I was a PC, as I worked as a 'Gaoler' many times. This role is basically working with the custody sergeant and helping him out in the smooth running of the cells: hourly welfare checks on prisoners, feeding them, getting them out of the cells to hand over to officers for interviews or processing, and so on.

Unfortunately, there were so many things that could go wrong, and often did. People died in custody for many reasons, and the buck always stopped with the custody sergeant. Even when I'd saved the life of a detainee in the cell-block, I knew that, had she died that night, then the poor old custody sergeant would have had the book thrown at him.

It didn't help that they began to use me as temporary cover down there at a time when a previous, full-time Custody Sergeant was being investigated for crimes against the very people he had in his custody and welfare.

Thirty-three-year-old PS Paul Banfield had transferred into Cambridgeshire Police from another force the same year as I had joined up as a probationer. As an arresting officer, I'd met him on numerous occasions when he had been the Custody Sergeant responsible for receiving my prisoners. He always came across as a friendly chap, if a little distant.

The investigation into his actions was very hush-hush, and I recall investigating officers coming into the custody area to check on the CCTV and the recording system whilst I was temporary custody sergeant, and they'd give me very little detail of what they were up to, despite the custody office being my full responsibility at the time. It was not a very comfortable feeling at all.

Banfield was eventually found guilty of two rapes, four indecent assaults, and burglary with intent to commit rape. He was sentenced to eighteen years in prison, one of the longest sentences given to a serving police officer at that time. He had raped one of his detainees in the very cells I had responsibility for, as well as indecently assaulting several others there. What he did to those women in his care – in *our* care – was beyond comprehension. Even now, in the course of researching this investigation, finding his mug shot online turns my stomach. That he could do that to a vulnerable woman he had responsibility for is unfathomable.

Six other officers were disciplined in relation to this enquiry, most for mundane lapses of procedure (identified in the subsequent enquiry) such as not signing an entry on a custody record.

Sadly, as I write this book, I realise that Banfield's eighteen years incarceration for crimes against those innocent women is now up. I've been reliably informed he is now out of prison and living his life in a different part of the country.

As apprehensive trainee custody sergeants, you were broken in gently – just cover for lunch breaks, etc. As you built up your confidence and abilities, it meant that you could be in there for longer. Even so, it caused me so much stress. I hadn't been that stressed since a petrol bomb was thrown through the kitchen window of a friend's house when my wife was inside.

Around the same time, I realised that my relationship with my wife was in trouble. She kept hinting that she would leave me, and, to be fair, I thought it might be a good idea, although financially it could be awkward.

Then an idea came up that might resolve our practical difficulties and allow us to part our ways with no financial issues at all.

Her father wanted to sell his house to pay off his debts. He was a widower and had found himself another lady who also had a home, and he was contemplating moving in with her. His house was valued at £35,000, which was well below the market price, but he'd have been happy with that, the only problem being that it might take a while to sell, as it wasn't really habitable.

I knew that it could be worth almost twice as much, but it needed to be seriously worked on due to its neglected state. My father-in-law just wanted to sell it quickly, so I offered to do the house up in my spare time to bring it up to its true market value, and I suggested when it was sold he would get his £35,000, and my wife and I would pocket the rest. He agreed.

Initially I thought I'd taken on more than I could deal with, as the house was in a very serious, abandoned condition. I spent every rest day working at the house, repairing it, levelling the garden, decorating and so on. It took me six months to get it into reasonable condition before we put it on the market.

It sold immediately and we duly split the money. For our part, the windfall paid off all of our marital debts, and we divided what was left.

My wife then moved out with our daughter, leaving me alone in the big police house provided by my job. We stayed friends. I even went to visit her and ended up painting her new bathroom for her and doing odd jobs around her new place that she couldn't cope with.

With a nice amount of money sitting idly in my account, I chose to join a gymnasium in Cambridge with the aim of getting fit again – my waistline had expanded considerably over the last few years.

Our former family home felt empty with just me as the occupant. We'd been living in our police house rent-free for twelve years. It was a large semi-detached house in an upmarket cul-de-sac in Girton, a lovely village on the outskirts of Cambridge. Despite being relatively neglected by the police, the house was a great place to live and had a massive garden and huge potential. I didn't want to vacate my home following our separation, and, fortunately, the police allowed me to continue to live there alone due to the fact that I often had my daughter over to stay – she had her own bedroom in the house, after all.

Another reason the police were so relaxed about it was that the force was finally off-loading their complete housing stock in an attempt to save yet more money. The police were no longer required to provide accommodation for new officers – although current officers were ring-fenced – because the properties were a huge drain on finances. They were to be sold off as we lived in them, and many rumours were circulating as to how this would happen.

As a sitting tenant, I was aware that I had certain rights, although I did fear the house being sold to a housing association, who would then charge me rent. However, much to our delight, sitting tenants were to be given first option to buy their homes.

With the money available from the sale of my father-in-law's house still in the bank, I dared to dream that I might be in a position to use that as a deposit to buy the house. It all depended, of course, on the valuation of the property. I knew the house was located in a prime position in a very posh part of the village, and that the police might just over-value the house and put it out of my reach, so I was never sure if I would be able to keep my home.

Before long, I was told the price: £107,000. It was very reasonable for a house located there, but there was no way any bank would be lending a single-salaried person that kind of money, even if I could pay the deposit (which I couldn't). It was well beyond my reach. I was devastated.

Then we received the news that officers living in police housing would be given a two percent discount on the overall price of the house, for *each year* that they had been living in the property. I'd been there for twelve years, which meant a twenty-four percent discount on the asking price. I quickly got my calculator out and did the maths: £82,000!

I checked with the bank, and they agreed it would be possible due to the capital I had available, having a secure job, my on-going pay rises as a sergeant, and the fact that I was likely to seek further promotion. I was a sure bet for them.

It suddenly dawned on me that I could in fact buy the house at the discounted price, and immediately sell it for the market value and make an instant profit of £25,000, if I were so inclined.

That was never my plan, but there was no way I was *not* going to buy my home. I knew I wouldn't be selling it, as, in time, the value of the property would surely increase, especially if I spent some time and money doing it up. Also, it would mean that I would have something to leave my daughter when my time was up.

So, I snapped it up.

COP OUT Chapter Fifteen

THE EIGHT POLICE HOUSES SCATTERED ALONG OUR STREET stood out for a number of reasons. First, they were the only semi-detached homes in this completely detached housing area, i.e. it was a very well to do street with the odd police house here and there for the posh residents to stare at. Or complain about. Which they often did.

Second, the maintenance and upgrading of the houses had, little by little, been neglected since their construction in the mid-sixties to a point that they looked like they were from a bygone era.

The fact that I had a mortgage worth twenty-four percent less than the market value of the house meant that the bank was willing to lend me more money – up to the value of the house – to do it up.

I was deliriously happy. I had seriously wanted to get rid of the prehistoric, single-glazed, metal-framed windows that were a feature of the police house, ever since the day I'd moved in. The metal frames were such good conductors of cold and heat that they often froze during the winter and became too hot to touch at the height of summer – on the inside!

Not only would it transform the exterior of the house, making it look more modern and less like a police house, but it would also help with the huge heating bill I had to pay.

My life started to pick up once more; I approached the bank for the extra funds, I installed a DIY home alarm system to protect my most valuable asset, and I worked flat out at the gym to get fit for this new chapter in my life.

I really wanted my body back, so that I would feel confident enough to meet women again. For some reason, I just couldn't budge the last few inches of fat from around my waist. I'd been going to the gym daily, partly to get fit, and partly because there were so many pretty ladies working out, especially foreign ones. It was a newly single man's paradise, which I'd been enjoying for two months now, but I still considered myself too fat to make any introductions, other than a passing "Is it all right if I use that machine now, love?"

My prayers were answered in February – my third month at the gym – when a month-long competition was organised for the members. To enter, all you had to do was pick up an exercise-recording card from reception. Then, whenever you finished a session such as running, rowing, cross-trainer and so on, you simply got an instructor to sign the card with the total distance completed. At the end of the month, the person with the most mileage on the machines would win a prize and some local fame.

What a timely event – surely it'd help me to burn off those final few pounds? I was one of the first to pick up a card from reception.

After about three weeks of recording every mile completed, I slowed down on my treadmill and called over one of the instructors to sign my card. As he did so, I patted my stomach. I was amazed at how the fat had just been falling off me those past few weeks. I knew I was doing a lot of exercise, as I was really getting into the spirit of the competition, knowing that it would help me to lose the stubborn weight.

I knew the instructor well as I had hired him as a personal trainer when I first joined the gym. He counted up my miles and looked at me.

"Dave, you're one of the leaders so far! Well done, mate. Well done."

I didn't initially believe him. I hadn't been expecting to do anything other than burn off the fat. Being in with a chance of winning the actual competition just hadn't entered my head. He confirmed he wasn't joking, and promised he'd look into the other contenders for me.

The next day, my trainer ambled over as I began a running session.

"Second place!" he said, smiling. I nearly fell off the treadmill.

"Seriously?" I asked.

"Yup. Tim is in front of you by about thirty miles. I'll introduce him if he comes in." He glanced around the gym. "Thing is, Tim only comes in every other day, and he was in yesterday. You, on the other hand, are here *every* day."

It was true. Work permitting, I never missed a day at the gym. I quickly calculated that there were eight days left until the end of the month and therefore the end of the competition. That's eight days for me, and just four days for Tim.

"And third place?" I asked, checking my six.

"There are no other contenders, third place is a long, long way off. You needn't worry about her."

Naturally, I had a massive workout that day, making sure I reached the total thirty miles to my nearest competitor, and getting it recorded on my card. Every day after that, I went to the gym and ran, rowed or cycled until the sweat poured off me.

I soon lost track of the days. One of the things about working all hours is it plays havoc with your inner calendar. Shift workers often don't know what day of the week it is.

I was at the gym late one evening, working as hard as ever. About an hour before the gym was due to close, my trainer walked over, recorded my most recent effort, and totted up my total mileage. I was shattered and ready for a shower, home, and a glass of wine.

He whistled through his teeth. "Dave," he said. "You know what? I think you've actually won this."

I hadn't realised that it was February, the shortest month, and the twenty-eighth day of February, and therefore the last day of the competition. It was due to end that day, and I'd just assumed that we'd still got a few more days left until the end of the month.

"It finishes *today*? But I can't have won yet – the gym doesn't close for another hour. It's not over yet."

"Oh yes it is," he replied. "Look, you've actually overtaken Tim and are well ahead of him by …" He checked my card against his little notebook. "… about thirty-two miles by my reckoning, and he's not even here tonight. The gym closes in an hour, and even if he came in now – which he won't – there's no way he's gonna be able to do thirty-three miles in an hour, and beat you."

"Really?" I smiled, shaking my head in disbelief. I looked around at the other members in the gym, checking if any of the guys looked like a Tim.

The only other time in my life I had ever won *anything* was when I won a second place medal for a martial arts competition at police college. There was absolutely no way I was about to risk Tim sneaking in and cycling like hell to pip me to the post. I stayed on that treadmill for the remaining sixty minutes, plodding along at a steady pace, keeping a suspicious eye out for any late arrivals. Whenever a guy came in, I'd look across the gym at my trainer, make eye contact, and nod at the new arrival. He'd look across at the guy from whatever he was doing, then turn to me and shake his head.

And so it was that I won something for only the second time in my life. I received over £100 worth of gym equipment, including a really useful heart rate monitor, as well as some local fame when my photo and name were displayed in the reception area. Surely, a bit of local celebrity might help me break the ice with the ladies now, especially with my newfound, ultra slim stomach?

My total distance covered for the month was a whopping 895 miles, completed on the cycle, rowing machine, treadmill, and cross-trainer. That was an unbelievable average of thirty-two miles for *every* single day of the month in February, and I hadn't even gone to the gym every day in the beginning, due to working night shift.

It was no wonder that the fat was just rolling off me, and not just during that month. For weeks after, I was still losing weight, despite eating whatever I wanted to. The last time I'd been able to stuff my face with sticky buns and not worry about it was when I was nineteen and in the army.

I'd lost so much weight by the time I visited home in March, my mother suspected that I was dying of AIDS. Seriously.

My whole training regime was now focused on toning and building muscle before I disappeared completely. It was an enjoyable time for me as lots of people were congratulating me, and engaging me in conversation, asking how I'd managed it, and if it was even possible to cover so many miles every day.

That month of exercising had one other benefit for me too, one that would change the course of my life forever, and bring about a close to these police stories.

As that intense month had finally burned away my embarrassing *Michelin* tyre, my confidence with the ladies was growing. It wasn't that I was following them around the gym or anything, but it was easy to be working out next to some cutie, and to be able to make small talk with them.

Cambridge is a very cosmopolitan city and is always full of international tourists, students, and business people. I'd lost count of the number of foreign tourist photos taken of that smiling British Bobby as I patrolled those streets over the years. My smiling face must pop up all over the world when people open their old photo albums. *Oh, and this is of a lovely, smiling Bobby in Cambridge ...* The gym was just a microcosm of the city. There were many British girls, of course, numerous girls from neighbouring European countries, and a handful from the other side of the world, too.

One particular girl always seemed to be working out in front of me when I was on the cross-trainer (or it might have been the other way around – I can't really recall). I'd noticed her earlier due to her intense abs workout. I'd never seen anybody do an abs routine like she did, and, as a result, she had a perfectly sexy set.

It was clear she was foreign, not least because of the delicious olive colour of her skin. She had a great body, and wore Lycra gym clothes to complement it in a very stylish way. She was extremely toned and athletic, and I couldn't help but want to get to know her, despite the fact that I thought she was well out of my league.

I started out with some fine, smooth-talking gym phrases such as 'Have you finished with this?' and 'Is this your towel?' I slowly progressed to 'No, you go first – I insist' to show her how much of a gentleman I was. And, finally, I became more daring with 'We can alternate on this machine if you like?'

The alternating proposal worked out just as anticipated. Difficult to refuse without seeming rude. I knew she'd accept. And then, of course, polite small talk is guaranteed to follow.

After a few days of deliberately using the same machine as she was using, we got into a routine of sharing and chatting. I learnt that she was a student in Cambridge and that her name was Laura (pronounced *Lhow-ra*). I loved her accent, but couldn't quite place it, and didn't really like to ask.

I started to ask her, out of politeness, when she would come to the gym next. Then I would do my utmost to ensure I was there at the same time, although shift-work often meant that I couldn't be.

One time, she arrived with another guy, shared her workout with him, and left with him. It felt like she was avoiding me during that visit. I wasn't sure who he was, as he seemed to be much older than she was. He turned out to be her boyfriend at the time, and they were living together. He was ten years older than her, but he did have a cottage in the countryside, an engineering PhD, a BMW, an Aprilia motorbike, *and* a Harley Davidson. Why anybody would want *two* motorbikes was beyond me. And a Harley, for that matter?

I had fine abs, a BRG Mini Cooper, and a house devoid of furniture and with dangerous-to-touch metal window frames. *No competition ...*

I didn't know who he was at the time, of course. Had I been told then, I would have left her well alone. But I was curious, so I decided that, when she next came in alone, I would ask her about the big bald bloke she had been with.

The next day, she was talking to a different guy in the gym. They seemed to get on well too. A short time later, she came over to talk to me.

"Hi," she purred.

"Hi," I replied. "You seem to have so many friends ..."

She looked back at the guy. "Oh, him? Yeah, he's Bruno Junqueira, a racing driver apparently."

My head shot up. "Really? What sort of racing?" I loved Formula One.

"Dunno, but he just told me he's got a Formula One test drive next week against some guy called Jensen Button. Have you heard of them?"

I hadn't, but despite Bruno being faster than the other guy, the then relatively unknown Jensen Button was given the F1 drive by the Williams team, and went on to become F1 World Champion nine years later. Bruno, who I got to know through Laura, went on to win the Formula 3000 World Championship that very year.

Bruno was painfully shy, whilst Jensen (as I discovered later) was very charismatic and marketable. Only then did I understand why Bruno had been unjustly overlooked for the F1 drive by Williams.

I was highly impressed by this lady's contacts, but I really wanted to know about the bald bloke from yesterday. I was trying to think of how to make her understand that my original comment about 'friends' had actually been in the *plural* without seeming pushy, when she said something that ended our budding relationship there and then.

She looked around our immediate area, leaned into me and spoke in a hushed voice.

"Look, I know you said you're a policeman, but do you know where I can buy some marijuana?"

COP OUT Chapter Sixteen

ONE OF MY GYM BUDDIES WAS A COLLEAGUE called Craig, who I'd worked with over a number of years as PCs on the same team. He was also a neighbour in the same street, and, same as me, had bought his own police house with dodgy windows. I was now Craig's patrol sergeant and, as we were on duty at 3.00pm that day, we'd agreed to meet at the gym around lunchtime. We'd had our workout and were chilling in the warm, bubbly jacuzzi, counting down the minutes until we'd have to get out and leave for work with all its stresses and unpredictable dangers. We decided that we would have a very quick shower afterwards, which meant we were able to linger for another ten minutes in the jacuzzi.

It'd been just two days since my budding relationship with Laura had gone up in a whiff of sweet smelling smoke. I was half suspecting she'd been some kind of trap to entice me into illegal activities. I was also trying to forget her perfect body. No, it was time to find somebody perhaps more on my own level to chase after. And, preferably, foreign. With an accent …

I didn't know it at that time, but something was about to happen in that jacuzzi that would be one of the few memories that gets so seared into your memory bank that you carry it with you for the rest of your life, completely untarnished by the ravages of time and age. It was also a new crossroads opening up in my life.

The door directly opposite us opened. I glanced lazily towards the sound. It was the door to the ladies' changing rooms, and out of that door walked Laura. I stopped breathing when I saw her.

She was wearing a *tiny* black bikini that showed off her amazing body and tan to perfection. I suddenly realised that I – like Craig – was staring open-mouthed, so I abruptly got a grip of myself before she turned and fled. It couldn't have been a very comfortable situation for any girl to have to walk into, but she just smiled, hung her towel up and, deliciously, lowered herself into the water directly opposite us. I could *hear* Craig smiling beside me.

I introduced her to him and chatted with her, and she responded in her confident, friendly way, in that delicious accent.

"I've never asked," I said. "Where are you from? Because I can't really place your accent."

"Where do you think I am from?" she purred back. *I so hate it when they do that.*

It was really difficult for me to place, but I assumed she was a native speaker of English.

"South Africa?" I grasped.

She laughed out loud. She had such an easy and comfortable way about her.

"Canada? Australia …?"

"No, I'm actually from Brazil."

I wanted to say something witty and interesting, and quickly tried to recall everything I knew about Brazil, which wasn't much beyond Pelé, Samba, Carnival, Rio, Carmen bleedin' Miranda, the Amazon rain forest and, of course, Ayrton Senna. Had I known that Bruno, the racing driver friend, was in fact Brazilian, I might have made a connection and mentioned him. I had to tread carefully. She'd probably heard all the ridiculous clichés about Brazil before, so I veered away from that minefield and said something much more profound instead.

"Are you a doctor?" I asked her, out of the blue. She looked baffled and shook her head in disbelief. OK, so I'd just blown it. Craig knew why I'd asked the stupidest of questions from when we were comparing our ideal women earlier. I loved the idea of being with a smart woman, and you don't get much smarter than a doctor with a PhD. Like Amanda Burton.

"Come on," said Craig, silently agreeing I'd messed up, nodding at the clock on the wall as he stood up. "It's time to go. We're gonna be late."

He was right, of course. As patrol sergeant, I needed to be in early and get briefed in preparation to brief the team. However, I also knew that my fellow sergeant, Batty, would be in early, and he'd no doubt enthusiastically do all of that before I got there anyway. He was always like that, so keen and committed.

"Yeah, I'll be along in a minute," I said, as he smirked back at me, reading my mind. I waited for him to disappear whilst thinking of how to correct my earlier foolish comment. I still didn't know who baldy was, and when she'd walked through that door, I'd instantly forgotten all about her indiscreet request from the other day.

"It's hot in here," she said, as she stood up, her face flushed red. "I'm just going to go to the steam room."

Oh bugger, message received and understood. I knew what it meant, and as much as I wanted to, there was no way I was going to follow her into the steam room like some creepy guy, so it looked like I wouldn't be making excuses to Batty after all.

You. Dick. Head.

As she climbed up the steps opposite me, she glanced back and caught me staring at her ass. I turned away quickly.

Double. Dick. Head.

She slithered out and sauntered across to the steam room adjacent to the sauna.

As she opened the door to the steam room, she paused and looked back at me. My gaze was unable to break away from her.

"Do you want to keep me company in here?"

COP OUT Epilogue

OVER THE NEXT WEEK, WE MADE SURE we bumped into each other in the gym, sauna and steam room. It got very hot in there. A week after that jacuzzi meeting, Laura left her wealthy boyfriend and moved in with me, in my big empty house.

The first question she asked me when she moved in was, "Where are all your books?"

"It's here," I replied, picking up my hardback copy of Nelson Mandela's *Long Walk to Freedom*, the only book I possessed. "I gave all the others away," I lied.

Over the next year or so I supported her through her English studies right up until she qualified as a TEFL teacher and began teaching in a local language academy in the village.

During those first few years together, we travelled extensively, and she taught me things I didn't know. I began to grow in a way I hadn't expected.

A few years later, after suffering too much stress on the front line for twelve years, and one violent attack too many, I walked away from my job and never went back. I didn't officially quit, just walked out on them, as I did from my A-levels all those years ago.

In 2002, I was forced to sell my beloved ex-police house and my only home by a divorce court, in order to pay my ex-wife fifteen percent of a house I bought *after* she had left me. As a cop, one knows of injustice, but that took the biscuit.

So, in 2003, Laura and I took my considerable profit from the sale of my home to Brazil, and invested it in a dream property there, before moving to Spain to teach English, where we've been ever since.

Seven years later, we sold our Brazilian home for another tidy profit, which we transferred to Spain, where we bought a language school, and settled down for good.

We now live in a dream villa in Spain, and, in 2020, I took the decision to use my police pension fund to semi-retire, meaning I will become a full-time writer of books.

Yes, there will now be a cascade of new books coming out over the next few years. Watch this space. And thank you for your commitment and dependability in reading this far.

The next book is for you.

Meanwhile, if you wish to help me with my new writing career, please leave an honest review of this book at the place where you bought it.

Many thanks.

Diem

Book Zero in THE ROZZERS Series

COP STOPPER

A TRUE STORY by

DIEM BURDEN

BOOKS IN THIS SERIES

THE ROZZERS COLLECTION contains all five published parts of the series, but there is a sixth book which you might not be aware of: Book Zero. This eBook is a prequel to *The Rozzers* series, and it cannot be bought anywhere on this planet.

COP STOPPER

COP STOPPER relates the antics the author got up to as a child and teenager, including several run-ins with the law. Should they have precluded him from the office of constable years later, or did they contribute to making him a better police officer? Why don't you decide!

You can't buy this book, but you *can* have it for FREE!

Simply sign up to my newsletter to get it.
https://www.diemburden.com/diem-s-newsletter

COMING SOON

THE LISTENING ROOM

After falling in with the wrong crowd and coming under continuous family pressure, Ben decides to make a new start in northern Spain. He quickly secures a job teaching English, and soon meets and falls in love with the girl of his dreams. When offered a well-paid job working on a secret operation for the paramilitary police, eavesdropping on British gangsters on the Costa del Sol, Ben initially hesitates, but circumstances soon take over. Life just couldn't get any better for Ben, right up until the point that his past forces him to make a life-changing decision.

This debut novel from Diem Burden is coming soon.

CONTACT THE AUTHOR

Diem loves to hear from his readers. You can EMAIL him anytime at diemburden@gmail.com, visit his BLOG at https://www.diemburden.com, or follow him on one of his social media accounts.

NEWSLETTER: https://www.DiemBurden.com/diem-s-newsletter
Be sure to sign up for Diem's newsletter and receive the free, exclusive eBook, *Cop Stopper*, which cannot be obtained anywhere else on earth. You'll gain access to discount codes, sneak peeks at future releases and book covers, and the latest updates of his works-in-progress. He'll occasionally ask for your opinion or feedback, and he'll share some elements of his life with you.

FACEBOOK: https://www.facebook.com/DiemBurden/
Diem posts updates regarding his books, and progress on his writings on Facebook.

TWITTER: https://twitter.com/DiemBurden
As well as keeping you up-to-date on details of his own work, @DiemBurden tweets about the processes of writing, particularly articles and tips for newer writers, as well as stories of the joys and challenges of self-publishing.

INSTAGRAM: https://www.instagram.com/Diem_Burden/
Diem posts some of his amazing photos on Instagram, including many of his life in sunny Spain, especially of his two gorgeous dogs: a German Shepherd called *Adah* and adopted Pitbull cross, *Rasta*.

ACKNOWLEDGEMENTS

END OF THE ROAD
A big thank you goes to the following folk for their honest and helpful advice in the creation of Book One.

Patrick Volpe
Jessie Stan
Debby C Foulkes
K Wodke
Miles Brough
and Paula Carvalho Burden

COPS DON'T RUN
A big thank you goes to the following folk for their honest and helpful advice and support in the creation of Book Two.

Jessie Stank: For her usual unselfish advice and time, whenever I drop a text on her out of the blue.
Brian Buncombe: For showing me how to be a cop with compassion, and for allowing me to use his real name in this book.

ONE FOR THE ROAD
A big thank you goes to Jan Marshall, my cover designer, editor, and overall adviser, for her honest and helpful advice in the creation of this book.

THIEF TAKER

I'd like to thank the following ex-colleagues – great thief takers – for their help in reminding me of certain events during our time together, as my memory sadly fades into old age.

Neil Smith: Neil is still a serving officer after having transferred out of Cambridgeshire Police some years ago. He presently holds the rank of DCI (Detective Chief Inspector). Needless to say, I'm seriously impressed.
Nick: Nick is currently serving as a sergeant in Cambridgeshire.
Simon: After 14 years with Cambridgeshire Police, Simon transferred out to work at the Eurostar Station at St Pancras International, London. Despite loving the job, two years later he quit the police completely, citing the targets and politics, etc. He is now the site manager of a large comprehensive school just outside of Cambridge, and is very happy.

COP OUT

First, I'd like to thank *you* for getting to the end of my memoirs, my first foray into writing books, which has been a massive learning curve for me and a totally unforgettable experience. For you to read this far means that maybe – just maybe – I am getting this writing business correct. It is for people like you that I do this, as well as the need to satisfy my uncontrollable urge to create something. Thanks for the vote of confidence. You feed me, you really do.
One other thing I learnt whilst writing *Cop Out* was that the *scroats* referred to throughout the series by the police of Cambridgeshire are in fact *scrotes*, which is an abbreviation of the word *scrotum*. I seriously didn't know that. (I've changed the spelling throughout this print book.)

Finally, the biggest thank you has to go to Jan Marshall, my cover designer, editor, and overall adviser and cheerleader, for her honest and helpful advice in the creation of these books, not to mention her amazing covers.

Every effort has been made to make this book as complete and accurate as possible. However, no matter how hard we try, a mistake can sometimes slip through. Please feel free to email me directly should you find any, and I'll see to it that it is rectified in future editions. Thank you.

Printed in Great Britain
by Amazon